Third Edition

Mathematics

for

Elementary Teachers

via

Problem Solving

STUDENT RESOURCE HANDBOOK

Joanna O. Masingila
Syracuse University

Frank K. Lester
Indiana University

Anne M. Raymond
Bellarmine University

Change the course.

Change the course.

530 Great Road
Acton, Massachusetts 01720
800-562-2147

BRIEF CONTENTS

CHAPTER

1   Getting Started in Learning Mathematics
via Problem Solving 1

2   Numeration 28

3   Operations on Natural Numbers, Whole Numbers,
& Integers 43

4   Number Theory 101

5   Data & Chance 126

6   Fraction Models & Operations 168

7   Real Numbers: Rationals & Irrationals 179

8   Patterns & Functions 226

9   Geometry 251

10   Measurement 311

Resources and Tools 361

Glossary 389

Index 397

CONTENTS

CHAPTER 1	Getting Started in Learning Mathematics via Problem Solving....1

SET THEORY

TOPIC 1.1...........2   **Sets and Set Terminology**
 1.1.1 Sets, Elements, and Set Notation 2
 1.1.2 Empty Set, Finite Sets and Infinite Sets 3

TOPIC 1.2...........4   **Subsets and Set Relationships**
 1.2.1 Subsets 4
 1.2.2 Venn Diagrams, Sets, and Disjoint Sets 4
 1.2.3 One-to-One Correspondence 5
 1.2.4 Equivalent Sets 5
 1.2.5 Equal Sets 6

TOPIC 1.3...........7   **Set Operations**
 1.3.1 Union of Sets 7
 1.3.2 Intersection of Sets 7
 1.3.3 Complement of a Set 8
 1.3.4 Relative Complement (or Difference Set) 8
 1.3.5 Cartesian Product of Sets 9
 1.3.6 Properties of Set Operations 9

LOGIC AND PROBLEM SOLVING

TOPIC 1.4.........11   **Logic**
 1.4.1 Inductive Reasoning 11
 1.4.2 Deductive Reasoning 12
 1.4.3 Conjectures, Hypotheses, Conclusions. 14
 1.4.4 Statements and the Negation of Statements 15
 1.4.5 Compound Statements 15
 1.4.6 Truth Tables 16
 1.4.7 Conditional Statements. 16
 1.4.8 Inverse, Converse, and Contrapositive Statements 17
 1.4.9 If and Only If Statements 17
 1.4.10 Direct and Indirect Reasoning 17

TOPIC 1.5.........19   **Problem-Solving Topics**
 1.5.1 Polya's Process of Problem Solving. 19
 1.5.2 Problem Solving Strategies 20

 In the Classroom 26
 Bibliography 27

CHAPTER 2	Numeration 28

TOPIC 2.1.........29   **Characteristics of Numeration Systems**
 2.1.1 Characteristics of the Hindu-Arabic System 29
 2.1.2 Unique Representation 29
 2.1.3 Historical/Social/Cultural Notes about
     Numeration Systems 29
 2.1.4 The Development of the Hindu-Arabic
     Numeration System 30

TOPIC 2.2.........34   **Base-Ten Introduction**
 2.2.1 Characteristics of the Egyptian Numeration System 34
 2.2.2 A Subtractive Characteristic Not Associated with the
     Hindu Arabic System 35
 2.2.3 Other Bases: The Example of Base Two 35

TOPIC 2.3........... 37   **Problem-Solving Topics**
      2.3.1   Place Value 38
      2.3.2   A Symbol for Zero 38

TOPIC 2.4........... 39   **Decimal System and More on Base Ten**
      2.4.1   Decimal System and Expanded Notation 39
      2.4.2   Multiplicative Characteristic 40

      In the Classroom 41
      Bibliography 42

CHAPTER 3   **Operations on Natural Numbers, Whole Numbers** 43

TOPIC 3.1........... 44   **Natural Numbers**

WHOLE NUMBERS

TOPIC 3.2........... 45   **Introduction to Whole Numbers**
      3.2.1   Number Representations. 45
      3.2.2   One-to-One Correspondence 46
      3.2.3   Whole Numbers and the Set of Whole Numbers 47
      3.2.4   Whole Numbers and Counting 47

TOPIC 3.3........... 48   **Addition with Whole Numbers**
      3.3.1   Definition of Addition: Joining Sets 48
      3.3.2   Addition Terminology and Pictorial Representation 48
      3.3.3   The Number-Line Model of Addition. 49
      3.3.4   Addition and Mental Mathematics 49

TOPIC 3.4........... 51   **Addition Properties and Patterns (Whole Numbers)**
      3.4.1   Whole Number Addition Table. 51
      3.4.2   General Patterns in the Addition Table. 51
      3.4.3   Additive Identity Property .52
      3.4.4   Commutative Property 52
      3.4.5   Closure Property. 52
      3.4.6   Associative Property. 52

TOPIC 3.5........... 53   **Addition Algorithms (Whole Numbers)**
      3.5.1   Addition Algorithms. 54
      3.5.2   Base-Ten Block Model 54
      3.5.3   The Traditional Addition Algorithm. 55
      3.5.4   Partial Sums Algorithm 55
      3.5.5   Scratch Algorithm. 56
      3.5.6   The Scratch Algorithm in Other Bases. 57

TOPIC 3.6........... 58   **Subtraction with Whole Numbers**
      3.6.1   Definition of Terms. 58
      3.6.2   Take-Away Subtraction 58
      3.6.3   Missing-Addend Subtraction 58
      3.6.4   Comparison Subtraction 59
      3.6.5   A Pictorial Model 59
      3.6.6   Number-Line Model 59
      3.6.7   Subtraction and Mental Mathematics 59

TOPIC 3.7........... 60   **Subtraction Algorithms (Whole Numbers)**
      3.7.1   Connections to Addition. 60
      3.7.2   Subtraction Using Base-Ten Blocks 60
      3.7.3   Notation for the Subtraction Algorithm 61
      3.7.4   Subtraction in Base Six. 62

TOPIC 3.8.......... 63   **Multiplication with Whole Numbers**

3.8.1   Definition and Terminology 63
3.8.2   Repeated Addition Multiplication 63
3.8.3   Array Multiplication. 63
3.8.4   Cartesian Product 64
3.8.5   Tree Diagram 64
3.8.6   Array Model and Area Model. 65
3.8.7   Number-Line Model 65

TOPIC 3.9........... 66   **Multiplication Properties and Patterns (Whole Numbers)**

3.9.1   Multiplication Table 66
3.9.2   Zero Property of Multiplication .67
3.9.3   Multiplicative Identity 67
3.9.4   Commutative Property 67
3.9.5   Closure Property. 67
3.9.6   Associative Property. 67
3.9.7   Distributive Property of Multiplication over Addition 68

TOPIC 3.10......... 69   **Multiplication Algorithms**

3.10.1   Multiplication Algorithm 69
3.10.2   Base-Ten Blocks 69
3.10.3   Partial-Products Multiplication Algorithm 70
3.10.4   Standard Multiplication Algorithm. 71

TOPIC 3.11......... 72   **Whole-Number Division**

3.11.1   Definition and Terminology 72
3.11.2   Repeated Subtraction 72
3.11.3   Sharing 73
3.11.4   Repeated Subtraction versus Partitioning. 73
3.11.5   Discrete Models of Division. 74
3.11.6   Array Model 74
3.11.7   Number-Line Model 75
3.11.8   Division by Zero. 75

TOPIC 3.12......... 76   **Division Algorithms**

3.12.1   Concrete Models of the Algorithm. 76
3.12.2   Scaffolding 78
3.12.3   Another Transitional Algorithm .78
3.12.4   Links to Estimating Products 78

INTEGERS

TOPIC 3.13......... 79   **Introduction to Integers**

3.13.1   Natural Numbers and Whole Numbers. 79
3.13.2   Positive and Negative Numbers .79
3.13.3   Notation for Positive and Negative Numbers. 79
3.13.4   Opposites 80
3.13.5   Absolute Value 80
3.13.6   Integers and the Set of Integers .80

TOPIC 3.14......... 81   **Integer Addition**

3.14.1   Properties of Integer Addition 81
3.14.2   The Additive Inverse Property 81
3.14.3   Addition Rules for Integers 81
3.14.4   Models of Integer Addition. 82

TOPIC 3.15......... 85   **Integer Subtraction**

3.15.1   Closure Property for Integer Subtraction 85
3.15.2   Rules for Integer Subtraction 85
3.15.3   Models of Integer Subtraction 86

TOPIC 3.16........ 89   **Integer Multiplication**

     3.16.1   Properties of Integer Multiplication 89

     3.16.2   Multiplication Rules for Integers .89

     3.16.3   Models of Integer Multiplication 90

TOPIC 3.17........ 93   **Integer Division**

     3.17.1   Rules for Dividing Integers 93

     3.17.2   The Set Model for Illustrating Integer Division 93

TOPIC 3.18........ 96   **Order of Operations**

     3.18.1   Definition of the Term Order of Operations 96

     3.18.2   The Rules of Order of Operations 96

     3.18.3   The Calculator and Order of Operations 97

     In the Classroom 98

     Bibliography 99

CHAPTER 4   **Number Theory** **101**

TOPIC 4.1..........102   **Prime and Composite Numbers**

     4.1.1   Definitions of Prime and Composite 102

     4.1.2   Sieve of Eratosthenes 102

TOPIC 4.2......... 104   **Prime Factorization and Tree Diagrams**

     4.2.1   Definition of Prime Factorization 104

     4.2.2   Tree Diagrams 104

     4.2.3   Notation of Prime Factorization 105

TOPIC 4.3......... 106   **Fundamental Theorem of Arithmetic**

TOPIC 4.4......... 107   **Divisibility**

     4.4.1   Definition of Divisibility 107

     4.4.2   Divisibility Notation 107

     4.4.3   Divisibility Theorems 107

     4.4.4   False, But Often Believed, Divisibility Theorems 108

     4.4.5   Related Terms 108

     4.4.6   Divisibility Tests 108

TOPIC 4.5......... 112   **Greatest Common Divisor**

     4.5.1   Definition of Greatest Common Divisor 112

     4.5.2   Relatively Prime 112

     4.5.3   Notation for GCD 112

     4.5.4   Methods for Finding the GCD .112

TOPIC 4.6......... 115   **Least Common Multiple**

     4.6.1   Definition of Least Common Multiple 115

     4.6.2   Notation for LCM 115

     4.6.3   Methods for Finding the LCM .115

     4.6.4   Relationships Between the LCM and GCD 116

TOPIC 4.7......... 117   **Clock Arithmetic & Modular Arithmetic**

     4.7.1   Telling Time 117

     4.7.2   Clock Arithmetic 117

     4.7.3   Modular Arithmetic 118

TOPIC 4.8......... 120   **Patterns**

     4.8.1   Definition of a Pattern 120

     4.8.2   Arithmetic Sequences 120

     4.8.3   Geometric Sequences 121

     4.8.4   Growing Patterns 121

     4.8.5   Fibonacci Sequences 121

4.8.6   Finding the nth Term 121
4.8.7   Figurate Numbers 122

In the Classroom 124
Bibliography 125

CHAPTER 5	Data & Chance 126

PROBABILITY

TOPIC 5.1 127   **Probability Notions**
5.1.1   Probability Terminology 127
5.1.2   Computing a Simple Probability 127
5.1.3   Simulation with a Spinner 128

TOPIC 5.2 129   **Equally Likely Outcomes**
5.2.1   Equally Likely 129
5.2.2   Certain and Impossible Events 129
5.2.3   Theoretical Probability 130
5.2.4   Empirical Probability 130
5.2.5   Relating Empirical and Theoretical Probabilities 131
5.2.6   Expected Value 131

TOPIC 5.3 132   **Mutually Exclusive and Complementary Events**
5.3.1   Mutually Exclusive Events 132
5.3.2   Non-Mutually Exclusive Events 132
5.3.3   Understanding "Or" Probability Situations 132
5.3.4   Using a Venn Diagram to Look at
         Mutually Exclusive Events 133
5.3.5   Interpreting an "Or" Situation 134
5.3.6   Table of Data Simulation 134
5.3.7   Complementary Events 135
5.3.8   Odds In Favor and Odds Against 136

TOPIC 5.4 137   **Multistep Experiments**
5.4.1   Independent versus Dependent Events 137
5.4.2   Conditional Probability 137
5.4.3   Understanding "And" Probability Situations 138
5.4.4   Tree Diagrams 139

TOPIC 5.5 141   **Counting Principles**
5.5.1   Factorial 141
5.5.2   Definition of Permutations 142
5.5.3   Computing Permutations 142
5.5.4   Permutation Notation and the Calculator 142
5.5.5   Definition of Combinations 142
5.5.6   Computing Combinations 142
5.5.7   Combination Notation and the Calculator 143
5.5.8   Fundamental Counting Principle 143

STATISTICS

TOPIC 5.6 144   **Statistics Notions**
5.6.1   Statistics and Statistical Data 144
5.6.2   Hypotheses 144
5.6.3   Populations, Samples and Types of Sampling 145

TOPIC 5.7 146   **Measures of Central Tendency**
5.7.1   Mean 146
5.7.2   Mode 147
5.7.3   Median 148

5.7.4   Range and Midrange. 148

5.7.5   Weighted Average 149

TOPIC 5.8 150   **Data Dispersion**

5.8.1   Variance and Standard Deviation 150

5.8.2   Z-Scores 151

5.8.3   Normal Distribution of Data. 152

5.8.4   Skewed and Bimodal Data Distributions 152

5.8.5   Quartiles 154

5.8.6   Percentiles. 154

5.8.7   Box-and-Whisker Plots. 155

TOPIC 5.9 156   **Representing Data**

5.9.1   Pictographs. 156

5.9.2   Bar Graphs 157

5.9.3   Frequency Tables 158

5.9.4   Histograms 159

5.9.5   Line Graphs and Frequency Polygons 160

5.9.6   Line Graphs and Scatter Plots 160

5.9.7   Circle Graphs/Pie Charts 161

5.9.8   Stem-and-Leaf Plots. 164

In the Classroom 166

Bibliography 167

CHAPTER 6   **Fraction Models & Operations** **168**

TOPIC 6.1 169   **Fractions**

6.1.1   Fractions Representing Part of a Whole 169

6.1.2   Fractions Representing Ratios 170

6.1.3   Fractions as Representing a Division Problem. 170

TOPIC 6.2 171   **Equivalent Fractions**

6.2.1   Finding Equivalent Fractions 171

6.2.2   Testing Whether Fractions are Equivalent 171

6.2.3   Ordering Fractions 172

TOPIC 6.3 173   **Simplifying Fractions**

6.3.1   Relatively Prime 173

6.3.2   Simplifying Fractions by Looking for Common Factors . .173

6.3.3   Simplifying Fractions Using Prime Factorization 174

TOPIC 6.4 175   **Improper Fractions and Mixed Numbers**

6.4.1   Improper Fractions and Mixed Numbers 175

6.4.2   Changing Mixed Numbers to Improper Fractions 176

6.4.3   Changing Improper Fractions to Mixed Numbers 176

In the Classroom 177

Bibliography 178

CHAPTER 7   **Real Numbers: Rationals & Irrationals** **179**

TOPIC 7.1 180   **Ratio**

7.1.1   Definition of Ratio 180

7.1.2   Ratio Notation. 180

7.1.3   Types of Ratios 180

7.1.4   Rates 181

7.1.5   Comparing Ratios and Fractions 181

TOPIC 7.2.......182   **Proportion**
                         7.2.1   Definition of Proportion 182
                         7.2.2   Solving Proportions Using Equivalent Ratios 182
                         7.2.3   Solving Proportions Using Cross Multiplication 182
                         7.2.4   Directly and Indirectly Proportional. 183

DECIMALS

TOPIC 7.3.......184   **Introduction to Decimals**
                         7.3.1   Definition of Decimal. 184
                         7.3.2   Decimals, Base Ten and Place Value 184
                         7.3.3   Expressing a Decimal Number. 185
                         7.3.4   Zeros in Decimals. 185
                         7.3.5   Base-Ten Blocks as a Model for Decimals. 185
                         7.3.6   Rounding of Decimals 186

TOPIC 7.4.......187   **Decimals and Fractions**
                         7.4.1   Decimals and Common Fractions. 187
                         7.4.2   Converting Decimals to Common Fraction Form 187
                         7.4.3   Converting Certain Common Fractions to Decimals 187
                         7.4.4   Fractions That Do Not Have Power-of-10 Denominators . 188
                         7.4.5   Using a Calculator for Converting 188
                         7.4.6   Comparing and Ordering Decimals
                                 Using Base-Ten Blocks 188
                         7.4.7   Ordering Decimals By Lining Up Decimal Points 189
                         7.4.8   Ordering Decimals On a Number Line 189

TOPIC 7.5.......190   **Terminating and Repeating Decimals**
                         7.5.1   Terminating Decimals. 190
                         7.5.2   Repeating Decimals 190
                         7.5.3   Rational Numbers as Repeating Decimals 190
                         7.5.4   Converting Repeating Decimals to
                                 Rational Number Form. 191

TOPIC 7.6.......193   **Decimal Addition and Subtraction**
                         7.6.1   Adding Decimals 193
                         7.6.2   Modeling the Addition of Decimals 193
                         7.6.3   Subtracting Decimals 194
                         7.6.4   Modeling the Subtraction of Decimals. 195

TOPIC 7.7.......196   **Decimal Multiplication**
                         7.7.1   Rule for Decimal Multiplication. 196
                         7.7.2   Connection Between Decimal and
                                 Fraction Multiplication. 196
                         7.7.3   Area Model of Decimal Multiplication 197

TOPIC 7.8.......198   **Decimal Division**
                         7.8.1   Rule for Decimal Division 198
                         7.8.2   A Key Fact About Division 199
                         7.8.3   Connection Between Decimal and Fraction Division 199

TOPIC 7.9.......200   **Percent**
                         7.9.1   Definition of Percent. 200
                         7.9.2   Percents and Decimals 200
                         7.9.3   Solving Basic Percent Problems. 200
                         7.9.4   Percent Change. 201

TOPIC 7.10.....202   **Interest**
                         7.10.1 Basic Terms in an Interest Problem 202
                         7.10.2 Computing Simple Interest. 202
                         7.10.3 Computing Compound Interest 203

RATIONAL NUMBERS

TOPIC 7.11.....204   **Rational Numbers**
                         7.11.1 Definition of a Rational Number 204
                         7.11.2 Rational Numbers versus Fractions 204
                         7.11.3 Three Models of Rational Numbers 204

TOPIC 7.12.....206   **Looking at Rational Numbers as the Set of Rational Numbers**
                         7.12.1 Comparing Sets of Numbers. .206
                         7.12.2 Infinite Sets. 207
                         7.12.3 The Density of the Set of Rational Numbers 207
                         7.12.4 Other Properties of Rational Numbers 208

TOPIC 7.13.....210   **Adding Rational Numbers**
                         7.13.1 Addition of Rational Numbers with
                                 Common Denominators 210
                         7.13.2 Formal Definition of the Addition of Rational Numbers . .210
                         7.13.3 Addition of Mixed Numbers. .211

TOPIC 7.14.....212   **Subtracting Rational Numbers**
                         7.14.1 Subtraction of Rational Numbers with
                                 Common Denominators 212
                         7.14.2 Formal Definition of the Subtraction of
                                 Rational Numbers. 212
                         7.14.3 Subtraction of Mixed Numbers 213

TOPIC 7.15.....215   **Multiplying Rational Numbers**
                         7.15.1 Understanding Multiplication of Two Rational Numbers .215
                         7.15.2 Definition of Multiplication of Rational Numbers 216
                         7.15.3 Multiplication of Mixed Numbers 216

TOPIC 7.16.....217   **Dividing Rational Numbers**
                         7.16.1 Understanding Division of Rational Numbers 217
                         7.16.2 Definition of Reciprocal 218
                         7.16.3 Definition of Dividing Rational Numbers 218
                         7.16.4 Why Can We Multiply by the Reciprocal? 218
                         7.16.5 Dividing Mixed Numbers 219

TOPIC 7.17.....220   **Irrational Numbers**
                         7.17.1 Nonterminating, Nonrepeating Decimals 220
                         7.17.2 Definition of Irrational Numbers 220
                         7.17.3 Square Roots. 220
                         7.17.4 Roots. 221
                         7.17.5 Rational Exponents. 221

TOPIC 7.18.....222   **Real Numbers**
                         7.18.1 The Set of Real Numbers 222
                         7.18.2 Relationship Between the Reals and
                                 Other Number Systems. 222
                         7.18.3 Properties of the Real Numbers 222

                         In the Classroom 224
                         Bibliography 225

CHAPTER 8	**Patterns & Functions**. **226**	

TOPIC 8.1.......227   **Functions**
8.1.1   Definition of Functions and Function Notation 227
8.1.2   Domain and Range 227
8.1.3   Ways to Describe Functions 228
8.1.4   Vertical-Line Test 230
8.1.5   Composition of Functions 230

TOPIC 8.2.......232   **Equations and Inequalities**
8.2.1   Definition of Equation 232
8.2.2   Properties of Equations. 232
8.2.3   Definition and Notation of Inequalities 233
8.2.4   Properties of Inequalities 233

TOPIC 8.3.......234   **Cartesian Coordinate System**
8.3.1   Definition of the Cartesian Coordinate System
          and Related Terms 234
8.3.2   Equations of Horizontal and Vertical Lines 235

TOPIC 8.4.......236   **Graphs and Equations of Lines**
8.4.1   Slopes of Lines. 236
8.4.2   Computing the Slope of a Line. 237
8.4.3   Lines of the Form $y = mx$ 237
8.4.4   X- and Y-Intercepts. 238
8.4.5   Slope-Intercept Form of a Line $y = mx + b$ 239
8.4.6   Point-Slope Formula for the Equation of a Line 239

TOPIC 8.5.......240   **Systems of Linear Equations**
8.5.1   Simultaneous Equations 240
8.5.2   Geometrical Relationships of the Graphs of Two Lines. . .240
8.5.3   Solving Simultaneous Linear Equations. 242

TOPIC 8.6.......243   **Solving Systems of Linear Equations Symbolically**
8.6.1   Solving Systems of Equations by Substitution. 243
8.6.2   Solving Systems of Equations by Elimination 243
8.6.3   Determining the Equation of a Line Through Two Points .244

TOPIC 8.7.......245   **Exponents**
8.7.1   Definitions of Terms Associated with Exponents. 245
8.7.2   Squares and Cubes 245
8.7.3   Zero as an Exponent 245
8.7.4   Negative Exponents 246
8.7.5   Properties of Exponents 246

TOPIC 8.8.......247   **Scientific Notation**
8.8.1   Definition of Scientific Notation. 247
8.8.2   Writing Numbers Expressed in Scientific Notation
          as Decimals. 247
8.8.3   Writing Decimal Numbers in Scientific Notation 248

In the Classroom 249
Bibliography 250

CHAPTER 9	**Geometry**. **251**	

TWO-DIMENSIONAL GEOMETRY

TOPIC 9.1.......252   **Two-dimensional Geometry Basics**
9.1.1   Points and Lines 252
9.1.2   Relationships Among Points and Lines 253

TOPIC 9.2.......254   **Planes**
                          9.2.1   Planes 254
                          9.2.2   Relationships Among Points, Lines, and Planes 255

TOPIC 9.3.......256   **Line Relationships**
                          9.3.1   Coplanar, Noncoplanar, and Skew Lines 256
                          9.3.2   Intersecting and Concurrent Lines 257
                          9.3.3   Parallel and Perpendicular Lines 258
                          9.3.4   Relationships Among Lines and Planes 258

TOPIC 9.4.......259   **Line Segments**

TOPIC 9.5.......260   **Rays and Angles**
                          9.5.1   Rays 260
                          9.5.2   Angles. 260

TOPIC 9.6.......262   **Angle Relationships**
                          9.6.1   Adjacent Angles, Linear Pair Angles, and Vertical Angles.262
                          9.6.2   Complementary and Supplementary Angles 263
                          9.6.3   Angles Formed by a Transversal and Two Lines 263
                          9.6.4   Angles Formed by a Transversal and Two Parallel Lines. .263

TOPIC 9.7.......264   **Polygons**
                          9.7.1   A Polygon and Its Features. .264
                          9.7.2   Convex and Concave Polygons 265
                          9.7.3   Names of Polygons. 265

TOPIC 9.8.......266   **Regular Polygons**
                          9.8.1   Regular Polygons 266
                          9.8.2   Sum of the Measures of Angles in a Convex Polygon 266
                          9.8.3   Sum of the Measures of the Exterior Angles
                                   in a Convex Polygon. 267

TOPIC 9.9.......269   **Triangles**
                          9.9.1   Features of a Triangle. 269
                          9.9.2   Special Kinds of Triangles 269
                          9.9.3   Sum of the Measures of the Interior Angles in a Triangle .270

TOPIC 9.10.....271   **Quadrilaterals**
                          9.10.1   Features of a Quadrilateral 271
                          9.10.2   Special Kinds of Quadrilaterals 271

TOPIC 9.11.....273   **Circles**
                          9.11.1   Features of a Circle. 273
                          9.11.2   The Compass 274

TOPIC 9.12.....275   **Congruence**
                          9.12.1   Congruent Segments. 275
                          9.12.2   Congruent Angles. 275
                          9.12.3   Congruent Polygons. 275

TOPIC 9.13.....276   **Symmetry**
                          9.13.1   Reflection Symmetry 276
                          9.13.2   Rotational Symmetry 276
                          9.13.3   Plane Symmetry 277

CONSTRUCTIONS
TOPIC 9.14.....278   **Line and Angles Constructions**
                          9.14.1   Geometric Tools 278

    9.14.2 Constructing a Line Segment Congruent to a
    Given Line Segment 278

    9.14.3 Constructing an Angle Congruent to a Given Angle 279

TOPIC 9.15.....280   **Angle Bisector Constructions**

    9.15.1 Angle Bisector 280

    9.15.2 Constructing an Angle Bisector 280

TOPIC 9.16.....281   **Perpendicular-Line-Through-a-Point Constructions**

    9.16.1 Constructing a Line Perpendicular to a
    Line Through a Point on the Line. 281

    9.16.2 Constructing a Line Perpendicular to a
    Line Through a Point Not on the Line 281

    9.16.3 Constructing a Perpendicular Bisector
    of a Line Segment. 282

TOPIC 9.17.....283   **Parallel-Line Construction**

TOPIC 9.18.....284   **Circumscribed-Circle Constructions**

    9.18.1 Circumscribed Circles 284

    9.18.2 Constructing a Circumscribed Circle About a Triangle . . .284

TOPIC 9.19.....286   **Inscribed-Circle Constructions**

    9.19.1 Inscribed Circles. 286

    9.19.2 Constructing an Inscribed Circle Within a Triangle 286

    9.19.3 Orthocenters and Centroids 287

TOPIC 9.20.....288   **Triangle Congruence**

    9.20.1 Congruent Triangles and Their Features 288

    9.20.2 How Two Triangles May or May Not be Congruent 288

TOPIC 9.21.....289   **Triangle-Congruence Properties**

    9.21.1 Side-Side-Side Triangle-Congruence Property. 289

    9.21.2 Side-Angle-Side Triangle-Congruence Property 289

    9.21.3 Angle-Side-Angle Triangle-Congruence Property 290

    9.21.4 Angle-Angle-Side Triangle-Congruence Property 290

    9.21.5 Isosceles-Triangle-Congruence Properties 290

TOPIC 9.22.....291   **Quadrilateral Properties**

    9.22.1 Properties of Trapezoids. 291

    9.22.2 Properties of Parallelograms. 292

    9.22.3 Properties of Rectangles. 292

    9.22.4 Properties of Kites 293

    9.22.5 Properties of Rhombi 294

    9.22.6 Properties of Squares 294

TOPIC 9.23.....295   **Similarity**

    9.23.1 Similarity and Similar Figures 295

    9.23.2 Similar Triangles. 295

    9.23.3 Indirect Measurement. 296

TOPIC 9.24.....297   **Triangle Proportion Properties**

TOPIC 9.25.....298   **Fractals and Rep-tiles**

    9.25.1 Fractals 298

    9.25.2 Rep-tiles 299

THREE-DIMENSIONAL GEOMETRY

TOPIC 9.26.....300   **Three-dimensional Geometry Basics**

    9.26.1 Plane Relationships. 300

    9.26.2 Dihedral Angles 301

TOPIC 9.27.....302   **Polyhedra, Prisms, and Pyramids**
9.27.1 A Simple Closed Surface 302
9.27.2 A Polyhedron and its Features .302
9.27.3 Convex and Concave Polyhedra 303
9.27.4 Prisms 303
9.27.5 Pyramids 304

TOPIC 9.28.....305   **Regular Polyhedra**
9.28.1 Regular Polyhedra 305
9.28.2 Semiregular Polyhedra 305

TOPIC 9.29.....306   **Cylinders, Cones, and Spheres**
9.29.1 Cylinders. 306
9.29.2 Cones 307
9.29.3 Spheres 307

TOPIC 9.30.....308   **van Hiele Levels**

In the Classroom 309
Bibliography 310

CHAPTER 10   **Measurement** **311**

TOPIC 10.1.....312   **Angle Measurement**
10.1.1 Angle Measurement and Notation 312
10.1.2 How to Use a Protractor 312
10.1.3 Angle Classification 313
10.1.4 Dihedral Angle Measurement. .313

TOPIC 10.2.....314   **Linear Measurement**
10.2.1 Length and How to Measure It. 314
10.2.2 The English System of Linear Measurement 314
10.2.3 The Metric System of Linear Measurement. 315

TOPIC 10.3.....316   **Perimeter**
10.3.1 Perimeter. 316
10.3.2 Perimeters of Polygons. 316

TOPIC 10.4.....317   **Circumference**
10.4.1 Circumference and π 317
10.4.2 Arc Length 317

TOPIC 10.5.....319   **Measuring Area**
10.5.1 Area and How to Measure It. 319
10.5.2 The English System of Area Measurement 319
10.5.3 The Metric System of Area Measurement 320

TOPIC 10.6.....321   **Area of Quadrilaterals**
10.6.1 Area of a Square 321
10.6.2 Area of a Rectangle 321
10.6.3 Area of a Parallelogram 322
10.6.4 Area of a Trapezoid 322

TOPIC 10.7.....323   **Area of Triangles**
TOPIC 10.8.....324   **Area of Regular Polygons and Circles**
10.8.1 Area of a Regular Polygon 324
10.8.2 Area of a Circle. 324
10.8.3 Area of a Sector 325

TOPIC 10.9.....326   **Surface Area of Prisms and Cylinders**
10.9.1 Surface Area. 326

10.9.2 Surface Area of a Right Prism 326
10.9.3 Surface Area of a Right Circular Cylinder 327

TOPIC 10.10...329   **Surface Area of Pyramids, Cones, and Spheres**
10.10.1 Surface Area of a Right Regular Pyramid 329
10.10.2 Surface Area of a Right Circular cone 330
10.10.3 Surface Area of a Sphere 330

TOPIC 10.11...331   **Measuring Volume**
10.11.1 Volume and How to Measure It 331
10.11.2 The English System of Volume Measurement 331
10.11.3 The Metric System of Volume Measurement 332

TOPIC 10.12...333   **Volume of Prisms and Cylinders**
10.12.1 Volume of a Right Prism 333
10.12.2 Volume of a Right Circular Cylinder 333

TOPIC 10.13...335   **Volume of Pyramids, Cones, and Spheres**
10.13.1 Volume of a Right Pyramid 335
10.13.2 Volume of a Right Circular Cone 335
10.13.3 Volume of a Sphere. 336

TOPIC 10.14...337   **Cavalieri's Principle**
TOPIC 10.15...338   **Mass and Temperature**
10.15.1 Mass and Weight. 338
10.15.2 Temperature 338

TOPIC 10.16...340   **Pythagorean Theorem and Other Triangle Relationships**
10.16.1 The Pythagorean Theorem 340
10.16.2 The Converse of the Pythagorean Theorem 341
10.16.3 Special Right Triangles. 341
10.16.4 The Triangle Inequality 342

TOPIC 10.17...343   **Distance Formula**
TOPIC 10.18...345   **Tessellations**
10.18.1 What is a Tessellation? 345
10.18.2 Any Triangle Can Tessellate the Plane 345
10.18.3 Any Quadrilateral Can Tessellate the Plane 346

TOPIC 10.19...347   **Tessellations of Regular Polygons**
10.19.1 Which Regular Polygons Can Tessellate the Plane? 347
10.19.2 Semiregular Tessellations 348

TOPIC 10.20...349   **Transformations**
TOPIC 10.21...351   **Translations**
TOPIC 10.22...353   **Rotations**
TOPIC 10.23...354   **Reflections and Glide Reflections**
TOPIC 10.24...356   **Size Transformations**

In the Classroom 357
Bibliography 358

APPENDIX A   **Resources and Tools** **361**

Glossary **389**

Index **397**

GETTING STARTED IN MATHEMATICS VIA PROBLEM SOLVING

1

TOPIC

1.1 Sets and Set Terminology
1.2 Subsets and Set Relationships
1.3 Set Operations
1.4 Logic
1.5 Problem Solving Topics

CHAPTER OVERVIEW

Most mathematics educators agree that problem solving is a very important, if not the most important, goal of mathematics instruction at every level. In this chapter you can learn some interesting facts about problem solving, and examine eight of the most commonly used problem-solving strategies. You will also learn about set-theory ideas and logic.

BIG MATHEMATICAL IDEAS

- Problem-solving Strategies
- Generalizing
- Verifying
- Using Language and Symbolism
- Multiple Representations

NCTM PRINCIPLES & STANDARDS LINKS

Problem Solving
Reasoning
Communication
Connections
Representation

TOPIC 1.1 SETS AND SET TERMINOLOGY

INTRODUCTION

Sets provide a means of categorizing and organizing objects into specific groups. Sets can be large, like the set of people living in the United States, and sets can be small, like the set of days in the week. In this section, we introduce the concept of sets and ways to describe sets. We also explain terminology of sets, including the notions of finite and infinite sets.

DID YOU KNOW?

Renowned mathematician Georg Cantor (1845–1918) spent most of his childhood in Germany and completed his doctoral studies in mathematics at the University of Berlin. His research in mathematics centered on sets and comparing the size of infinite sets. He is known particularly for his work with the set of numbers in the closed interval [0,1] that are not in the open middle third of [0, 1] and not in the open middle third of any interval obtained by separating [0, 1] into three equal intervals, then dividing each of these intervals into three equal intervals, etc. This fascinating set has been named the *Cantor Set* after Cantor himself.

For More Information: Bunt, L. N. H., Jones, P. S., & Bedient, J. D. (1988). *The Historical Roots of Elementary Mathematics*. New York: Dover Publications.

1.1.1
Sets, Elements and Set Notation

A **set** is a collection of objects or ideas and is typically denoted by a list or description of what is in the set in brackets. For example,

- The set of Natural Numbers could be described this way: {1, 2, 3, 4, 5, ...}.

- The set of vowels could be described this way: {a, e, i, o, u}

- The set of boys on the debate team is:
  {Jay, Tommy, Chris, Mike, John, Frank}

An **element** of a set is a member of the set. The notation meaning, "is an element of" is represented by the symbol, $\in$. The letter "a" is an element of the set A = {a, e, i, o, u}; we denote this by writing, a $\in$ A. Likewise, because the letter "h" is not an element of set A, we can denote the phrase, "is not an element of" using the symbol $\notin$, saying h $\notin$ A.

Rather than indicate a set by listing all the elements in a set within brackets, we can describe a set using **set-builder notation**; that is, we can summarize the members of a set using the notation $\{x \mid x$ is $\mid ...\}$ read as "x such that x is" to describe the elements.

For example, instead of describing set A = {a, e, i, o, u} by listing all the elements, we could say A = $\{x \mid x$ is a vowel} which is read " the set of all x such that x is a vowel."

Another example of a set written in set-builder notation includes B = $\{x \mid x$ is an even whole number less than 20}, read as "the set of all x such that x is an even whole number less than 20," meaning the set {0, 2, 4, 6, 8, 10, 12, 14, 16, 18}.

A set with no elements is called the **empty set** or **null set**. The empty set is denoted either as { } or ∅.

Sets can be **finite**, that is, have a limited number of elements, or **infinite**, have an unlimited number of elements.

Examples of finite sets include:
{1, 2, 3, 4, 5, 6}
$\{x \mid x$ is a student in this class$\}$.
{red, yellow, blue}
$\{x \mid x$ is a prime number between 1 and 100$\}$.

Examples of infinite sets are:
$\{x \mid x$ is a whole number$\}$.
{1, 3, 5, 7, 9, ...}
{..., -2, -1, 0, 1, 2, 3, ...}
$\{x \mid x$ is an idea$\}$.

Notice that infinite sets are often described using ellipses, which are the symbols, "..." indicating that the pattern described by the previous elements in the set is continued in the same manner.

Subset and Set Relationships | Set Operations | Set of Whole Numbers   **RELATED TOPICS**

TOPIC 1.2 SUBSETS AND SET RELATIONSHIPS

CORNERSTONE Sets and Set Terminology

INTRODUCTION *Many relationships we observe involve noting how one set relates to another. For example, when we invite a few friends to go to the movies, we are identifying a subset of our total set of friends. In fact, we usually categorize our total set of friends into a variety of subsets such as our friends from high school, our friends from college, our friends from the neighborhood, our friends at work, and so on. In this section, we investigate relationships between sets, particularly focusing on the concepts of subsets, disjoint sets, and equivalent and equal sets.*

DID YOU KNOW? Venn diagrams, which are used to illustrate logical relationships between sets, are named after John Venn (1834–1923), an Englishman who studied logic and logical symbols. Figures 1.1 and 1.2 are examples of Venn diagrams.

For More Information: Bunt, L. N. H., Jones, P. S., & Bedient, J. D. (1988). *The Historical Roots of Elementary Mathematics.* New York: Dover Publications.

1.2.1
Subsets

A set A is a **subset** of another set B if every element in set A is also in set B. We denote this relationship symbolically as A ⊆ B. For example, the set A={a, e, i, o, u} is a subset of the set B={$x \mid x$ is a letter of the alphabet}. It is important to note that the empty set is considered a subset of every set. Also, every set is considered a subset of itself. Using set notation we say that A ⊆ A to denote that A is a subset of itself and that ∅ ⊆ A to denote that the empty set is a subset of set A.

We say A is a **proper subset** of B, denoted A ⊂ B, if A is a subset of B, but there is at least one element of B that is not an element of A. For example, the set {1, 2} is a proper subset of {1, 2, 3, 4}. However, although {1, 2, 3, 4} is a subset of the set {1, 2, 3, 4}, it is NOT a proper subset. Using notation, we say, {1, 2, 3, 4} ⊄ {1, 2, 3, 4}; instead we would write {1, 2, 3, 4} = {1, 2, 3, 4} or {1, 2, 3, 4} ⊆ {1, 2, 3, 4}.

1.2.2
Venn Diagrams, Sets, and Disjoint Sets

We can illustrate sets and relationships between sets using **Venn Diagrams**. For example, given set A = {1, 3, 5, 7, 9, 11, 13, 15} and set B = {1, 5, 9, 13} we note that B ⊂ A. We can show this subset relationship with the Venn diagram shown in Figure 1.1.

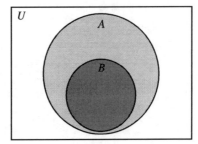

Figure 1.1

Note that the Venn diagram shows set B inside of set A, indicating that all elements in set B are also in set A. Also note that the sets A and B are shown within a rectangular box labeled *U*. We usually show sets in a Venn diagram situated within the **Universe**, U, of a larger set of elements. Sometimes, we are very specific about U. For example, in Figure 1.1, U could stand for the set of all counting numbers. Thus, A and B are shown as being sets within the larger universal set.

Sometimes sets have no elements in common. If two sets share no elements, then we say that these sets are **disjoint**. For example, given set A = {Bill, Bob, Bart} and set B = {Jack, Jill}, we would say sets A and B are disjoint. A Venn diagram representation of the disjoint sets A and B can be seen in Figure 1.2.

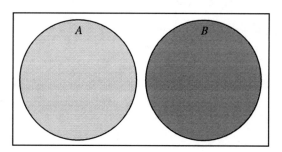

Figure 1.2

We say two sets, A and B, have **one-to-one correspondence** if and only if each element of A can be paired with exactly one element of set B and each element of set B can be paired with exactly one element of A. For example, Figure 1.3 shows a one-to-one correspondence between two sets.

1.2.3
One-to-One Correspondence

$$A = \{1, 2, 3, 4, 5\}$$
$$\Big\updownarrow\ \Big\updownarrow\ \Big\updownarrow\ \Big\updownarrow\ \Big\updownarrow$$
$$B = \{a, b, c, d, e\}$$

Figure 1.3

We say two sets A and B are **equivalent**, denoted A~B, if we can show a one-to-one correspondence between them. For example, we say A= {Sue, Sally, Sara, Sam} is equivalent to B={red, blue, green, yellow} because we can show a one-to-one correspondence between them (see Figure 1.4).

1.2.4
Equivalent Sets

$$A = \{Sue, Sally, Sara, \ Sam\}$$

$$B = \{red, blue, green, yellow\}$$

Figure 1.4

Another way of describing equivalence is by saying that two sets are equivalent if they have the same number of elements. In set language, we say the number of elements in set A, denoted *n(A)* is called the **order** of set A. For example,

- Given A={a, b, c, d, e}, n(A) = 5.

- Given B= {x lx is a letter in the alphabet}, n(B) = 26.

- Given C= {1, 2, 3, 4, ...}, n(C) is infinite.

We say two sets A and B are **equal** if they contain the exact same elements. This is denoted A = B. For example, set A= {2, 4, 6, 8} is exactly the same as set B={x|x is an even counting number less than 10} because they both describe exactly the same elements: 2, 4, 6, and 8.

RELATED TOPICS   Set Operations

TOPIC 1.3 SET OPERATIONS

Sets and Set Terminology | Subsets and Set Relationships

CORNERSTONE

The thinking involved in set operations arises in everyday situations. For example, couples planning their wedding often talk about inviting friends on the groom's side of the family and friends on the bride's side of the family, but acknowledging that there are some friends that fit into both categories. In this situation, we must deal with combining two sets, with an eye on noting where the two sets overlap. In this section, we examine the mathematical process of operations between sets including finding the union of sets, determining the intersection of sets, and we explore a means of illustrating these operations through Venn diagrams.

INTRODUCTION

Many people know Lewis Carroll (1832–1898) as the author of the children's story, *Alice in Wonderland*. However, what many people do not know is that Lewis Carroll (his real name was Charles Lutwidge Dodgson) was a mathematics lecturer at Oxford University. In 1896, he published a book entitled, *Symbolic Logic: A Fascinating Mental Recreation for the Young*, which was filled with logical puzzle problems to be solved for fun.

For More Information: Reimer, L., & Reimer W. (1995). *Mathematicians are people, too: Stories from the lives of great mathematicians, Volume 2.* Palo Alto, CA: Dale Seymour Publications.

DID YOU KNOW?

The **union** of sets A and B, denoted A ∪ B, is the set of all elements that are in either set A or Set B or in both sets. For example, given A = {1, 2, 3, 4, 5} and B = {2, 4, 6, 8, 10}, we find A ∪ B = {1, 2, 3, 4, 5, 6, 8, 10}. Notice that even though the numbers 2 and 4 are in both sets, they are each presented only once in the union of the two sets.

Suppose we have sets C = {1, 2, 3} and D = {4, 5, 6} that have no elements in common. We can find the union of the sets by combining the two sets. Thus, C ∪ D = {1, 2, 3, 4, 5, 6}.

Figure 1.5 illustrates a Venn diagram representation of the union of sets A and B. The shaded portion shows the union.

1.3.1
Union of Sets

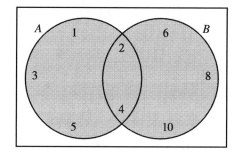

Figure 1.5

The intersection of sets A and B, denoted A ∩ B, is the set of all elements that are in both sets A and B. For example, working with the sets A = {1, 2, 3, 4, 5} and B = {2, 4, 6, 8, 10}, we find A ∩ B = {2, 4}. Note that when two sets are disjoint, their intersection is the empty set. For example, given C = {a, b, c} and D = {x, y, z}, we say, C ∩ D = ∅.

1.3.2
Intersection of Sets

The Venn diagram in Figure 1.6 illustrates the intersection of sets A and B. Notice that the shaded portion, the overlap, shows the intersection.

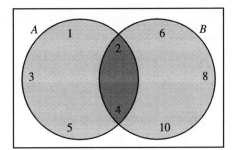

Figure 1.6

1.3.3
Complement of a Set

Given a set A within a universal set U, we say the **complement** of set A, denoted $\overline{A}$, is the set of all elements in the universe that are not in set A. We can write this as $\overline{A} = \{x \in U \,|\, x \notin A$. For example, if the universe we are working within is the set of Whole Numbers and set A = $\{x \,|\, x$ is an odd whole number$\}$, then $\overline{A} = \{x \,|\, x$ is an even whole number$\}$.

To show the complement of set A in a Venn diagram, Figure 1.7 shows set A within the universe, U. The shaded portion represents the complement of set A.

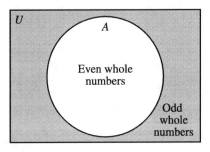

Figure 1.7

In another example, suppose
U = $\{x \,|\, x$ is a Whole Number less than 20$\}$
A = $\{x \,|\, x$ is a multiple of 5 less than 20$\}$
B = $\{x \,|\, x$ is an even number less than 20$\}$.

Then we can determine that
$A \cup B = \{0, 2, 4, 5, 6, 8, 10, 12, 14, 15, 16, 18\}$
$A \cap B = \{0, 10\}$
$\overline{A \cup B} = \{1, 3, 7, 9, 11, 13, 17, 19\}$
$\overline{A \cap B} = \{1, 2, 3, 4, 5, 6, 7, 8, 9, 11, 12, 13, 14, 15, 16, 17, 18, 19\}$.

1.3.4
Relative Complement (or Difference Set)

Given sets A and B in a universal set U, we define the **complement of A relative to B** as the set of all elements in A that are not in B. This is denoted symbolically as $A - B = \{x \in U \,|\, x \in A$ and $x \notin B\}$. For example, suppose U = $\{x \,|\, x$ is a Whole Number less than 20$\}$, A = $\{x \,|\, x$ is an odd number less than 20$\}$ and B = $\{x \,|\, s$ is a multiple of three less than 20$\}$. Then $A - B = \{1, 5, 7, 11, 13, 17, 19\}$. The Venn diagram in Figure 1.8 illustrates sets A and B, and the shaded portion represents A – B.

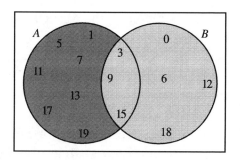

Figure 1.8

The **Cartesian product** of sets A and B, denoted A × B, is the set of ordered pairs (x,y) you can form where the first element in the ordered pair, x, is an element from set A and the second element in the ordered pair, y, is an element from set B. We can write the Cartesian product A × B = $\{(x,y)|x \in A,\ y \in B\}$. For example, given set A = $\{1, 2, 3\}$ and set B = $\{a, b\}$, we find A × B = $\{(1, a), (1, b), (2, a), (2, b), (3, a), (3, b)\}$. Note that there are six elements in the set A × B and each element in the set is an ordered pair written in parenthetical notation.

In a second example, suppose we want to form singing duets matching one soprano singer with one bass singer. The set of soprano singers include = {Janet, Dina, Jean} and the set of bass singers include = {Paul, Ted, Dale}. The duets that can be formed are Soprano × Bass = {(Janet, Paul), (Janet, Ted), (Janet, Dale), (Dina, Paul), (Dina, Ted), (Dina, Dale), (Jean, Paul), (Jean, Ted), (Jean, Dale)}. Note that there are 9 elements in the Cartesian product..

From both examples, we can confirm that the size or order of a set formed by a Cartesian product, given sets A and B, is n(A × B) = n(A) × n(B).

**1.3.5
Cartesian Product
of Sets**

There are five properties associated with set operations. The first property is the **Commutative Property of the Union of Sets**. This property says, given sets A and B, A ∪ B = B ∪ A. Take, for example, sets A = $\{x|x$ is a vowel in the alphabet} and B = $\{x|x$ is a consonant in the alphabet}. A ∪ B is the set of all elements that are in A, in B, or in both A and B. Similarly, $B \cup A$ is the set of all elements that are in B, in A, or in both A and B. Therefore, A ∪ B = B ∪ A = $\{x|x$ is a letter in the alphabet}.

Another property of set operations is the **Commutative Property of the Intersection of Sets.** This property states that given sets A and B, A ∩ B = B ∩ A. Given A = {red, yellow, blue} and B = {blue, red, green, black}, we would say that A ∩ B is the set of all elements that A and B have in common and that B ∩ A is also the set of all elements that A and B have in common. Therefore, A ∩ B = B ∩ A = {blue, red}.

Next we consider the **Associative Property of the Union of Sets**, that is, given sets A, B, and C, (A ∪ B) ∪ C = A ∪ (B ∪ C). Suppose we have set A = {a, b, c, d, e}, B = {a, e, i, o, u}, and C = {e, f, g, h, i}. We find (A ∪ B) ∪ C by first finding (A ∪ B) = {a, b, c, d, e, i, o, u}. Then (A ∪ B) ∪ C = {a, b, c, d, e, i, o, u} ∪ {e, f, g, h, i} = {a, b, c, d, e, i, o, u, f, g, h}. Now, to find A ∪ (B ∪ C), we first find (B ∪ C) = {a, e, i, o, u, f, g, h}. Then, we find A ∪ (B ∪ C) = {a, b, c, d, e} ∪ {a, e, i, o, u, f, g, h}= {a, b, c, d, e, i, o, u, f, g, h}. Thus we have confirmed that (A ∪ B) ∪ C = A ∪ (B ∪ C).

**1.3.6
Properties of
Set Operations**

A fourth property of set operations is the **Associative Property of the Intersection of Sets**. This property states that given sets A, B, and C, (A ∩ B) ∩ C = A ∩ (B ∩ C). To show this is true, consider again the sets A = {a, b, c, d, e}, B = {a, e, i, o, u}, and C = {e, f, g, h, i}. First let us find (A ∩ B) ∩ C. We determine (A ∩ B) = {a, e}. Then (A ∩ B) ∩ C = {a, e} ∩ {e, f, g, h, i} = {e}. Now, to compute A ∩ (B ∩ C), we first find (B ∩ C) = {e, i}. Then A ∩ (B ∩ C) = {a, b, c, d, e} ∩ {e, i} = {e}. Therefore, (A ∩ B) ∩ C = A ∩ (B ∩ C).

A final property of set operations is the **Distributive Property of Intersection over Union**. This distributive property asserts that given sets A, B, and C, A ∩ (B ∪ C) = (A ∩ B) ∪ (A ∩ C). Given A = {1, 3, 5, 7, 9, 11}, then B = {1, 5, 10, 20}, and C = {5, 10, 15, 20}. To show that the left- and right-hand sides of the distributive property equation are equal, we compute both sides and compare.

To compute the left-hand side, we find A ∩ (B ∪ C). First, we find (B ∪ C) = {1, 5, 10, 20, 15}. Then A ∩ (B ∪ C) = {1, 3, 5, 7, 9, 11} ∩ {1, 5, 10, 20, 15}= {1, 5}. Now, computing the right-hand side, we find (A ∩ B) ∪ (A ∩ C). First, we find (A ∩ B) = {1, 5}. We also find (A ∩ C) = {5}. Then, we determine (A ∩ B) ∪ (A ∩ C) = {1, 5} ∪ {5} = {1, 5}. Therefore, we have shown that A ∩ (B ∪ C) = (A ∩ B) ∪ (A ∩ C).

RELATED TOPICS   Functions

TOPIC 1.4 LOGIC

Logical reasoning plays a role in many conversations that we have. When we try to convince someone to support a certain stance, we have to provide compelling and valid arguments. In mathematics, we use the same tools of deductive and inductive reasoning that are used in the courtroom in settling cases, to solve mathematical problems and prove mathematical theorems. In this section, we examine the rubrics of deductive and inductive reasoning and the types of statements involved in logical arguments.

Mathematician Thales of Miletus (636 - 546 B.C.) was the first known Greek philosopher and scientist. He is considered the first person to have made use of deductive methods in mathematics. Once, while traveling in the desert of Giza in Egypt, a guide commented to Thales that the base of the pyramid they were viewing measured 518 cubits on each side. Interested, Thales asked the guide how high the pyramid stood. The guide was embarrassed that he did not know. After a short period, Thales announced that he had figured out the height of the pyramid to be 329 cubits. Thales explained that he used the pyramid's shadow and his own shadow to find the height of the pyramid by solving the proportion:

$$\frac{\text{Height of Thales}}{\text{Height of Thales's shadow}} = \frac{\text{Height of pyramid}}{\text{Height of pyramid's shadow}}$$

Many people were impressed with Thales' ability to solve problems. He was the first name on the list of "Seven Wise Men" of Greece compiled by the Greeks themselves.

For More Information: Reimer, L., & Reimer W. (1990). *Mathematicians are people, too: Stories from the lives of great mathematicians, Volume 1.* Palo Alto, CA: Dale Seymour Publications.

Inductive reasoning is reasoning from the particular to the general; that is, given a set of specific cases, we induce a generalization by observing patterns. There are a number of mathematical problems that can be solved using inductive reasoning. For example, consider the following problem:

> *At the class reunion in the conventional hall, there was a first knock on the door and one person entered the room. At the second knock, two more people entered than on the first knock. On each successive knock, two more people entered than on the previous knock. After the 200th knock, how many people had entered the room for the reunion?*

It is not likely that we would want to work each step of the problem out to the 200th knock. Instead, we can generate a table that helps us create specific information about how many people were in the room after certain knocks. We can then use these specific pieces of data to look for a pattern and induce a generalization of how many people will be in the room after the nth knock. We can then use this generalization to say how many people will be in the room after the 200th knock. See Table 1.1 for the table of information.

After observing a number of cases, we might notice the pattern that after knock number 1, the total number of people in the room is $1^2 = 1$, after knock number 2, the total number of people in the room is $2^2 = 4$, after knock number 3, the total number of people in the room is $3^2 = 9$, and so on. Thus, after knock number n, the total number of people in the room will be n^2. Thus, after the 200th knock, there will be $200^2 = 40,000$ people at the reunion.

Table 1.1

KNOCK #	HOW MANY ENTERED	TOTAL # IN THE ROOM
1	1	1
2	3	4
3	5	9
4	7	16
5	9	25
6	11	36
7	13	49
8	15	64
9	17	81
10	19	100
•	•	•
•	•	•
•	•	•
n		

Note that there are limitations to inductive reasoning. For example, there are some mathematical problems that appear to generate a pattern that could lead to a generalizable solution, but at some point, the pattern fails. However, not all mathematical problems can be solved using inductive reasoning. Rather, sometimes other types of reasoning or problem-solving strategies are more likely to lead to a solution. Further, in some cases a combination of strategies will lead to a solution, particularly the combination of inductive and deductive reasoning.

**1.4.2
Deductive
Reasoning**

Deductive reasoning involves working from a set of axioms or given general statements, and striving to derive or prove other specific statements or conclusions. Unlike inductive reasoning which is reasoning from specific to general, deductive reasoning is reasoning from general to specific. A mathematical problem that can be solved using deductive reasoning is the following:

Four friends, Nancy, Molly, Erin and Caroline, are going away to college together. They each are pursuing different majors, English, Mathematics, Biology, and Education. Erin and Caroline usually get help from tutors on their mathematics homework. Nancy was hired as a feature writer for the school newspaper. Caroline's volunteer work with children at a local elementary school will count for credit in her major. Match each girl with her major.

To solve this problem deductively, we can create a grid that shows each girl and each major as shown in Figure 1.10. As we work through the given general information provided about the girls, we can eliminate possibilities, noting these eliminations on the grid.

	math	biology	english	education
Nancy				
Erin				
Molly				
Caroline				

Figure 1.10

From the first clue, "Erin and Caroline usually get help from tutors on their mathematics homework," we can eliminate Erin and Caroline as the pursuing the math major. Thus, in Figure 1.11, we eliminate the possibility of Erin and Caroline as math majors by crossing an X through the boxes indicating the connection between Erin and math, and Caroline and math. This leaves either Nancy or Molly as the math major.

	math	biology	english	education
Nancy				
Erin	X			
Molly				
Caroline	X			

Figure 1.11

The next clue, "Nancy was hired as a feature writer for the school newspaper," implies that Nancy is probably the English major. Thus, not only can we pinpoint Nancy with this major, but we can eliminate others from this major and eliminate Nancy from the other majors, leaving Molly as the math major. We can then eliminate Molly from the other majors. See Figure 1.12.

	math	biology	english	education
Nancy	X	X	Yes	X
Erin	X		X	
Molly	Yes	X	X	X
Caroline	X		X	

Figure 1.12

After the second clue, we only have two people left to match with their majors. The final clue, "Caroline's volunteer work with children at a local elementary school will count for credit in her major," leads us to believe that Caroline must be the education major. Therefore, we can eliminate the possibility that Erin is the education major, leaving Erin as the biology major. See Figure 1.13.

	math	biology	english	education
Nancy	X	X	Yes	X
Erin	X	Yes	X	X
Molly	Yes	X	X	X
Caroline	X	X	X	Yes

Figure 1.13

Thus, from a few general statements, we were able to draw a specific conclusion using the process of elimination in our deductive reasoning.

1.4.3
Conjectures,
Hypotheses,
Conclusions

A **conjecture** is a guess or opinion based on inconclusive evidence. Conjectures often lead to investigations that can show whether or not the guess or opinion has any merit. To test a conjecture, we can form a hypothesis. A **hypothesis** is a statement that is assumed to be true. We generally prove whether or not a hypothesis is actually true through deductive reasoning. A **conclusion** is a decision or judgment made regarding the truth of a hypothesis. The conclusion is drawn through a valid deductive process.

For example, suppose Gina notices that $3 \times 1 = 3$, $5 \times 7 = 35$, $3 \times 13 = 39$ makes the conjecture, "When I multiply whole numbers by an odd number my answer is odd." We can form the hypothesis, "The product of an odd number times any whole number is an odd number." We can try to prove or disprove this hypothesis by forming an organized table showing the multiplication of an odd number times a variety of whole numbers.

Table 1.2 shows a table of products. One column of factors includes representative whole numbers starting with 0. The other column of factors includes several odd numbers.

Table 1.2

WHOLE NUMBERS	ODD NUMBERS	PRODUCT
0	3	0
1	3	3
2	3	6
3	3	9
4	5	20
5	5	25
6	5	30
7	7	49
8	7	56
9	7	63
•	•	•
•	•	•
•	•	•

We find from the list of products that not all the products are odd. Therefore, the hypothesis is shown to be false. However, while looking at the list of factors and products, Gina makes another hypothesis. She notices that all of the odd products came from two factors that were both odd. We form the hypothesis, "the product of two odd factors will always be odd." Testing this hypothesis, we can see that all of our examples indicate that this hypothesis is true.

To prove formally that the hypothesis is true, we can work with the following given statements. Any number of the form $2m$ where m is a whole number is an even number. So, a number of the form $2m + 1$ is odd. Suppose we have two odd numbers expressed generally as $2m + 1$, and $2n + 1$. The product of these two numbers is $(2m + 1)(2n + 1) = 4mn + 2n + 2m + 1$. This number can be re-written as: $2(2mn + n + m) + 1$. This product is also an odd number. Thus, we can draw the conclusion that the hypothesis, that the product of any two odd numbers is an odd number, is true.

In logical reasoning, we work with **statements** that are declarative sentences that are either true or false (not both). Examples of statements are: (a) It is raining.; (b) The door is open.; (c) 5 + 6 = 11; (d) I won the game.; and (e) Babies can drive. In symbolic logic, we usually denote a statement by a symbol, either p or q.

The **negation** of a statement p, which is denoted $\sim p$, is the statement "it is false that p." For example, if p is the statement "it is raining," then $\sim p$ is the statement "it is false that it is raining," or, rather, "it is not raining." If p is the statement, "No numbers between 10 and 20 are prime numbers," then $\sim p$ is the statement, "At least one number between 10 and 20 is a prime number."

1.4.4
**Statements and
the Negation of
Statements**

Compound statements are formed by combining two statements. We can combine two statements with the words (operations) "and" and "or." If p and q are each statements, then the compound statement, **p and q**, denoted $p \cap q$, is true when both p and q are true, and is false when either p, q, or both p and q are false. Such a compound statement is called a **conjuction**.

1.4.5
**Compound
Statements**

For example, suppose p is the statement "5 is a prime number" and q is the statement "8 is an even number." The statement p is true and the statement q is true. Therefore, the statement p *and* q, that is, "5 is a prime number and 8 is an even number," is also true.

Consider the example where p is the statement "5 is a prime number and q is the statement "10 is an odd number." The statement p is true, but the statement q is false. Therefore, the compound statement p *and* q, which says, "5 is a prime number and 10 is an odd number," is false.

Given statements p and q, the compound statement **p or q**, denoted p $\cup$ q, is true when either p or q or both p and q are true, and is false when both p and q are false. For example, suppose the statement p is "2 + 3 = 5" and the statement q is "5 > 8." Because the statement p is true and statement q is false, then the statement p *or* q, which reads "2 + 3 = 5 or 5 > 8" is true. Such a compound statement is called a **disjunction**.

Suppose p is the statements "dogs can fly" and q is the statement "everyone speaks Spanish." The compound statement "dogs can fly or everyone speaks Spanish" is false because both individual statements are false.

1.4.6
Truth Tables

We can form logical tables, called **truth tables**, that list all the possible outcomes regarding the truth or falsity of statements and related compound statements. If we have statements p and q, the possible combinations of the truth or falsity of these statements are: (a) both statements are true, (b) p is true and q is false, (c) p is false and q is true, and (d) both statements are false. We can place these possibilities in a table as shown in Table 1.3.

If we expand the truth table in Table 1.3 to include the possible outcomes of truth or falsity of compound statements involving p and q, we create the truth table shown in Table 1.4. Note that the table shows the cases when the statement p and q is true and false and cases when the statement p or q is false.

We can use truth tables to determine any combinations of statements. Suppose we want to determine outcomes associated with the compound statement ~p ∩ q. We can make the truth table shown in Table 1.5 to determine the answer.

Table 1.3

p	q
T	T
T	F
F	T
F	F

Table 1.4

p	q	$p \cup q$	$p \cap q$
T	T	T	T
T	F	T	F
F	T	T	F
F	F	F	F

Table 1.5

p	q	$\sim p$	$\sim p \cap q$
T	T	F	F
T	F	F	F
F	T	T	T
F	F	T	F

Truth tables can help find the possible outcomes associated with even more complex statements such as ~(p ∪ ~q) ∩ r, where p, q, and r are all simple statements. See Table 1.6 for the truth table.

Table 1.6

p	q	r	$\sim q$	$p \cup \sim q$	$\sim (p \cup \sim q)$	$\sim (p \cup \sim q) \cap r$
T	T	T	F	T	F	F
T	F	T	T	T	F	F
T	T	F	F	T	F	F
T	F	F	T	T	F	F
F	T	T	F	F	T	T
F	F	T	T	T	F	F
F	T	F	F	F	T	F
F	F	F	T	T	F	F

1.4.7
Conditional Statements

A **conditional statement** is a statement of the form "*if p then q*," denoted $p \rightarrow q$. The statement p is called the hypothesis and the statement q is called the conclusion. We can determine the truth or falsity of a conditional statement by the rule that $p \rightarrow q$ is true except in the case when p is true and q is false. The truth table associated with the conditional statement is shown in Table 1.7.

Table 1.7

p	q	$p \rightarrow q$
T	T	T
T	F	T
F	T	T
F	F	F

For example, suppose the statement p is "I weigh more than 150 pounds" and q is the statement "I will skip breakfast," then the statement. The conditional statement reads, "If I weigh more than 150 pounds, then I will skip breakfast." If the hypothesis is true and the conclusion is true, then the conditional statement is true. However, if the hypothesis is false, and the conclusion is true, read as "If

I don't weigh more than 150 pounds, then I will skip breakfast," the conditional statement is still true. This makes sense because the conclusion that "I will skip breakfast" may still come about even though the hypothesis is not true.

For every conditional statement $p \rightarrow q$, we have a related **contrapositive statement**, denoted $\sim q \rightarrow \sim p$. For example, given the conditional statement, "If it snows then school will be canceled." The contrapositive of this statement is "If school is not canceled, then it did not snow."

Every conditional statement $p \rightarrow q$ also has a related **converse statement**, denoted $q \rightarrow p$. For example, given the conditional statement "If I run fast then I win the race," the converse of this statement would read, "If I win the race, then I run fast."

Finally, for a conditional statement $p \rightarrow q$, there is an **inverse statement**, denoted $\sim p \rightarrow \sim q$. For example, given the conditional statement "If $a + b$ is even, then a and b are both even," the inverse of this statement is "If $a + b$ is not even, then a and b are not both even."

**1.4.8
Inverse, Converse, and Contrapositive Statements**

Given statements p and q, we make the statement "**p if and only if q**," denoted p *iff* q or $p \leftrightarrow q$, to describe the situation where both of the conditional statements $p \rightarrow q$ and $q \rightarrow p$ hold true. For example, consider the *if and only if* statement, "A number is divisible by 2 if and only if the digit in the ones place is divisible by 2." The truth of this *if and only if* statement implies that both the conditional statements "If a number is divisible by 2 then the digit in the ones place is divisible by 2" and "If a digit in the ones place is divisible by 2 then the number is divisible by 2" are true.

**1.4.9
If and Only If Statements**

Direct reasoning is a mode of deductive reasoning that follows through the logic of a conditional statement $p \rightarrow q$. Direct reasoning follows these steps:

**1.4.10
Direct and Indirect Reasoning**

Hypothesis: $p \rightarrow q$
$$\frac{\qquad\qquad p}{}$$
Conclusion: q

For example,

Hypothesis: If it rains, then I bring my umbrella.
It rains.
Conclusion: I bring my umbrella.

Generally, with direct reasoning, if we want to prove the conditional statement is true, we assume the hypothesis is true and show how the conclusion follows from the hypothesis through deductive reasoning.

An example of direct reasoning in problem solving is this. Let us prove the statement, "If we add two even numbers then our sum will be an even number." By definition, an even number is any number of the form 2 times a whole number. Given any two even numbers, which can be expressed as $2m$, and $2n$ (where m, n are whole numbers), we find the sum to be $2m + 2n = 2(m + n)$. Because $m + n$ is a whole number, the sum is expressed in the form of 2 times a whole number, and, therefore, is an even number.

Indirect reasoning uses reasoning that makes use of the contrapositive. The steps of indirect reasoning are:

$$\text{Hypothesis: } \quad \sim q \to \sim p$$
$$\underline{\qquad\qquad\qquad p \qquad}$$
$$\text{Conclusion: } \qquad q$$

For example, suppose we have the conditional statement "If there is a traffic jam, then I will be late for work." We can use indirect reasoning with the contrapositive statement "If I am not late for work then there is not a traffic jam" to work through the logical possibilities of this statement.

Hypothesis: If I am not late for work, then there is not a traffic jam.
There is a traffic jam.
Conclusion: I am late for work.

In general with indirect reasoning, in trying to prove that a certain conclusion follows from hypothesis, we assume the conclusion is not true and try to show, then, that the hypothesis is not true. What happens is that we find that the hypothesis is in fact true (we find a contradiction to our false assumption), which means that the conclusion cannot be false. Therefore, the conclusion is true.

An example of indirect reasoning in problem solving is this. Let us prove that there are infinitely many Natural Numbers. To do so, we will assume there are finitely many Natural Numbers. Through deductive reasoning, we will show that this false assumption leads to a contradiction of a fundamental mathematical property, and therefore, we prove that our original assumption is false. Therefore, we will conclude that there must be an infinite number of Natural Numbers.

Proof: Assume there is a finite number of Natural Numbers. Then there is a largest Natural Number, n. However, the set of Natural Numbers is closed under addition; that is, the sum of any two Natural Numbers is also a Natural Number. Therefore, because both n and 1 are Natural Numbers, the sum $n + 1$ will be a Natural Number. But, $n + 1$ is greater than n, which contradicts the assumption that n is the largest Natural Number. Therefore, there must be an infinite number of Natural Numbers.

RELATED TOPICS   Patterns | Problem-Solving

TOPIC 1.5 PROBLEM-SOLVING TOPICS

Of course solving problems is not restricted only to mathematics. There are examples of problems being posed and solved in many ancient cultures. What is new about the idea of problem solving is the fact that more and more people are coming to believe that solving problems is at the very heart of learning mathematics. In this section, we examine the process of solving mathematics problems, giving special attention to four key phases of problem solving and eight popular strategies for solving a variety of mathematical problems.

INTRODUCTION

DID YOU KNOW?

George Polya is credited for developing a methodical process for finding solutions to mathematical problems. This **process of problem solving**, along with a description of what each step involves for the problem solver, includes:

1.5.1
Polya's Process of Problem-Solving

Understand the Problem. In order to be successful in solving any problem, you must understand it well. To help yourself understand the problem, you can (a) restate the problem in language that is clear and sensible to you; (b) clarify the question being asked, including any hidden questions; (c) organize the information in the problem by identifying key information and getting rid of unnecessary information.

Devise a Plan. Analyze the problem with the goal of identifying a systematic method for solving the problem. At this step in the process, you can (a) ask yourself, "Have I ever solved a problem like this one before? In what ways was it like this one? What did I do to solve that problems that might be helpful in solving this one?"; (b) consider the various problem-solving strategies that you have learned and decide if any of them will help; and (c) determine what you want to do first, second, etc.

Carry Out the Plan. Carry out the plan you have chose, being sure to implement it correctly. When carrying out your plan (a) check your work along the way as you proceed with your solution effort; (b) don't be content to check only your computations. Also, check to make sure that you are using all the important information and that and that you have not misinterpreted anything; (c) ask yourself, "Is this plan getting me anywhere? Am I following the plan I chose, or am I getting sidetracked? Should I abandon this plan and try to think of another way to solve the problem?"

Look Back. Make sure that you have clearly answered the question at hand and decide if your solution is reasonable. Also, consider what you have learned by solving the problem, not only about mathematics, but also about yourself as a doer of mathematics. At this point, (a) check your solution with the important information given in the problem and determine if there are other possible solutions, (b) check all your computations and other work one more time; (c) think about the plan you used and ask yourself, "Could I have solved this problem another, better way? Would my plan work if the numbers in the problem were larger? Would my plan work in general? Could I now solve other problems similar to this one?"

Although the four phases seem chronological in order, it is important to remember that you might need to go back and forth between the different stages before a solution is achieved.

**1.5.2
Problem-Solving
Strategies**

In mathematics, there are many standard strategies that can help in the process of problem solving, when applied appropriately. In this section we discuss eight of these strategies and work through a sample problem for each strategy.

Guess and Check. As the name suggests, this strategy consists of guessing the answer to a problem and then verifying whether the solution you guessed satisfies all the conditions of the problem. Once you determine the degree to which your first guess satisfied the problem, you can make a second, more informed guess and check this guess to see if this guess satisfies the problem. This strategy works particularly well if there are only a limited number of possible answers to choose from. At times, this strategy may not give you the solution directly. However, it will help you to eliminate some possibilities, and suggest where you may look for possible solutions.

For example, you are given nine specific numbers to place without repetition in a 3-by-3 square such that the sum of the numbers in any row or column or along any diagonal is always the same. It would help you to start by guessing at some of the number positions and then work with that guess to make revised guesses. Figure 1.13 shows guesses 1, 2, and 3.

Figure 1.13

GUESS 1
Checking we find that row 1 adds to 11, row 2 adds to 21, and row 3 adds to 13. Decide that the smallest numbers can't be in the same rows and the largest numbers can't be in the same row. Try again.

GUESS 2
In this guess, we tried to distribute high and low numbers more evenly in different rows (and columns). In this guess, the row sums, 16, 15, 14, are at least closer to each other. Now decide that if the first nine numbers add to 45 and each row must be the same sum, then each row must sum to 15. So now try to make each row sum to 15.

GUESS 3
In this guess, each row adds to 15. Now we have to work with this guess so that all the columns and the diagonals as well also add to 15.

From our conclusions in Figure 1.13, we make more informed guesses as shown in Figure 1.14.

Figure 1.14

GUESS 4
In this guess, each row adds to 15, and both diagonals add to 15. Also, 1 of the 3 columns adds to 15. We just need to adjust the guess slightly to arrive at a final answer.

GUESS 5
Each row, column, and diagonal sums to 15.

Use a Visual Aid. There are different ways in which one can use a visual aid in order to look for a solution to a problem. Such visual aids include drawing a picture, using physical manipulatives, or even connecting the problem to some situation that you have experienced in your life so that you can make sense of it using your own experience.

Drawing a picture or diagram is particularly useful when the problem one is dealing with involves a physical situation. A picture will help to show the relative position of various objects in the problem. Often, it is also a useful way to organize the given information. Once you have drawn a picture, it can help you to interpret the problem and the conditions in it. It may also suggest a possible strategy to solve the problem. While it may not be always essential, it is usually helpful for you to draw a clear and well-labeled picture. Firstly, such a picture is easier to interpret, and secondly, seeing all the information in one place may make it easier to find a solution.

Similarly, one may use such physical manipulatives as tiles, pencils, candy, boxes, cones, or cans in order to understand a problem or to look for a solution. These manipulatives may be particularly useful in case our problem involves three dimensional objects or moving objects from one place to another when looking for a solution.

Example: John is supposed to run 4 laps around a rectangular field that measures 100 by 85 feet. However he feels a little lazy and cuts across the corners each time, leaving each side 12 feet before the edge, and hitting the other side 5 feet from its edge. By what distance has John cut short his run?

Solution: It is easy to see that in this case, drawing the field and marking the distances on it would help to see the problem more clearly and find its solution. Consider the diagram shown in Figure 1.15.

Figure 1.15

If John did not cut corners, the total distance around that he would run per lap is found by computing $2 \times (100 + 85) = 370$ feet. Each time he cuts a corner, instead of running $(12 + 5) = 17$ feet, he actually runs a distance of only 13 feet. This is determined by using the Pythagorean theorem to find the hypotenuse of the right triangle formed with side lengths 12 and 5. The hypotenuse would be $\sqrt{12^2 + 5^2} = \sqrt{169} = 13$. Thus, finding the distance of the shortcut path we compute: $2 \times ((100 - (12 + 5) + 13 + (85 - (12 + 5) + 13) = 354$ feet. So, in one lap, John cuts his run short by $370 - 354 = 16$ feet. Therefore, in 4 laps he cuts his run short by $4 \times 16 = 64$ feet.

Look for a Pattern. Another useful strategy that often helps in looking for a solution to a problem is looking for patterns. This strategy is particularly useful when one is trying to generalize an idea or to look for an algebraic formula. The strategy is to look at specific cases of the solution of a problem, and to see if an identifiable pattern emerges. Once you have identified the patterns, it is usually a good idea to verify it with other randomly chosen instances before you feel reasonably convinced of it.

Example: Given n points in a plane, no three of which are collinear, how many line segments must be drawn to connect all pairs of points?

Solution: To begin the solution, it is perhaps best to actually draw points in a plane and connect them by line segments. We should do this systematically. So, start with 2 points, then three points, then four, and so on. Then, from these trials, create a table and try to observe a pattern to generalize a solution to the problem (see Figure 1.16).

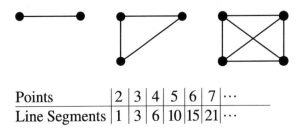

Figure 1.16

Points	2	3	4	5	6	7	⋯
Line Segments	1	3	6	10	15	21	⋯

To try to establish a pattern, we can observe a pattern that can be illustrated in Table 1.8.

Table 1.8

Points	2	3	4	5	6
Line Segments	1	1+2	1+2+3	1+2+3+4	1+2+3+4+5

From this table, the pattern becomes clear. For 3 points, we have $1+2$ line segments; for 4 points, we have $1 + 2 + 3$ line segments, and so on. Thus, for n points, we will have $1 + 2 + 3 + \cdots + (n - 1)$ line segments. This gives us the general formula to find the number of segments that connect any number of (non-collinear if more than two) point, in pairs, to each other.

Make a Table. As we have seen in the previous problem, a table is a useful tool to use when the problem has several related components that build upon one another or when we have a list of possibilities and need to manipulate each possibility in several stages.

Example: On opening night, the director counted 56 people and noticed that 1 out of every 5 seats in the theater was empty. How many empty seats were there?

Solution: A table will facilitate finding a solution to this problem. Consider Table 1.9.

Table 1.9

Total Seats	5	10	15	20	⋯
Filled Seats	4	8	12	16	⋯
Empty Seats	1	2	3	4	⋯

The table helps us organize the situation and generate a list of possible total seats and a breakdown of how many of the total seats would be empty and how many filled. For example, if there were 5 seats total, then 1 of the 5 would be empty and 4 of the 5 would be filled. If there were 10 seats, 2 would be empty and 8 would be filled. Thus, we can use the table to project how many seats will be empty if there are 56 filled seats. We note a relationship between filled seats and empty seats in that the number of filled seats is four times the number of empty seats. Thus, if there are 56 filled seats, there would be 56 ÷ 4 = 14 empty seats. Therefore, we can conclude that the theater must seat 70 people, and that 14 of those seats were empty on opening night.

Make an Organized List. When solving problems with multiple solutions, making an organized list is a useful strategy. It is also useful when solving problems regarding various ways of combining or arranging things. Organized lists can be created within a table to facilitate the organization process.

Example: There are four infielders on the junior baseball league and the coach is trying to determine the best batting order of the four infielders: first base, second base, third base, and short stop. What are all the possible batting order combinations he could try with the four players?

Solution: To make sure we find all possible combinations, it is important that we generate a list of possibilities in an organized fashion. Therefore, let us first refer to the first base player using the symbol, 1, second base with the symbol 2, third base with the symbol 3, and short stop with the letter S. Thus, one possible batting order might be (1, 2, 3, S). Another possibility would be (S, 3, 2, 1). We can continue to configure batting orders, but the best means is to organize the list so that we won't mistakenly leave out some of the possibilities. Here is a sample of the organized list:

1, 2, 3, S	2, 1, 3, S	3, 1, 2, S	S, 1, 2, 3
1, 2, S, 3	2, 1, S, 3	3, 1, S, 2	S, 1, 3, 2
1, 3, 2, S	2, 3, 1, S	3, 2, 1, S	S, 2, 1, 3
1, 3, S, 2	2, 3, S, 1	3, 2, S , 1	S, 2, 3, 1
1, S, 2, 3	2, S, 1, 3	3, S, 1, 2	S, 3, 1, 2
1, S, 3, 2	2, S, 3, 1	3, S, 2, 1	S, 3, 2, 1

By starting the list with all the possibilities where the first basement bats first, and combine the first basemen with each of the ways to arrange the remaining three batters, we begin an organized list. Continuing by considering all possibilities where the second basement is first maintains the organization of the list. In this fashion, we find all 24 possible batting orders of the four infielders.

Work Backward. In some problems, you are given a series of related data. In order to work through the data to uncover a solution to your problem, you need to start the last and most specific piece of the data and work backward through the other related pieces of data. For example, suppose you visit a friend in an unfamiliar city. Your friend gives you directions to reach her house from the highway. After spending some time with her, you are ready to return. This time you need to reach the highway from your friend's house, but you do not have a map. Your best way to solve your problem is to try to work backwards from the directions given to you earlier.

Example. April is thinking of a number. If you add 7 to the number, multiply the result by 2 and then subtract 10, you get 26. What was the original number that April thought of?

Solution. We do not know the number that April started with, but we do know what she ended up with. So, we start at the end and work our way backward, unraveling the information at each stage. Starting with 26, we add back the 10 that had been subtracted to get the difference of 26 and have 36. Then, undoing the fact that this number was found by multiplying by two, we divide the number by 2 to find 18. Finally, to undo the fact that 7 had been added to the original number, we subtract 7 from 18 to yield a solution of 11. To check that we indeed found the correct original number, start with 11, add 7 to get 18, multiply by 2 and get 36, and then subtract 10 to get 26. We have verified that 11 was April's original number.

Use Algebra. Using algebra is probably one strategy that every student in high school becomes familiar with in order to solve problems. In fact, algebra is often the only strategy that students try to use to solve a problem. While not all problems can be solved using algebra, it certainly is a very useful problem-solving tool, particularly when it is combined with other strategies, such as drawing a picture, making a table, or looking for patterns. Just as a reminder, this strategy involves replacing an unknown quantity (or quantities) with a variable (or variables) using letters such as x or y, setting up equation using these variables to satisfy the condition given in the problem, and then solving the equation for the variable through symbolic manipulation.

Example. Show that the sum of any five consecutive multiples of 3 is a multiple of 15.

Solution. To solve this problem, we will introduce a variable and develop an algebraic expression to show the sum of five consecutive numbers. We can write a multiple of 3 as $3m$, where m is any integer. Then the next multiple of 3 will be $3m + 3$. Thus, five consecutive multiples of 3 can be written as $3m$, $3m + 3$, $3m + 6$, $3m + 9$, $3m + 12$. Their sum will be $3m + (3m + 3) + (3m + 6) + (3m + 9) + (3m + 12) = 15m + 30 = 15(m + 2)$ which is clearly a multiple of 15.

Solve a Simpler Problem. Sometimes a mathematical problem may seem overwhelming simply because it has too many conditions that need to be satisfied, or it involves big and complicated numbers, or there are simply too many tasks that need to be done to get the final answer. In such cases, it may be helpful to look for a simpler, related problem to solve. Once you find the solution to the easier problem, you can examine its solution, and see what insight it gives you for the big, complex problem. Often, this process may make your task much easier.

Example. How many squares are there on an 8 × 8 checkerboard?

Solution. To find the total number of squares on an 8 × 8 checkerboard may be difficult to do directly. Instead, we can try to solve a simpler problem by looking at smaller checkerboards. We can start with the 1 × 1 and 2 × 2 boards (See Figure 1.17).

The 1 × 1 board clearly has just one square. The 2 × 2 board has 4 small (1 × 1) squares and 1 big (2 × 2) square, for a total of 5 squares. Now, we can look at a 3 × 3 board (see Figure 1.18). From our experience with the 2 × 2 board, we can conclude that counting will be much easier if we do it systematically. That is, by looking at how many 1 × 1 squares, how many 2 × 2 squares, and how many 3 × 3 squares in the 3 × 3 board.

In Figure 1.18 we find 9 1 × 1 squares, 4 2 × 2 squares, and 1 3 × 3 squares for a total of 14 squares in the 3 × 3 board. Now, we examine the 4 × 4 board in Figure 1.19. Within the 4 × 4 board, we find 16 1 × 1 squares, 9 2 × 2 squares, 4 3 × 3 squares, and 1 4 × 4 squares for a total of 30 squares in the 4 × 4 board.

Figure 1.17   **Figure 1.18**   **Figure 1.19**

1 × 1   2 × 2

Having examined these simpler versions of the problem, we have learned a systematic means of counting the number of squares in an $n \times n$ board. Now, we can combine what we have learned from these simpler problems with the strategies of making a table and looking for a pattern (see Table 1.10) to determine the number of squares in an 8 × 8 board.

From the table, we see that the number of squares in the 1 × 1 board is 1 (the first square number). The number of squares in the 2 × 2 board is found by adding the first two square numbers (1 + 4). The number of squares in the 3 x 3 board can be found by adding the first three square numbers (1 + 4 + 9). The number of squares in the 4 × 4 boards can be found by adding the first four square numbers (1 + 4 + 9 + 16). Thus, we can determine the number of squares in the 8 × 8 checkerboard by adding the first eight square numbers to find the sum 204.

Size of Board	Number of Squares	Total	Table 1.10
1 × 1	1	1	
2 × 2	1 + 4	5	
3 × 3	1 + 4 + 9	14	
4 × 4	1 + 4 + 9 + 16	30	
•	•	•	
•	•	•	
•	•	•	
8 × 8	1 + 4 + 9 + 16 + 25 + 36 + 49 + 64	204	

Logic | Patterns   **RELATED TOPICS**

IN THE CLASSROOM

Some expectations of your future students

From the Problem Solving Standard (NCTM, 2000, p. 52)	build new mathematical knowledge through problem solving
	solve problems that arise in mathematics and in other contexts
	apply and adapt a variety of appropriate strategies to solve problems
	monitor and reflect on the process of mathematical problem solving
From the Reasoning & Proof, Communication, Connections & Representation Standards (NCTM, 2000, pp. 56, 60, 64, 67)	recognize reasoning and proof as fundamental aspects of mathematics
	communicate their mathematical thinking coherently and clearly to peers, teachers, and others
	recognize and use connections among mathematical ideas
	create and use representations to organize, record, and communicate mathematical ideas

In this first chapter we emphasize the five *Process Standards* outlined in the National Council of Teachers of Mathematics *Principles and Standards for School Mathematics* (NCTM, 2000).

Standards are descriptions of what mathematics instruction should enable students to know and do. They specify the understanding, knowledge, and skills that students should acquire from prekindergarten through grade 12. The Content Standards—Number and Operations, Algebra, Geometry, Measurement, and Data Analysis and Probability—explicitly describe the content that students should learn. The Process Standards—Problem Solving, Reasoning and Proof, Communication, Connections, and Representation—highlight ways of acquiring and using content knowledge (p. 29).

How Activities 1.1-1.10 help you develop an adult-level perspective on the above expectations.

- By stacking cereal boxes or laying patio tiles, you solve problems that may arise in everyday contexts yet have important connections to number, geometry, and algebra. This activity also gives you the opportunity to apply different problem solving strategies as well as adapt a strategy used to solve one problem to solve another.

- By modeling situations such as the Valentine's Day Party or the Hefty Hippos puzzle, you learn to communicate your mathematical thinking coherently and clearly to each other, while gaining an opportunity to formally monitor and reflect on the process of mathematical problem solving.

- By creating and using representations to visualize a situation or understand relationships, you learn to organize, record, and communicate mathematical ideas in activities such as Making Dice and the Tower of Hanoi.

- By exploring the mathematics in the pages of a newspaper and the activity constructing numbers, you build new mathematical knowledge through problem solving.

- By playing games such as What's my Number? and Poison, and exploring Family Relations, you realize that reasoning and proof are fundamental aspects of mathematics and develop strategies for justifying the general case by analyzing the specific.

BIBLIOGRAPHY

Averback, W. B., & Orin, C. (1980). *Problem solving through recreational mathematics.* New York: Freeman.

Gardiner, A. (1996). *Discovering mathematics: The art of investigation.* New York: Oxford Scientific Publications.

Akaishi, A., & Saul, M. (1991). Exploring, learning, sharing: Vignettes from the classroom. *Arithmetic Teacher, 39,* 12-16.

Bledsoe, G. J. (1989). Hook your students on problem solving. *Arithmetic Teacher, 37,* 16-20.

Borassi, R. (1992). *Learning mathematics through inquiry.* Portsmouth. NH: Heinemann.

Brown, S. I., & Walter, M. I. (1990). *The art of problem posing* (2nd edition). Hillsdale, NJ: Erlbaum.

Brown, S. I., & Walter, M. I. (Eds.). (1993). *Problem posing: Reflections and applications.* Hillsdale, NJ: Erlbaum.

Bush, W. S., & Fiala, A. (1986). Problem stories: A new twist on problem posing. *Arithmetic Teacher, 34,* 6-9.

Campbell, P. F., & Bamberger, H. J. (1990). Implementing the *Standards*: The vision of problem solving in the *Standards*. *Arithmetic Teacher, 37,* 14-17.

Cemen, P. B. (1989). Developing a problem-solving lesson. *Arithmetic Teacher, 37,* 14- 19.

Chambers, D. L. (1995). Improving instruction by listening to children. *Teaching Children Mathematics, 1,* 378-380.

Charles, R., & Lester, F. K. (1982). *Teaching problem solving: What, why and how.* Palo Alto, CA: Dale Seymour Publications.

Corwin, R. B. (1993). Doing mathematics together: Creating a mathematical culture. *Arithmetic Teacher, 40,* 336-341.

Day, R. P. (1986). A problem-solving component for junior high school mathematics. *Arithmetic Teacher, 34,* 14-17.

English, L. D., Cudmore, D., & Tilley, D. (1998). Problem posing and critiquing: how it can happen in your classroom. *Mathematics Teaching in the Middle School, 4,* 124-129.

Esty, W. W., & Teppo, A. R. (1996). Algebraic thinking, language, and word problems. In P. C. Elliott (Ed.), *Communication in mathematics: K-12 and beyond* (pp. 45-55) Reston, VA: National Council of Teachers of Mathematics.

Fortunato, I., Hecht, D., Tittle, C. K., & Alvarez, L. (1991). Metacognition and problem solving. *Arithmetic Teacher, 39,* 38-40.

Fulkerson, P. (1992). Getting the most from a problem. *Arithmetic Teacher, 40,* 178-179.

Garofalo, J. (1987). Metacognition and school mathematics. *Arithmetic Teacher, 34*(9), 22-23.

Garofalo, J., & Lester, F. K. (1985). Metacognition, cognitive monitoring, and mathematical performance. *Journal for Research in Mathematics Education, 16,* 163-176.

Garofalo, J., & Bryant, J. (1992). Assessing reasonableness: Some observations and suggestions. *Arithmetic Teacher, 40,* 210-212.

Goodnow, J., Hoogeboom, S., Moretti, G., Stephens, M., & Scanlin, A. (1987). *The problem solver: Activities for learning problem solving strategies.* Palo Alto, CA Creative Publications.

Hembree, R., & Marsh, H. (1993). Problem solving in early childhood: Building foundations. In R. J. Jensen (Ed.), *Research ideas for the classroom: Early childhood mathematics* (pp. 151-170). Old Tappan, NJ: Macmillan.

Henningsen, M., & Stein, M. K. (1997). Mathematical tasks and student cognition: Classroom-based factors that support and inhibit high-level mathematical thinking and reasoning. *Journal for Research in Mathematics Education, 28,* 524-549.

Hyde, A. A., & Hyde, P. R. (1991). *Mathwise: Teaching mathematical thinking and problem solving.* Portsmouth, NH: Heinemann.

Kersh, M. E., & McDonald, J. (1991). How do I solve Thee? Let me count the ways!" *Arithmetic Teacher, 39,* 38-41.

Kimball, R. L. (1991). Activities: Make your own problems-and then solve them. *Mathematics Teacher, 84,* 647-655.

Kroll, D. L., & Miller, T. (1993). Insights from research on mathematical problem solving in the middle grades. In D. T. Owens (Ed.*), Research ideas for the classroom: Middle grades mathematics* (pp. 58-77). Old Tappan, NJ: Macmillan.

Kruliks, S., & Rudnick, J. A. (1985). Developing problem-solving skills. *Mathematics Teacher, 78,* 685-692, 697-698.

Lester, F. K. (1989). Research into practice: Mathematical problem solving in and out of school. *Arithmetic Teacher, 39,* 33-35.

Lester, F. K., Jr., Masingila, J. O., Mau, S. T., Lambdin, D. V., Santos, V. M. P., & Raymond, A. M. (1994). Learning how to teach via problem solving. In D. Aichele (Ed.), *Professional development for teachers of mathematics* (pp. 152-166). Reston, VA: National Council of Teachers of Mathematics.

Lubienski, S. T. (1999). Problem-centered mathematics teaching. *Mathematics Teaching in the Middle School, 5,* 250-255.

Manouchegri, A., & Enderson, M. C. (1999). Promoting mathematical discourse: Learning from classroom examples. *Mathematics Teaching in the Middle School, 4,* 216-222.

Masingila, J. O. (1997). Let's be realistic. *Mathematics Teaching in the Middle School, 2* (3), 136-137.

Masingila, J. O. (1998). Thinking deeply about knowing mathematics. *Mathematics Teacher, 91* (7), 610-614.

Masingila, J. O., & Moellwald, F. E. (1993). Using Polya to foster a classroom environment for real-world problem solving. *School Science and Mathematics, 93* (5), 245-249.

Mason, J., Burton, L. & Stacey, K. (1985). *Thinking mathematically* (Revised edition). Menlo Park, CA: Addison-Wesley.

Matz, K. A., & Leier, C. (1992). Word Problems and the Language Connection. *Arithmetic Teacher, 39,* 14-17.

McNeal, B. (1995). Learning not to think in a textbook-baled mathematics class. *Journal of Mathematical Behavior, 14,* 205-234.

Meyer, C., & Sallee, T. (1983). *Make it simpler: A practical guide to problem solving in mathematics.* Menlo Park, CA: Addison-Wesley.

Ritchhart, R. (1999). Generative topics: Building a curriculum around big ideas. *Teaching Children Mathematics, 5,* 462-468.

Rowan, T. E., & Robles, J. (1998). Using questions to help children build mathematical power. *Teaching Children Mathematics, 4,* 504-509.

Sigurdson, S. E., Olson, A T., & Mason, R. (1994). Problem solving and mathematics reaming *Journal of Mathematical Behavior, 13,* 361-388.

Silver, E. A., Kilpatrick, J., & Schlesinger, B (1990). *Thinking through mathematics: Fostering inquiry and communication in mathematics classrooms .* New York: College Entrance Examination Board.

Silverman, F. L., Winograd, K., & Strohauer, D. (1992). Student-generated story problems. *Arithmetic Teacher, 39,* 6- 12.

Smith, M. S., & Stein, M. K. (1998). Selecting and creating mathematical tasks: From research to practice. *Mathematics Teaching in the Middle School, 3,* 344-350.

Stein, M. K., & Smith, M. S. (1998). Mathematical tasks as a framework for reflection: From research to practice. *Mathematics Teaching in the Middle School, 3,* 268-275.

Stimpson, V. C. (1989). Using diagrams to solve problems. *Mathematics Teacher, 82,* 194-200.

Szetela, W. (1986). The checkerboard problem extended, extended, extended. School Science and Mathematics, *86,* 205-222.

Talton, C. F. (1988). Let's solve the problem before we find the answer. *Arithmetic Teacher, 36*(1), 40~5.

Whitin, D. J. (1987). Problem solving in action: The bulletin-board dilemma. *Arithmetic Teacher, 35, 48-50.*

2 NUMERATION

CHAPTER OVERVIEW

Among the most important topics in elementary school mathematics are those concerned with systems of recording and naming numbers: numeration systems. In this chapter you can learn some interesting facts about numeration, and examine some concepts and procedures involving numeration ideas.

BIG MATHEMATICAL IDEAS

- Generalizing
- Problem-solving Strategies
- Decomposing
- Mathematical Structure
- Multiple Representations

NCTM PRINCIPLES & STANDARDS LINKS

Number and Operation
Problem Solving
Reasoning
Communication
Connections
Representation

TOPIC

2.1 Characteristics of Numeration Systems

2.2 Base-Ten Introduction

2.3 Place Value and Zero

2.4 Decimal System and More on Base Ten

In the Classroom

Bibliography

TOPIC 2.1 CHARACTERISTICS OF NUMERATION SYSTEMS

Whole Numbers

CORNERSTONE

A numeration system is a collection of numerals with a set of characteristics that determine how to interpret those symbols, and algorithms that depict methods of calculating amounts with those numerals. Characteristics associated with a variety of numeration systems include having place value, having a base, and having a zero. The Hindu-Arabic numeration system, the prevailing system used today, has all of these characteristics and more. In this section we list the six basic characteristics of the Hindu-Arabic numeration system as an introduction to the sections that follow and briefly examine the characteristics of unique representation. The remaining five characteristics of the Hindu-Arabic numeration system are examined in subsequent sections within this Topic.

INTRODUCTION

Did you know that the numeration characteristic of being **additive** shows up in most of the numeration systems about which we know? Even the Primitive Numeration System, which consists of a tally-marking process that seems almost too basic to be defined by any characteristics, is an additive system. Take, for example, the amount represented in the Primitive system, | | | | | |. To interpret the value of these symbols, we simply add the singular values of each of the tally marks. Because each tally mark represents "1," we can interpret the number | | | | | | as $1 + 1 + 1 + 1 + 1 + 1 = 6$.

DID YOU KNOW?

The Hindu-Arabic numeration system has six key characteristics: place value, base ten, having a zero, additivity, multiplicativity, and unique representation. Although many of these characteristics are found in other numeration systems, having the combination of these six characteristics is what makes the Hindu-Arabic system singularly its own.

2.1.1
**Characteristics of
the Hindu-Arabic System**

One key outcome of the Hindu-Arabic system due to the combination of five of the six characteristics, those being place value, base ten, having a zero, additivity, and multiplicativity, is that we are guaranteed **unique representation**. We all agree that there is one, and only one, way to represent the amount five hundred forty six using the Hindu-Arabic numeration system, that is, by the symbols 546. This characteristic of unique representation, while seemingly such a simple feature, provides a clarity of number representation that is not present in all numeration systems.

2.1.2
**Unique
Representation**

Unlike the Hindu-Arabic system, the Roman numeration system allows for multiple representation of some numbers. For example, when representing the amount 49 using the Roman numeration system, some may use the combination of symbols XLIX while others may simply use IL. Although multiple representations are not inherently bad, it is important in our technologically-advancing world that we have a precise, unambiguous, and indisputable means of representing numbers in society.

The earliest roots of mathematics can probably be traced back to a need for counting and recording numbers. From as far back as historians can tell, every society has had some means of recording numerical quantities. This is true even of those societies for which no written records of numerals are available. Evidence of this fact comes from archaeological excavations from different parts of the world.

2.1.3
**Historical/Social/
Cultural Notes
about Numeration**

The handle of a bone tool etched with some clear markings found amongst the remains of the Ishango community in central Africa bear testimony to the fact that this neolithic community had some means of keeping tally of numerical quantities.

Another culture from which archaeologists have dug up evidence of recording numerical quantities is that of the Incas, a culture that flourished until about the fifteenth century A.D., in parts of modern Peru, Bolivia, Chile, Ecuador, and Argentina. The Incas had a device called *quipu* that they used for recording numbers. A quipu consists of a collection of cords, containing knots of different kinds. There are records of a quipu being used as a tool to record data during a household census in 1567.

The earliest system of spoken and written symbols used to represent numbers may have used small numbers such as 2, 3, or 4 as a **base**. The use of such systems has been reported from communities that lived in Africa, southern Australia, and South America.

Definition: A numeration system has a **base** if it reflects a process of repeated grouping by some number greater than 1. This number is called the base of the system, and all numbers in that system are written in terms of powers of the base. If b is the base, numbers are written in terms of 1, b, b^2, b^3, etc.

Numeration systems in early societies often reveal interesting aspects of the culture that prevailed, and what was regarded as important in these societies. The Aztecs of central America had such written symbols for numbers as a blob representing a maize pod for a unit, a diagrammatic sketch of a maize plant to represent the number 400, and (what is commonly believed to be) a maize doll to represent the number 8000. The use of the base 10 in many cultures evolved from the practice of using fingers of the hands for counting. Zulu words for the numbers 1 through 10 are clearly based on this practice. In warmer climates, on the other hand, people could even use their toes for counting and this led to the use of the number 20 as a base, in such cultures as the Maya of central America, and the Yoruba in western Africa.

2.1.4
The Development of the Hindu-Arabic Numeration System

The system of numbers that we use today, called the Hindu-Arabic numeration system, has a fascinating and checkered history. While it is commonly believed to have been invented by Hindu mathematicians in India around 500 A.D., from where it was carried to other parts of the world by the Arabs, it took a long time before it became universally accepted. Meanwhile, in other parts of the world, different civilizations developed different ways of bringing order to their system of numeration. We now turn to a brief glimpse of these systems, and how each in its own way contributed to the advancement of human understanding of numbers.

The Egyptian Numeration System. The Egyptian system of numbers dates back to about 3400 B.C. Our information on this civilization is derived from papyrus documents that the Egyptians used for record keeping. They used ink brushes to write upon the papyrus. Initially, it was a simple system based on using a series of vertical strokes, called tally marks, the number of which was in one to one correspondence with the items being counted. Later, this cumbersome method was improved upon by using some system of grouping numbers bigger than 9. The Egyptians drew upon their environment to introduce pictographic symbols to represent the different powers of 10, from 10^0 to 10^6. The following table shows these Egyptian numerals.

Egyptian Numeral	Description	Hindu-Arabic Equivalent
	vertical staff	1
	heel bone	10
	scroll	100
	lotus flower	1,000
	pointing finger	10,000
	polliwog or burbot	100,000
	astonished person	1,000,000

Definition: A symbol used to represent a number is called a **numeral**. For example, the symbol "3" is a numeral that represents the quantity three.

Numbers written in the Egyptian system used an additive property. Thus, the value of the number was the sum of the values of the numerals used to write the number. The following example illustrates this idea.

	represents	100,000
	represents	20,000
	represents	400
	represents	30
	represents	1

Thus, ![Egyptian numerals] represents 120,431.

The Babylonian Numeration System. The Babylonian numeration system developed at about the same time as the Egyptian but it has been much better preserved because of the use of clay tablets, as opposed to papyrus, by the Babylonians. They used a reed, shaped at one end, to make wedge shaped marks on wet clay. Once these tablets dried, the marks on them were preserved for posterity.

The most outstanding achievement of the Babylonian numeration system was the invention of a place value system, that is, a numeration system in which the value of a numeral depended on its placement with respect to other numerals while writing a number. The Babylonians used the following symbols.

Babylonian Numeral	Hindu-Arabic Equivalent
	1
	10

These symbols were combined to write numbers as, for example, ![Babylonian numeral] represented 32. Numbers greater than 59 were represented using repeated groupings of 60. Spaces were used to separate multiples of powers of 60. The following examples illustrate this idea.

represents $30 \cdot 60 + 1$, or 1801

represents $10 \cdot 60^2 + 11 \cdot 60 + 2$, or 36,662

The Babylonian system was somewhat confusing as it lacked the concept of zero, until about 300 B.C. Thus, ![Babylonian numeral] could represent $3 \cdot 60$ or 3.

The Chinese Numeration System. The Chinese civilization, in about 1300 B.C., had a system of numeration that was simpler and in many ways more advanced than most contemporary civilizations. This is because, in this system, it was possible to write any number, however large, by the use of ten basic symbols, along with additional ones to represent 100's and 1000's. The following table shows the symbols used by this civilization.

Chinese Numeral	Hindu-Arabic Equivalent
一	1
二	2
三	3
四	4
五	5
六	6
七	7
八	8
九	9
十	10
百	100
千	1,000

Here is an example of 247 written using the Chinese system:

$$2(100)+4(10)+7 = 247$$

二	(2)
百	(100)
四	(4)
十	(10)
七	(7)

The Mayan Numeration System. The Mayan system, developed about 400 B.C., was one of the most economical ones developed. It used only three symbols, given in the table below.

Mayan Numeral	Hindu-Arabic Equivalent
•	1
—	5
👁	0

The Mayan system was a base 20 system. Numbers were written vertically in this system, with the greatest values on top. One of the curious features in this system was the value of the symbols in the third position from the bottom. Keeping in mind the fact that this was a base 20 system, the value of the symbol in this position should be a multiple of 20^2, or 400. However, it appears that the Mayans used $20 \cdot 18$, or 360, in this position. It has been conjectured that the number 360 may have been used because it is the approximate length of the calendar year (18 months consisting of 20 days each, with an additional 5 unlucky days). Given below are some examples of numbers written in the Mayan system.

••	$7 \cdot 360 =$	2520		•	$6 \cdot 360 =$	2160
••	$12 \cdot 20 =$	240		👁	$0 \cdot 20 =$	0
•	$6 \cdot 1 =$	6		•••	$3 \cdot 1 =$	3
		2766				2163

The Roman Numeration System. The Roman system of numeration is one of the few ancient ones that continues to be in use today. It can be seen on the faces of some watches and clocks, on cornerstones, and in the names of monarchs.

The table given below shows the numerals used in the Roman numeration system.

Roman Numeral	Hindu-Arabic Equivalent
I	1
V	5
X	10
L	50
C	100
D	500
M	1000

An additive property is used to combine numerals. Thus, MDLXII represents 1000 + 500 + 50 + 10 + 2 = 1562. Similarly, DCCXXI represents 721.

A subtractive property was introduced in this system in order to avoid writing a symbol more than three times. This was done by placing symbols representing smaller numbers to the left of symbols representing larger ones, as, in writing 4 as IV, instead of IIII, or 900 as CM, instead of DCCCC.

A limited multiplicative property is also evident in the Roman numeration system. A bar placed over a symbol indicates that the value of the symbol must be multiplied by 1000. Thus $\overline{V}$ represents 5000, and $\overline{CDX}$ represents 410 • 1000.

More than one bar can be placed over symbols to indicate multiplication by greater powers of 1000. Thus, $\overline{\overline{LX}}$ represents 60 • 1000^2.

The Hindu-Arabic Numeration System. The Hindu Arabic numeration system used today originated in India. While different versions of this system existed even earlier, a system which is very close to the system we know today, developed around 850 A.D.

The Hindu-Arabic system is a base ten system, and hence is said to be a decimal system (*decem* is a Latin word indicating ten). It has ten basic symbols called digits: 0, 1, 2, 3, 4, 5, 6, 7, 8, and 9. In this system, all numbers can be written as a combination of these digits. It is a place value system, where the place values are based on groupings by powers of 10.

Each digit in a numeral has two main functions. The digit indicates its face value, and its position in the numeral indicates its place value. Thus in the number 247, the symbol "4" has a face value of four, and being in the second place from the right in the number, it represents 4 • 10. Similarly, "2" represents the face value of two, and by its place indicates that it represents 2 • 10^2. The system becomes clear when numbers are written in their expanded form. For example,

$$65031 = 6 • 10^4 + 5 • 10^3 + 0 • 10^2 + 3 • 10^1 + 1 • 10^0$$

Base-Ten Introduction | Decimal System and More on Base Ten
Place Value and Zero   **RELATED TOPICS**

TOPIC 2.2 LINE RELATIONSHIPS

CORNERSTONE	Whole Numbers

INTRODUCTION

The Hindu-Arabic numeration system that we use today is a base-ten system. This system is more sophisticated than some of the earlier systems, such as the Egyptian Numeration System, that had symbols to represent certain powers of ten. The base ten system Hindu-Arabic system is useful in its ability to represent numbers concisely. For example, we can represent the amount four hundred fifty-nine in the Hindu-Arabic system using the symbols 459, with the 4 representing four sets of 100, the 5 representing 5 sets of ten and the 9 representing 9 ones. Other numeration systems often require a larger set of symbols such as the symbols ???? ∩∩∩∩ ||||||||| to represent 459 in the Egyptian system. In the following sections, we explore base ten and other characteristics of our numeration system.

DID YOU KNOW?

Numeration systems in early societies often reveal interesting aspects of the culture that prevailed, and what was regarded as important in these societies. It is generally accepted that the use of the base ten in many cultures evolved from the practice of using fingers of the hands for counting. In warmer climates, on the other hand, people could even use their toes for counting and this may have led to the use of the number 20 as a base in such cultures as the Maya of Central America and the Yoruba in western Africa.

For More Information: Zaslavsky, C. (1996). *The multicultural math classroom: Bringing in the world.* Portsmouth, NH: Heinemann.

2.2.1 Characteristics of the Egyptian Numeration System

Understanding our own numeration system can be enhanced by examining the characteristics of other systems. The Egyptian Numeration System illustrates several features that our Hindu-Arabic System shares. Note that the Egyptian Numeration System uses the following symbols: ⸕ = 1000, ? = 100, ∩ = 10, | = 1.

Additive Characteristic. The Egyptian Numeration System is **additive**, meaning that the overall value of the number represented by a series of symbols is equal to the sum of the values of the individual symbols. For example, the number represented by the string of symbols ∩∩∩∩||| can be found by adding together the values of the symbols such as:

∩ + ∩ + ∩ + ∩ + | + | + | = 10 + 10 + 10 + 10 + 1 + 1 + 1 = 43.

Our Hindu-Arabic system is also additive in that the value of the numeral 324, for example, is determined by adding together the values that each of the symbols represents as follows: 300 + 20 + 4.

Powers of 10. All of the symbols in the Egyptian system represent various **powers of 10**; that is, the symbols are worth 1, 10, 100, 1000, 10000, and so on, which are numbers that can all be expressed as 10 or 10 times itself some number of times. For example, $10 = 10$, $100 = 10 \times 10$, $1000 = 10 \times 10 \times 10$, $10000 = 10 \times 10 \times 10 \times 10$, and so on. Each of these numbers could be alternatively written in exponential form such as 10^1, 10^2, 10^3, 10^4, and so on, where the exponent in this notation stands for the "power" of ten. Even the number one represented by the symbol "|" in the Egyptian System can be represented as a power of ten. We write the number 1 as 10^0.

Base-Ten System. Although the Egyptian system has symbols that themselves are each powers of ten, the system is considered to be as limited as a base-ten system. It is limited because there is no association of the powers of ten with the specific placement of the digits. Consequently, the symbols alone do not provide a concise and unique means of representing large numbers even though they represent powers of ten. For example, ∩∩| is the same as ∩|∩.

On the other hand, in the Hindu-Arabic system, the **base ten** means that each digit in a numeral is associated with a **place value** that is a power of ten. That is, each of the places (or locations of a digit)—ones, tens, hundreds, thousands, etc.—is a power of ten. This association of unique powers of ten with places allows us to write large numbers easily and uniquely, using only a few digits. See Figure 2.1.

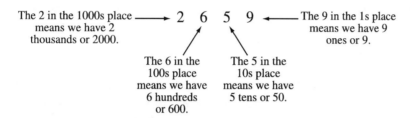

Figure 2.1

Without place value, both out Hindu-Arabic system and the Egyptian system would have awkward, non-unique representation for a number such as 2,659 (see Figure 2.2).

Without place value, 2659 may be written as:

Egyptian	∦∦???????∩∩∩∩∩ |||||||||
Hindu-Arabic	1000 + 1000 + 100 + 100 + 100 + 100 + 100 + 100 + 10 + 10 + 10 + 10 + 10 + 1 + 1 + 1 + 1 + 1 + 1 + 1 + 1 + 1

Figure 2.2

Some numeration systems, such as the Roman Numeration System, have features that our Hindu-Arabic System does not have. For example, the Roman system has the characteristic of being **subtractive** in that sometimes, instead of adding the values of the symbols together, one must subtract the value of one digit from another to determine the value. Note that the Roman system uses the symbols: M = 1000, D = 500, C = 100, L = 50, X = 10, V = 5, I = 1. When we see the symbols VII in the Roman system, we add the value of the symbols together: V + I + I = 5 + 1 + 1 = 7. However, when we see symbols positioned such that a smaller-valued digit precedes a larger-valued digit, as in the number IX where the symbol for 1 (I) precedes the symbol for 10 (X), we subtract the value of the smaller digit from the value of the larger digit. Thus, we interpret the number IX as X - I = 10 - 1 = 9.

2.2.2
A Subtractive Characteristic Not Associated with the Hindu-Arabic System

It is often useful to consider systems that operate like the Hindu-Arabic system except for having a different base. For example, consider the **base-two system** where each of the places is a power of 2 (instead of a power of 10 as in our base ten system) and which only uses the two digits 0 and 1 (unlike the ten digits used in our base ten system). A base two system is often referred to

2.2.3
Other Bases: The Example of Base Two

as a **binary system** (the prefix "*bi*" meaning two), particularly in the context of computer codes. In a digital computer, data and instructions are encoded as bits, which are the digits 0 and 1. The technology in a digital computer system relies on the state of an electronic circuit to represent a bit. The circuit must be capable of being in two states, one representing 1, the other 0.

An example of interpreting a base two number in its base ten equivalent is seen in the following. Given the base-two number 110011_{two}, we can translate the value of these symbols into terms we understand in base ten by figuring out what each symbol represents in each of the base two places. That is,

$$110,011_{two} = (1 \times 2^5) + (1 \times 2^4) + (0 \times 2^3) + (0 \times 2^2) + (1 \times 2^1) + (1 \times 2^0)$$
$$= 32 + 16 + 0 + 0 + 2 + 1 = 51_{ten}$$

Similarly, we can start with a base-ten number, say 19, and determine how to represent this amount in a base two system. To translate 19 to its base-two equivalent, we must consider the place values in base two up to the largest place that does not exceed 19. Thus the places to consider would be $2^4 = 16$, $2^3 = 8$, $2^2 = 4$, $2^1 = 2$, $2^0 = 1$. Note that because $2^5 = 32$ exceeds 19, we can conclude that the base-two representation of 19 will be a five-digit number, and we must determine what digits (0 or 1) belong in each of the places $\overline{2^4}\,\overline{2^3}\,\overline{2^2}\,\overline{2^1}\,\overline{2^0}$. Because we can express 19 as $16 + 2 + 1$, we determine that 19 can be represented in base two by placing the digit 1 in the 2^4, 2^1, and 2^0 places, and the digit 0 in the 2^3 *and* 2^2 places. Thus, 19 can be expressed as $\frac{1}{2^4}\frac{0}{2^3}\frac{0}{2^2}\frac{1}{2^1}\frac{1}{2^0}$ in base two or, more concisely written, $19 = 10011_{two}$.

RELATED TOPICS Properties of Whole Number Addition
Properties of Whole Number Multiplication | Place Value and Zero
Decimal System and More on Base Ten

TOPIC 2.3 PLACE VALUE AND ZERO

Whole Numbers | Base-Ten Introduction

CORNERSTONE

INTRODUCTION

The characteristics of place value and a symbol for zero work together in the Hindu-Arabic Numeration System in that the symbol for zero serves as a place holder when representing number amounts. However, early place value systems did not always have a symbol for zero, which presented some limitations to those systems. In the sections that follow, we explore place value and our symbol for zero through examples.

DID YOU KNOW?

The most outstanding achievement of the Babylonian numeration system was the invention of a place value system. The Babylonian system is an example of a numeration system in which the value of a numeral depends on its placement with respect to other numerals when writing a number. The Babylonians had two symbols, ∇, which represented 1, and $<$, which represented 10. The system was also additive, meaning that the value represented by the set of symbols was equal to the sum of each individual symbol value. For example, the number represented by the symbols $<\,<\,<\,\nabla\,\nabla$ is $10 + 10 + 10 + 1 + 1 = 32$.

The Babylonian system was also a base-60 system. So the places are all powers of 60: $60^0 (60^0 = 1)$, 60^1, 60^2, and so on. Thus, to write numbers larger than 59, they used spaces to separate the powers of 60. For example, the symbols $<\,<\ \ <\,\nabla\,\nabla$ represent $20 \times 60^1 + 12 \times 1 = 1,212$. The space, in this case, separates the ones place from the 60s place. In another example, the symbols $<\ \ <\,\nabla\ \ \nabla\,\nabla$ represent $10 \times 60^2 + 11 \times 60^1 + 2 \times 1 = 36,662$ (see Figure 2.3 for how these place values can be interpreted in a place value table). Because the Babylonians implemented a place value feature in its number system, they were able to represent fairly large numbers with only a few symbols.

$3600 = 60^2$	sixty $= 60^1$	ones $= 60^0$
$<$	$<\,\nabla$	$\nabla\,\nabla$

Figure 2.3

The limitations to the approach of leaving a space to indicate a new place include the danger of perhaps not indicating the space clearly enough. However, what is probably more limiting with this system is how to represent having a set of digits in the 60^2 place and in the ones place, but no digits in the 60^1 place. Perhaps they simply left a bigger space initially to indicate that they were skipping a place. However, at some point they decided that they needed a symbol to represent zero and introduced this new symbol, $/\,/$, to their system to indicate where a place was being skipped. Thus, they, in effect, created a symbol as a place holder, much like our present day symbol for zero.

For More Information: Bunt, L. N. H., Jones, P. S., & Bedient, J. D. (1988). *The Historical Roots of Elementary Mathematics.* New York: Dover Publications.

2.3.1
Place Value

Place value refers to the value associated with a specific position a digit occupies in a number. In a place value numeration system, the position that a digit occupies dramatically affects the value of the digit. For example, in the number 540, the digit 4 is in the tens place, so the four represents four sets of ten or 40. On the other hand, in the number 504, the digit 4 is in the ones place and represents 4 ones. Thus, place value provides a means of representing each number amount in our number system in a unique way. See Table 2.1 for an abbreviated table of place values in the Hindu-Arabic Numeration System showing the place values associated with the digits of the number 504.

Table 2.1						
	etc.	Ten Thousands Place	Thousands Place	Hundreds Place	Tens Place	Ones Place
				5	0	4

2.3.2
A Symbol for Zero

With a **symbol for zero**, 0, in the Hindu-Arabic Number System we are able to maintain our place value, allowing for the possibility of representing numbers such as 504, meaning that there are 5 hundreds, zero tens, and 4 ones. Without a zero, how would we represent 504? Would we leave a blank line to indicate that we are skipping the tens place, such as 5 _ 4? Alternatively, a representation of 5 4 does not make clear whether there are five hundreds (because a space is left) or five tens. Without a symbol for zero, we would need some other clear way to distinguish the place values that different digits occupy. The zero in the number 504 helps to indicate that the digit 5 really stands for five hundreds. The use of a symbol for zero leaves no doubt of the placement of a digit, therefore leaving no doubt as to the overall value of the number represented. Besides playing the important role of a placeholder, recall that 0 is also the cardinal number representing the size of the empty set

RELATED TOPICS   Decimal System and More on Base Ten

TOPIC 2.4 DECIMAL SYSTEM AND MORE ON BASE TEN

| Whole Numbers | Base-Ten Introduction | Place Value and Zero | **CORNERSTONE** |

*The prefix "deci" comes from the Latin word, **decem**, meaning ten. Thus, referring to a decimal system is the same as referring to a base ten system. Today, when we hears the word "decimal" we might think of decimal fractions. What we will discover is that a decimal system not only allows us to write all whole numbers concisely, but also provides the means of representing many fractional amounts as well. Consequently, our decimal system has developed over time from its beginning use as a means of representing whole-number amounts to a sophisticated system where we can represent a myriad of whole number and fractional number amounts.*

INTRODUCTION

Every numeration system has two fundamental features: a collection of symbols and a set of rules by which we combine and interpret those symbols. Our decimal system has ten symbols: 0, 1, 2, 3, 4, 5, 6, 7, 8, and 9. These 10 symbols are also referred to as digits, which also corresponds to a name used to refer to our fingers or toes. These ten digits combined, with a base of ten, provide a means of representing any whole number uniquely.

Knowledge of the decimal number system allows us to answer questions that range from the most basic to very sophisticated. For example, we might ask what digit is in the tens place of the number 23,469? The problem solver could identify the tens place and see the digit 6 is in that place. On the other hand, a more complicated problem to solve that requires knowledge of the decimal number system would be the following. Consider what number meets the following criteria: Using some of the digits 0, 1, 2, 3, 4, 5, 6, 7, 8, 9 without using any digit more than once, determine the largest odd six-digit number with a 9 in the tens place. Through process of elimination, the problem solver can determine that the number 876,593 meets all the criteria.

DID YOU KNOW?

The **Hindu-Arabic System** is called a **decimal system** because it is based on powers of ten. The Hindu-Arabic decimal system is best understood when numbers are written in **expanded notation.** In expanded notation, numerals are broken down, digit by digit, writing the value of each digit as a product of its face value (that is the value of the symbol itself) times its place value (which is always a power of 10). For example, the number 6,023 can be written as $6 \times 1000 + 0 \times 100 + 2 \times 10 + 3 \times 1$. Further, expressing each place value as a power of 10, the formal expanded notation of 6,123 is written as:

$$(6 \times 10^3) + (0 \times 10^2) + (2 \times 10^1) + (3 \times 10^0).$$

Note that it is commonly accepted to represent the value of the digit in the ones place as the face value times 1. Thus, expanded forms in textbooks often represent a number such as 6,123 as:

$$(6 \times 10^3) + (0 \times 10^2) + (2 \times 10^1) + (3 \times 1).$$

2.4.1
Decimal System and Expanded Notation

**2.4.2
Multiplicative
Characteristic**

The fact that the value of digits in the Hindu-Arabic system are understood by multiplying face value times place value implies that the system is **multiplicative**. Thus, when numbers are written in expanded form, we clearly see the system as additive, multiplicative, having place value, having a base of ten, and having a zero.

RELATED TOPICS   Properties of Whole Number Addition |
Properties of Whole Number Multiplication

IN THE CLASSROOM

This chapter on numeration is the first of five chapters whose focus is on some aspect of the *Number and Operations Content Standard*. Given that "all mathematics proposed for pre-kindergarten through Grade 12 is strongly grounded in number" (NCTM, 2000, p. 32), we believe it is essential for you to develop a strong, connected understanding of (a) numeration systems as abstract, structured representations of number concepts (Activities 2.1-2.5), and (b) place value and base as fundamental to the structure of and operations on the base-ten numeration system we use (Activities 2.6-2.10).

How Activities 2.1-2.10 help you develop an adult-level perspective on the above expectations.

- By examining early numeration systems and comparing them and our base-ten system you work with different representations of number.

- By exploring the historical development of number concepts and representations, you distinguish between the idea of number as concept and numeral as representation. You appreciate the need to enable children to develop this understanding through appropriate experiences and over time. For example, many ancient systems did not have the concept of, or representation for, zero.

- By understanding the symbols used in a system and how they are arranged to represent different numbers, you examine the composition of a number as sums or products of other numbers.

- By working with base blocks and in bases other than base ten, you construct a conceptual understanding of place value. You thereby develop a conceptual understanding of the procedures we employ in basic arithmetic operations.

Some expectations of your future students

Pre-K-2 (NCTM, 2000, p. 78)	count with understanding and recognize "how many" in sets of objects
	connect number words and numerals to the quantities they represent using various physical models and representations
	use multiple models to develop initial understandings of place value and the base-ten number system
	understand the effects of adding and subtracting whole numbers
Grades 3-5 (NCTM, 2000, p. 148)	recognize equivalent representations of the same number and generate them by decomposing and composing numbers
	understand the place-value structure of the base-ten number system
	understand the effects of multiplying and dividing whole numbers

BIBLIOGRAPHY

Arithmetic Teacher. (1988, February). Focus issue on early childhood mathematics, *35*.

Baroody, A. J., & Wilkins, J. L. M. (1999). The development of informal counting, number, and arithmetic skills and concepts. In J. V. Copley (Ed.), *Mathematics in the early years* (pp. 48-65). Reston, VA: National Council of Teachers of Mathematics.

Bresser, R., & Holtzman, C. (1999). *Developing number sense.* Sausalito, CA: Math Solutions Publications.

Clements, D. H. (1999). Subitizing: What is it? Why teach it? *Teaching Children Mathematics, 5*, 400-405.

Flexer, R J. (1986). The power of five: The step before the power of ten. *Arithmetic Teacher, 34*(3), 5-9.

Frank, A. R. (1989). Counting skills—A foundation for early mathematics. *Arithmetic Teacher, 37*, 14-17.

Fuson, K. C., Wearne, D., Hiebert, J. C., Murray, H. G., Human, P. G., Olivier, A. I., Carpenter, T. P., & Fennema, E. (1997). Children's conceptual structures for multidigit numbers and methods of multidigit addition and subtraction. *Journal for Research in Mathematics Education, 28*, 130-162.

Gluck, D. H. (1991). Helping students understand place value. *Arithmetic Teacher, 38*, 10-13.

Harrison, M., & Harrison, B. (1986). Developing numeration concepts and skills. *Arithmetic Teacher, 33*, 18-21.

Ifrah, G. (1987). *From one to zero: A universal history of number.* New York: Penguin Books.

Krusen, K. (1991). A historical reconstruction of our number system. *Arithmetic Teacher, 38*, 46-48.

Labinowicz, E. (1985). *Learning from children: New beginnings for teaching numerical thinking.* Menlo Park, CA: Addison-Wesley.

Little, C. (1999). Counting grass. *Mathematics Teaching in the Middle Grades, 5*, 7-10.

McClain, K., & Cobb, P. (1999). Supporting students' ways of reasoning about patterns and partitions. In J. V. Copley (Ed.), *Mathematics in the early years* (pp. 112-118). Reston, VA: National Council of Teachers of Mathematics.

Menninger, K. (1992). *Number words & number Symbols: A cultural history of numbers.* New York: Dover.

Nagel, N. G., & Swingen, C. C. (1998). Students' explanations of place value in addition and subtraction. *Teaching Children Mathematics, 5*, 164-170.

Payne, J. N., & Huinker, D. M. (1993). Early number and numeration. In R. J. Jensen (Ed.), *Research ideas for the classroom: Early childhood mathematics* (pp. 4~71). Old Tappan, NJ: Macmillan.

Rathmell, E. E., & Leutzinger, L. P. (1991). Implementing the *Standards*: Number representations and relationships. *Arithmetic Teacher, 38*, 20-23.

Schwartz, S. L. (1995). Enchanting, fascinating, useful number. *Teaching Children Mathematics, 1*, 486-491.

Sutton, J. T., & Urbatsch, T. D. (1991). Transition boards: A good idea made better. *Arithmetic Teacher, 38*, 4-9.

Suydam, M. N. (1986). Research report: The process of counting. *Arithmetic Teacher, 33*, 29.

Thompson, C. S. (1990). Place value and larger numbers. In J. N. Payne (Ed.), *Mathematics for the young child* (pp. 89-108). Reston, VA: National Council of Teachers of Mathematics.

Thompson, C. S., & Van de Walle, J. A. (1984). The power of 10. *Arithmetic Teacher, 32*(3), 6-11.

Thompson, C. S. (1989). Number sense and numeration in grades K-8. *Arithmetic Teacher, 37*, 22-24.

Wearne, D., & Hiebert. J. (1994). Place value and addition and subtraction. *Arithmetic Teacher, 41*, 272-274.

Weinberg, S. (1996). Going beyond ten black dots. *Teaching Children Mathematics, 2*, 432-435.

Wicket, M. S. (1997). Serving up number sense and problem solving: *Dinner at the panda palace. Teaching Children Mathematics, 3*, 476-480.

Zepp, R. A. (1992). Numbers and codes in ancient Peru: The Quipi. *Arithmetic Teacher, 39*, 42-44.

OPERATIONS WITH NATURAL NUMBERS, WHOLE NUMBERS & INTEGERS

3

TOPIC

3.1 Natural Numbers

3.2 Introduction to Whole Numbers

3.3 Addition with Whole Numbers

3.4 Addition Properties and Patterns (Whole Numbers)

3.5 Addition Algorithms (Whole Numbers)

3.6 Subtraction with Whole Numbers

3.7 Subtraction Algorithms (Whole Numbers)

3.8 Multiplication with Whole Numbers

3.9 Multiplication Properties and Patterns (Whole Numbers)

3.10 Multiplication Algorithms

3.11 Whole Number Division

3.12 Division Algorithms

3.13 Introduction to Integers

3.14 Integer Addition

3.15 Integer Subtraction

3.16 Integer Multiplication

3.17 Integer Division

3.18 Order of Operations

In the Classroom

Bibliography

CHAPTER OVERVIEW

A solid understanding of addition, subtraction, multiplication, and division is crucial to being able to do mathematics and these operations play central parts in the elementary school mathematics curriculum. In this chapter you can learn some interesting facts about operations, and examine some concepts and procedures involving operation ideas.

BIG MATHEMATICAL IDEAS

- Mathematical Structure
- Verifying
- Generalizing
- Using Algorithms

NCTM PRINCIPLES & STANDARDS LINKS

Number and Operation
Problem Solving
Reasoning
Communication
Connections
Representation

TOPIC 3.1 NATURAL NUMBERS

CORNERSTONE   Characteristics of Numeration Systems

INTRODUCTION   *Natural numbers are the numbers we "naturally" use when we count objects. They are the most basic set of numbers that students are introduced to in elementary school. In this section we define Natural Numbers.*

DID YOU KNOW?   Natural numbers provide us with the most basic means of telling "how much." However, some cultures do not need many of these most basic numbers. For example, in some Australian tribes, members do not have use for numerals beyond the amount of four. In many cases, having number names for "one" and "two" are sufficient. Amounts beyond two are called "much" or "many." This reminds us that numeration systems match the needs of the cultures they serve. The more complicated numeration systems themselves began with basic elements, but grew as societal demands changed.

For More Information: Smith, D. E. (1958). *History of mathematics, Volume I.* New York: Dover Publications.

The **Natural Numbers**, also known as the **Counting Numbers**, are the numbers beginning with "1" and progressing as 1, 2, 3, 4, 5, … . The ellipses (…) indicate that this set of numbers continues on in this pattern and is infinite. **The Set of Natural Numbers**, written in set notation as N= {1, 2, 3, 4, 5, …} is often simply referred to as "N." The Natural Numbers are used to express "how much" or "how large a set is," with the exception of sets that are empty.

RELATED TOPICS   Whole Numbers | Integers

TOPIC 3.2 INTRODUCTION TO WHOLE NUMBERS

Natural Numbers | Sets

The earliest roots of mathematics can probably be traced back to a need for counting and recording numbers. From as far back as historians can tell, every society has had some means of recording numerical quantities. This is true even of those societies for which no written records of numerals are available. Evidence of this fact comes from archaeological excavations from different parts of the world. Whole numbers provide the symbols we use in our Hindu-Arabic Number System for counting and recording. Within this topic we examine the set of whole numbers and how they relate to other number representations and counting.

The Hindu-Arabic system we use today evolved slowly. It is commonly believed to have been invented by Hindu mathematicians in India around 500 A.D. It was carried to other parts of the world by the Arabs, it took a long time before it became universally accepted.

Today we see our whole number symbols displayed everywhere, representing the complexities of international finance and trade as well as facilitating computer programming and international internet communications. For example, the Dow Jones Industrial Average is a weighted average of stock prices for a number of prominent stocks. In the spring of 1999, the Dow Jones Industrial Average reached a record high of 10,000. The number 10,000, because of the large amount it represents, was significant to traders in the stock market. In computer programming, technologists are eager to have a large amount of computer memory. They often use expressions such as 500 megabytes or 10 gigabytes to describe this computer space. Without a numeration system to represent whole numbers, information could not be conveyed in this manner.

For More Information: Bunt, L. N. H., Jones, P. S., & Bedient, J. D. (1988). *The Historical Roots of Elementary Mathematics.* New York: Dover Publications.

The word **number** refers to an amount or quantity. A number can be represented in a several ways. One could place objects on a table to provide a **concrete representation of an amount**. For example, if you want to show the amount three, you could place three coins on a table, letting the coins physically represent the number. Traditionally we use number **names**, such as the words one, two, three, etc. to describe an amount. We also use **numerals**, or symbols, such as the digits 0, 1, 2, 3, etc. as symbolic representations of number amounts.

When we refer to the number of objects in a set, or a number that says "how many," this number is called a **cardinal number**. A cardinal number is usually represented by the numeral that corresponds to the amount; that is, if there are two objects, the numeral "2" can represent that amount. Also, the answer to the question, "how many objects are there?" can be answered by the cardinal number 2. On the other hand, a number that designates a comparative position or an order of some set of objects is called an **ordinal number**. For example, if I am "fourth" in line, the ordinal number "fourth" describes my position in line compared to others' positions in line. Figure 3.1 provides a summary of examples of number representations.

Number Representations

Figure 3.1

	Concrete Representation	Name	Numeral	Cardinal Number	Ordinal Number
Summary	Physical objects used to show an amount	The words we use to show an amount	The symbols we use	The amount itself	The comparative position of an object
Example 1	☐☐☐☐☐ five blocks	Five	5 (the symbol)	5 (the amount)	☐☐☐☐■ the fifth block
Example 2	⊢—┴—┴—⊣ 3 centimeters	Three	3 (the symbol)	3 (the amount)	the third centimeter

3.2.2
One-to-One Correspondence

Counting objects involves an understanding of **one-to-one correspondence.** One-to-one correspondence is the notion that you can match each item from one set with exactly one item from another set, and vice versa. For example, if six children come to a birthday party and you want to make sure each child goes home with exactly one of the six balloons you have, there are many ways you can distribute the balloons according to the children's color preferences. However, in the long run, no matter how you match children with balloons, each child leaves with exactly one balloon. See Figure 3.2.

In Figure 3.2, each child has selected his favorite balloon color. However, a different pairing of child with balloon (say Ted wanted red and Abby wanted yellow and all the others stayed the same) would still result in the fact that there is exactly one balloon for each child. In that sense, we could say that there is a one-to-one correspondence between the set of children and the set of balloons.

Figure 3.2

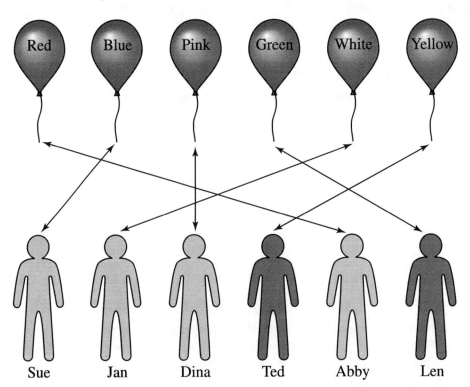

Whole numbers are cardinal numbers that describe the size of finite sets. That is, given a set, {a, b, c, d}, we use the whole number, 4, to describe the number of elements in the set. The **set of whole numbers** is traditionally expressed as W = {0, 1, 2, 3, . . . } which indicates that the whole numbers start with zero and continue on toward infinity. Whole numbers differ from the natural numbers N = {1, 2, 3, 4, . . . } in that they include the number zero, which allows for representing the cardinal number of an "empty set."

3.2.3
**Whole Numbers
and the Set of
Whole Numbers**

When we count a set of objects, we ultimately determine a whole number that states "how many" objects there are. Steps in counting are as follows: (a) point to each object to be counted exactly once, (b) recite the whole numbers *in order*, beginning with 1, associating exactly one number to correspond with each object being counted, and (c) conclude the total number of objects counted by identifying the last whole number stated when pointing to the last object.

3.2.4
**Whole Numbers
and Counting**

For example, if there is a group of coins on the table, we can determine how many there are by pointing to each coin exactly once and assigning consecutive numbers to each object, starting with the number one (see Figure 3.3). Each coin, then, corresponds to exactly one number. The last number stated, in this case 8, reveals the total number of coins on the table.

Coins

1   2   3   4   5   6   7   8

Figure 3.3

Properties of Whole Number Addition
Properties of Whole Number Multiplication | Base-Ten Introduction
Place Value and Zero | Decimal System and More on Base-Ten | Integers

RELATED TOPICS

TOPIC 3.3 ADDITION WITH WHOLE NUMBERS

CORNERSTONE | Whole Numbers | Place Value and Zero | Base-Ten Introduction
Decimal System and More on Base-Ten

INTRODUCTION | *The roots of whole number addition stem from combining sets together to determine how many are in the new, combined set. Further, the notation for the addition process, as well as the need for an addition algorithm when adding two numbers where carrying is required, springs from the simple notion of **joining** together. In this topic, we describe the meaning of addition and provide examples of mathematical problems that call for addition.*

DID YOU KNOW? | The operation, addition, has been referred to by many names throughout history. Famous mathematician, Fibonacci, used the terms *composition* and *collection* as well as *addition* to refer to this operation in the 13th century. At that same time, the French used the terms *add* and *assemble* to describe the process of addition. Two centuries later, the words *join* and *summation* were frequently used. Ultimately, in the 16th century, the word *addend*, coming from the Latin phrase *numeri addendi* meaning numbers to be added, became a popularly accepted term for the elements in an addition problem.

Some of the earliest written addition problems were written on clay tablets found in Mesopotamia. These tablets describe arithmetic calculations depicting business transactions. Addition computations were also written in sand on a *sand abacus* usually for the purpose of census-taking or business transactions. The operation of addition itself has not changed much since Hindu-Arabic numerals began being used.

For More Information: Smith, D. E. (1958). *History of mathematics, Volume II.* New York: Dover Publications.

3.3.1 Definition of Addition: Joining Sets

Whole-number addition is defined as the joining of two disjoint sets. **Disjoint sets** are sets that have no elements in common (other than the empty set). Suppose, then, that you have two sets, Set A and Set B, such that the sets have no common elements. When these two sets are combined, the total number of objects in the new set, more precisely expressed as A ∪ B read **"A union B"**, is the sum of the number of objects in set A plus the number of objects in set B. We denote the number of elements in set A as n(A) and the number of elements in B as n(B). Therefore, the number of elements in set A ∪ B (or A + B) is n(A ∪ B) = n(A) + n(B). See the example.

$$A = \{ball, bat, glove\} \qquad n(A) = 3$$
$$B = \{doll, brush\} \qquad n(B) = 2$$
$$A \cup B = \{ball, bat, glove, doll, brush\} \quad n(A + B) = 5$$

$$n(A) + n(B) = n(A \cup B); \text{ that is, } 3 + 2 = 5$$

3.3.2 Addition Terminology and Pictorial Representation

Although addition of whole numbers is initially defined as the joining of two sets, addition can be also be modeled **pictorially.** If we picture a set of objects, not necessarily expressed in set notation, but as a collection of distinct, countable objects, we can combine one set of objects with another and determine "how many altogether." For example, if I have 3 apples and pick 2 more apples, I then have 5 apples altogether. See Figure 3.4. This pictorial situation can be represented by the addition statement 3 + 2 = 5. We refer to the numbers 3 and 2 in the addition statement as the **addends** and to the number 5 in the addition statement as the **sum**.

Figure 3.4

Addition can also be represented via a **number line**. For example, on the number line below (See Figure 3.5), we see the addition of 4 + 2 by moving along the number line, starting with zero, to the first addend, 4. Then, moving 2 more places to the right (we move right to indicate addition), we end up at 6 (the sum) on the number line.

3.3.3
The Number-Line
Model of Addition

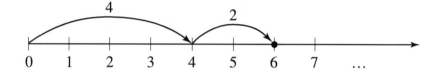

Figure 3.5

Using the pictorial and number line models, the definition of *addition* as the act of "joining together" is made clear. Ultimately, however, students need to be able to perform basic addition of whole numbers quickly in their heads, without the benefit of models. This refers to performing addition using **mental computation**. Three techniques that are useful in performing mental computations are counting up, compensation, and double plus 1 or 2.

3.3.4
Addition and Mental
Mathematics

Counting Up. After working with models, students should not only be able to picture the addition in their heads, but will have developed some mental math techniques to help them perform the operation quickly. For instance, when adding 1, 2, or 3 to any other addend, it is simple to merely say the larger addend in your head and then **count up** by 1, 2, or 3. Take, for example, adding 6 + 2. Using mental math, the student starts by thinking (or saying aloud) the number "6" and then counts up two more numbers: 7, 8. Thus, the conclusion is that 6 + 2 = 8.

Compensation. Other mental math techniques include the strategy of **compensation**. This strategy is useful when one of the addends is 8 or 9. Compensation essentially takes advantage of the fact that most students learn early on how to add a single-digit number to ten. So, when adding an addend that is close to ten, such as adding 8 or 9, the student can ask herself, "How much of the other addend would I have to add to this number (8 or 9) to get ten? And then ask, "How much of the other addend would be "left over" to add onto the amount of 10?"

For example, when adding the whole numbers 9 + 7, the student may think, "I need to add one more to the 9 to get 10, so if I take 1 away from the 7 and add it to the 9, that leaves 6. Then I just have to add 6 to 10 to get a sum of 16."

Essentially, when you "borrow" the 1 from the 7 to add to the 9 you have to "compensate" for this action by thinking of the second addend as a 6 rather than a 7. Thus the name, compensation.

Double Plus 1 or 2. Two other mental math techniques that help when adding two addends that are one or two numbers apart, such as when adding 4 + 5 or 5 + 7, are strategies referred to as **double plus one** or **double plus two**, respectively. Because most children easily learn the sum of an addend plus itself (1 + 1 = 2, 2 + 2 = 4, 5 + 5 = 10, etc.), they can use this knowledge to add other combinations of numbers. For example, when adding 4+5, a student might think, "4+5" is really one more than 4 + 4, and I know 4 + 4 is 8, so 4 + 5 must be 9." Similarly, when the addends are two apart, as in the case of 5 + 7, the student may mentally calculate, "seven is two more than 5, and I know that 5 + 5 is 10, so 5 + 7 must be two more than 10, so it's 12."

RELATED TOPICS   Addition Properties and Patterns (Whole Numbers) | Addition Algorithms

TOPIC 3.4 ADDITION PROPERTIES AND PATTERNS (WHOLE NUMBERS)

Whole Numbers | Addition with Whole Numbers

CORNERSTONE

INTRODUCTION

There are many observable patterns associated with the addition of whole numbers. Many of these patterns can be described through properties associated with whole number addition and can be observed in an addition table. In this topic, we demonstrate properties of whole number addition through examples.

DID YOU KNOW?

Properties of whole number addition stem from properties associated with combining sets. For example, we say the union of two sets A and B, written A ∪ B, is the set of all elements in set A or in set B, or in both. Thus, the union of sets is much like addition. We find when we determine the union of sets A and B that order does not matter; that is, A ∪ B yields the same result as B ∪ A. Thus, whether we start with the objects in set A and then add in the objects from set B or whether we start with the objects in set B and then add in the objects in set A, we will still end up with the set when the two are combined. This notion is called the *Commutative Property of the Union of Sets* and is similar to the *Commutative Property of the Addition of Whole Numbers* that we will see in this section. The commutative and other properties for sets are the precursors to the properties associated with whole–number addition.

When students are at the point of trying to memorize their **basic addition facts**, that is, all the addition problems that involve two single-digit addends, working with an addition table is quite useful. The addition table also illustrates properties associated with the addition of elements within the set of whole numbers. See the addition table for whole numbers in Table 3.1.

**3.4.1
Whole Number
Addition Table**

Students may notice a variety of patterns on the addition table. For example, diagonal rows that run from the bottom left to the top right have the same number throughout the diagonal. On the other hand, diagonal rows that run from the top left to the bottom right either contain only even numbers that increase as you move from left to right or only odd numbers that increase as you move from left to right. Students may also notice that as you move down row by row, a row begins with one larger number than the row before and the numbers in each row increase by one as you move across the row. Similarly, each column begins with one larger number than the column to its left, and the numbers in each column increase by one as you move down the column.

**3.4.2
General
Patterns in the
Addition Table**

Table 3.1

+	0	1	2	3	4	5	6	7	8	9
0	0	1	2	3	4	5	6	7	8	9
1	1	2	3	4	5	6	7	8	9	10
2	2	3	4	5	6	7	8	9	10	11
3	3	4	5	6	7	8	9	10	11	12
4	4	5	6	7	8	9	10	11	12	13
5	5	6	7	8	9	10	11	12	13	14
6	6	7	8	9	10	11	12	13	14	15
7	7	8	9	10	11	12	13	14	15	16
8	8	9	10	11	12	13	14	15	16	17
9	9	10	11	12	13	14	15	16	17	18

3.4.3
Additive Identity Property

When looking for more patterns in the addition table, students may immediately notice that the first row and first column match the addends that are being added to zero. Thus, at a glance, students easily see that having a zero as one of the addends yields a sum equal to the other addend. Therefore, the students have learned one of the four properties associated with whole number addition: *zero serves as an* **additive identity** *for the set of whole numbers* because when zero is added to a number, it does not change the identity (or value) of that number. In brief, for any whole number, a, the additive identity of zero ensures that $a + 0 = a$ (and, similarly, that $0 + a = a$).

3.4.4
Commutative Property

Other properties of whole number addition are evident from the addition table. For example, students might notice that the sum associated with $4 + 5$ is the same as the sum associated with $5 + 4$. Quickly, students begin to see a second property called the **Commutative Property of Whole-number Addition** (often referred to as the **Ordering Property** in elementary textbooks). They learn that it does not matter in what order the addends appear; the sum will always be the same. So, for any two whole numbers a and b, $a + b = b + a$. The commutative property is very helpful when students are learning to memorize their addition facts because once they know sum of $6 + 7$ is 13, they automatically know that the sum of $7 + 6$ is 13. In a way, this reduces the task of memorizing basic addition facts by one-half.

3.4.5
Closure Property

The addition table also illustrates a third property called the **Closure Property for Whole-number Addition**; that is, for any two whole numbers, a and b, $a + b = c$, where c is also a whole number. Essentially, this property says, whenever you add two whole numbers together, the sum will also be a whole number. Thus, all the sums seen within the addition table are whole numbers.

3.4.6
Associative Property

The fourth and final property of whole number addition that can be verified using the addition table is called the **Associative Property of Whole-number Addition** (often called the **Grouping Property** in elementary textbooks). This property says that when adding three (or more) whole numbers together, it does not matter which pairs of numbers you add together first. Once all three (or more) numbers are added together, the sum will always be the same.

For example, when adding $4 + 3 + 5$, we can group the 4 and 3 together and add them together. Then, take that sum, 7, and add it to 5 to get a grand total sum of 12. This might be written as $(4 + 3) + 5 = 12$ to indicate that we are adding the 4 and 3 together first. On the other hand, we get the same sum if we choose to add the 3 and 5 together first and then add that sum, 8, to the 4, again finding a total of 12. This would be written as $4 + (3 + 5) = 12$. In general, when adding any three whole numbers a, b, and c together, the associative property of whole number addition guarantees that $(a + b) + c = a + (b + c)$.

RELATED TOPICS Addition Algorithms
Multiplication Properties and Patterns (Whole Numbers)

TOPIC 3.5 ADDITION ALGORITHMS (WHOLE NUMBERS)

| Addition with Whole Numbers | Addition Properties and Patterns | **CORNERSTONE** |

INTRODUCTION

Learning the traditional addition algorithm occurs in various stages. An **algorithm** *is a set of steps or procedures to follow. The term* algorithm *grew from the word* algorism *(from the name of Arabic mathematician al-Khwārizmī), which refers to arithmetic done with Hindu-Arabic numerals that made use of a zero. An addition algorithm is a set of steps that allow us to add any two whole numbers together. Historically, addition algorithms developed as the need to add large amounts became necessary. As we show in the following sections, we begin to understand algorithms by learning to add two single-digit whole numbers and work toward being able to add two multi-digited whole numbers together, performing "carrying" (or more properly "regrouping" or "renaming") when necessary.*

DID YOU KNOW?

Hindu and Arab mathematicians performed addition problems in a variety of ways over the centuries. Their methods ultimately evolved to the methods we use today where we line addends up, one on top of the other, with like places aligned, and with the sum written below a line separating the addends from the sum. However, the early work of Hindu mathematician Bhaskara, generally known as *Bhaskara the Learned* (c. 1150), shows the addition of two, five, thirty-two, a hundred and ninety-three, eighteen, ten, and a hundred as shown in Figure 3.6a in a different manner. The Arabs, led by Maximus Planudes (c. 1340), wrote the sum at the top of an addition problem as seen in Figure 3.6b.

Sum of the units, 2, 5, 2, 3, 8, 0, 0	20
Sum of the tens,......3, 9, 1, 1, 0	14
Sum of the hundreds, . . 1, 0, 0, 1	2
Sum of the sums	360

Figure 3.6a

Note that the right-hand column in Figure 3.6b records the arithmetic checking method of "casting out nines" where next to each addend, after adding the digits in the addend, you record the remainder after you divide by nine. For example, with the first addend, 5687, we find $5 + 6 + 8 + 7 = 26$. Dividing 26 by 9 we find a quotient of 2 with a remainder of 8. The digit 8 is recorded to the right of 5687. Similarly, we find that 3 is the remainder when we add the digits in the addend 2343 and divide the sum by 9. The process of casting out nines is performed on the sum, 8030, as well. We check the arithmetic of adding 5687 + 2343 by verifying that the sum of the "cast out" amounts in the addends ($8 + 3 = 11$), when divided by 9, has a remainder of 2, which matches the amount "cast out" in the sum 8030.

8030	2
5687	8
2343	3

Figure 3.6b

In whole number addition, we often hear the expression *carrying* to indicate an exchange of ten 1's for one 10, or ten 10's for one 100, etc. The expression *to carry* is an old one. It dates from the time when a counter was actually carried on a line abacus to the space or line above, but it was not common in English works until the 17th century. An abacus is a mechanical means of recording and combining numbers. Early versions were drawing in the sand. More recent versions of the abacus keep track of place value with disks in columns representing the different places. Figure 3.7 shows a sample place value abacus representing 1,352.

Figure 3.7

Thousands   Hundreds   Tens   Ones

For More Information: Smith, D. E. (1958). *History of mathematics, Volume II*. New York: Dover Publications.

3.5.1
**Addition
Algorithms**

Once students have mastered the basic whole number addition facts (that is addition problems that involve adding 2 single-digit addends), they are ready to move forward and learn addition algorithms. **Addition algorithms** include procedures for adding a single-digit whole number to a 2-digit whole number, for adding two 2-digit whole numbers together, for adding a 2-digit whole number to a 3-digit whole number, and so on. When first introduced to such algorithms, it is useful for students to have a concrete model that helps illustrate the addition as well as reinforce the concept of place value.

3.5.2
**Base-Ten
Block Model**

Base-ten blocks are useful manipulatives when illustrating whole number addition. The blocks are particularly helpful because they reinforce place value and the need to add like-valued places to like-valued places, such as adding tens to tens or hundreds to hundreds.

Consider the simple addition of a two-digit addend to another two-digit addend in the problem 23 + 41. Figure 3.8 illustrates the addition problem with base-ten blocks.

Figure 3.8

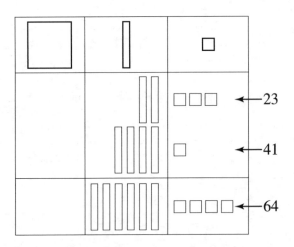

Using base-ten blocks, students can model each of the addends 23 and 41 and then show, when combined, how much they have altogether. In Figure 3.8, students can see that they have 6 longs (or 6 tens) and 4 units (or 4 ones) or 64 altogether.

Once students are comfortable with the idea of modeling addition with base-ten blocks, they can then move forward to situations where some "exchanging" or "carrying" is necessary. For example, when adding 23 and 48, students soon see that they have a total of 11 units and 6 longs with their base ten blocks (See Figure 3.9).

With this type of problem, students learn the step of trading in ten of the

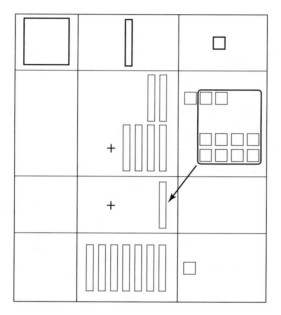

Figure 3.9

units for one of the longs (that is trading 10 ones for 1 ten) and adding that new long to the tens column. Then students can conclude that when they add 23 and 48, they will end up with 7 longs and 1 unit or a sum of 71.

Once students have had many experiences with the concrete materials, they are ready to translate this knowledge to the traditional addition algorithm. For example, students should learn that when finding a sum, such as the sum of 35 and 49, they must begin by adding the numbers in the ones' place together. If they find, as in this case, that they have more than ten ones, they should "carry" a set of ten over to the tens column and determine how many ones they will have left. This number of ones that remains is written in the ones column of the sum, and then the total number of tens is determined and recorded in the tens column of the sum.

3.5.3
The Traditional Addition Algorithm

$$
\begin{array}{r}
\overset{1}{3}5 \\
+49 \\
\hline
84
\end{array}
$$

Other transitional algorithms that students may find useful when working toward learning how to add any whole number to any other whole number with multiple carrying steps is the **partial sums algorithm.** For example, when add-

3.5.4
Partial Sums Algorithm

ing the whole numbers 348 and 595, students might find it useful to find the total number of units in the ones place, and record that sum, find the total number of tens in the tens place, and record that sum, and find the total number of hundreds in the hundreds place, and record that sum. Then, once these partial sums are determined, the student can find the total sum by adding the partial sums together. This is illustrated below.

$$
\begin{array}{r}
348 \\
+595 \\
\hline
13 \\
130 \\
\underline{800} \\
943
\end{array}
$$

The partial sums algorithm is a very useful **transitional algorithm**. It reinforces the idea that in our base ten system we add hundreds to hundreds, tens to tens, and ones to ones. Further, students can see that when they add the ones places together and get 13, as in the example above, that this really means that they should view that 13 as being 1 ten in the tens column and 3 ones in the ones column. It also parallels nicely with a transitional multiplication algorithm we will explore in Multiplication Algorithms called partial products.

3.5.5
Scratch Algorithm

The scratch algorithm is a useful way to keep track of how many sets of ten you need to carry over to the next column when adding a column of addends. Adding down a column, beginning with the ones place, the student should add until a sum of ten or greater is reached. Once the partial sum goes over ten, the students should scratch through the last digit added in, indicating that a set of ten will have to be carried over to the next column. The student then write the mow much the sum went over ten next to the number that was scratched out. The student then begins with this left-over amount and begins adding digits continuing down the same column. Once the bottom of a column has been reached, the last amount added that did not go over ten is written as the remaining amount that goes in the ones column. The student then counts up the number of scratches made in the ones column and carries that number over to the tens column and begins adding in that column using the same procedure.

For example, illustrating the scratch algorithm in the problem below with the problem 548 + 287 + 344 + 539 + 488, we find that when adding down the column of numbers, the first scratch is made through the 7 in the ones column because 8 + 7 = 15. The scratch indicates that a set of ten has been reached, and the small 5 written next to the scratched-out 7 indicates that a remainder of 5 is left when you take away that set of ten.

$$
\begin{array}{r}
548 \\
287 \\
344 \\
539 \\
+488 \\
\hline
2206
\end{array}
$$

Continuing, the 5 is added to the 4 for a sum of 9. This sum is added to the 9 for a sum of 18. At this point, a second scratch must be made and a small 8 written next to the scratch to indicate a set of ten has been reached with a remainder of 8. This 8 is added to the final 8 in that column for a total of 16. The 6 is recorded in the ones place, because we have reached the end of the column and a scratch is made through the 8. Then the number of scratches is found to be 3. Then a 3 is carried over to the next column and the process is continued.

The scratch algorithm can be useful when adding numbers in other bases. For example, when adding $1023_{four} + 2332_{four} + 2121_{four} + 1233_{four}$, the scratches in each column represent sets of four and the small number written next to each scratch represent the amount that the partial sum has gone higher than 4.

$$
\begin{array}{r}
2232 \\
1\ 0\ 2_03 \\
2_03_5 \cancel{3}\ 2_5 \\
\cancel{2}\ \cancel{1}\ 2_1 \cancel{1} \\
+\ 1\ 2\ \cancel{3}\ 3 \quad_{four} \\
\hline
2\ \cancel{0}\ \cancel{1}\ \cancel{0}\ \cancel{1} \quad_{four}
\end{array}
$$

Subtraction Algorithms | Multiplication Algorithms | Division Algorithms **RELATED TOPICS**

TOPIC 3.6 SUBTRACTION WITH WHOLE NUMBERS

CORNERSTONE   Addition with Whole Numbers
Addition Properties and Patterns (Whole Numbers)

INTRODUCTION   *Subtraction is considered the inverse operation to addition. It is often associated with the notion of having a set of objects, taking something away from the set, and determining how much of the set remains. We will find, however, that there are other representations of the concept of subtraction. In the following sections, we examine three interpretations of subtraction through sample story problems.*

DID YOU KNOW?   The names and process of the numbers used in subtraction have varied greatly over the centuries. Even today, the formal terms of subtraction are seldom used outside classroom instruction. For example, we might say *deduct what I owe and pay me the rest*, using the word *deduct* for *subtract* and the *rest* for the *difference*. Mathematician Fibonacci, in the 13th century, used the expression *extract* instead of subtract, and spoke of *extraction* instead of subtraction. In the 16th century the words *detract* and *subduct* were used for subtract.

Today's terms *minuend* and *subtrahend* are actually abbreviations of the Latin expressions *numerus minuendus* (number to be diminished) and *numerus subtrahendus* (number to be subtracted). The words *difference* and *remainder* have never been popular in spite of the fact that they are commonly found in textbooks today.

For More Information: Smith, D. E. (1958). *History of mathematics, Volume II.* New York: Dover Publications.

3.6.1
Definition of Terms

Whole-number subtraction is the inverse operation of whole number addition. In any subtraction statement such as $a - b = c$, we say that a is the **minuend**, b is the **subtrahend**, and c is the **difference**. Unlike addition, which is viewed only as the act of joining, subtraction has three interpretations. One can conceive of subtraction as the act of *taking away*, the act of *finding a missing addend*, or the act of *comparing two sets*.

3.6.2
Take-Away Subtraction

In a **take-away** view of subtraction, subtraction is called for when there is a starting amount, something is removed from that amount, and you want to determine how much remains. For example, suppose Ben has 5 letters to mail and drops one on the way to the mailbox. To determine how many letters he has left, the scenario suggests that we start with 5 letters, remove 1 of those 5 from the set, and find that there are 4 letters remaining. Consequently, the answer can be found by performing the subtraction $5 - 1 = 4$.

3.6.3
Missing-Addend Subtraction

Missing-addend subtraction is the appropriate interpretation when we know what amount we start with, know what we want to end up with, but do not know the difference between the starting and ending amount. For example, if Kate has 9 dollars but needs 12 dollars in order to buy the new doll she wants, how many more dollars does she need? We can think of this problem as an addition situation, saying, "I have to add 3 dollars to the 9 dollars I already have to then have a total of 12 dollars." Thus, there is the sense of finding the missing addend, or missing amount, [9 + _ = 12] that has to be added in order to reach a certain total. The required operation is subtraction because in order to find the missing amount, we subtract 12 − 9 = 3.

Finally, there is the **comparison subtraction** interpretation. In this situation, two amounts are compared and we ask how much larger one amount is than the other. For example, suppose Chris has 8 concert tickets and Allison has 3 concert tickets. How many more tickets does Chris have than Allison? In this case, we are determining *how much more* 8 is than 3, and so we subtract 8 − 3 = 5.

3.6.4
Comparison Subtraction

Like addition, subtraction can be modeled pictorially. We can illustrate the subtraction problem 7 − 4 = 3 with the pictorial model Figure 3.10 below. The picture indicates that we started with 7 letters and removed 4 from the set. This leaves 3 letters as the difference in this take-away, pictorial model.

3.6.5
A Pictorial Model

Figure 3.10

7 − 4 = 3

Subtraction can also be modeled with a number line. In Figure 3.11 we show the problem 8 − 2, beginning at 8 on the number line and moving two notches to the left (left to indicate the action of taking away), and ending at the point 6 on the number line.

3.6.6
Number-Line Model

Figure 3.11

Parallel to the learning of whole-number addition facts, students use mental-computation techniques in order to be able to perform subtraction facts quickly in their heads. Two useful techniques used when performing mental subtraction are *counting back* and *compensation*.

3.6.7
Subtraction and Mental Mathematics

Counting Back. A mental math strategy similar to counting up is a strategy called **counting back**. This strategy is useful in subtraction situations where the subtrahend is 1,2, or 3. For example to mentally subtract 6 − 2, it is appropriate to think of the minuend, 6, and then count backward two numbers (because the subtrahend is 2)—5,4—to determine that 6 − 2 is 4.

Compensation. Another subtraction strategy is **compensation** which was discussed in the addition of whole numbers. When the subtrahend is a number close to 10 we can subtract 10, but make sure to compensate for the change. For example, in the problem 15 − 8, we know that 15 − 10 = 5, but because we subtracted more than necessary by 2, we must add 2 to 5 to determine the difference of 7.

Subtraction Algorithms (Whole Numbers)   **RELATED TOPICS**

TOPIC 3.7 SUBTRACTION ALGORITHMS (WHOLE NUMBERS)

CORNERSTONE
Addition with Whole Numbers | Subtraction with Whole Numbers
Addition Properties and Patterns (Whole Numbers) | Addition Algorithms

INTRODUCTION

*Subtraction algorithms are related to addition algorithm in that both can involve exchanging. In addition, we traditionally exchange ten of one place (such as ten ones) for one of a larger place (such as one set of ten). This process is usually referred to as **carrying**. In subtraction, there is usually the need to exchange one item in a larger-valued place (such as 1 one-hundred) for ten of a smaller-valued place (such as 10 sets of ten) in order to be able to subtract. This process is often referred to as "borrowing" (or more properly "renaming" or "regrouping").*

DID YOU KNOW?

Calculations involving subtraction were first used in business transactions. There are four or five methods of subtraction in common use today. The borrowing method traditionally used in our schools is only one popular method. Another method used is the **equal additions method**. Essentially, in this method you add equal amounts to the minuend and subtrahend of the subtraction problem in a manner that makes the subtraction easier by not requiring regrouping. Instead, the equal additions method draws heavily upon understanding place value relationships between adjacent columns. An example is:

$$
\begin{array}{ccc}
842 + 10_{ones} & 84_{12} + 10_{tens} & 8_{14\,12} \\
-\ \underline{356 + 1_{ten}} & -\ \underline{366 + 1_{hundred}} & -\ \underline{466} \\
& & 486
\end{array}
$$

In this problem we see that the same amount was added to each number at each stage. In the first stage, 10 was added to each. In the top number, the 10 was added to the ones place so that there is 12 in the ones place. In the bottom number, the amount 10 was added to the tens place making the tens place 6 instead of 5. In the second adding stage, 100 was added to both numbers. The 100 was recorded as 10 tens and added to the tens column making it 14 sets of ten. The amount 100 was added to the bottom number in the hundreds place making it 400. Then, the subtraction was performed, place by place, without any regrouping required.

**3.7.1
Connections to
Addition**

Subtraction algorithms for whole numbers expand ideas developed in basic subtraction facts. The development of subtraction algorithms generally progresses from subtracting a 1-digit whole number from a two-digit whole number without requiring any borrowing (or exchanging) to subtracting any whole number from any other larger whole number with multiple exchanges required.

**3.7.2
Subtraction Using
Base-Ten Blocks**

Like addition algorithms, subtraction algorithms are best introduced using concrete models such as the base-ten blocks. Illustrated in Figure 3.12 is the subtraction 68 − 54. Borrowing is not necessary.

Once we observe that subtraction involves subtracting tens from tens, and ones from ones, etc., we then *exchange* one block for ten of the next smaller block in order to perform the necessary subtraction. For example, in the problem 81 − 54, there are not enough units in the ones column to take away 4 units. See Figure 3.13.

In Figure 3.13 we see the step of *exchanging* one of the longs in the tens' column for ten of the units so that 7 longs are in the longs column and 11 units are in the ones' column. Then the subtraction of 54, that is 5 longs and 4 units, is illustrated, leaving a difference of 2 longs and 7 units or 27.

Figure 3.12

Figure 3.13

The subtraction algorithm can be performed without using concrete models. However, we need to be aware of the exchanges of larger blocks for the next smaller blocks that must take place in order to complete the subtraction. Notation associated with the formal subtraction algorithm provides a means of recording when such an exchange has taken place. For example, the exchange required in the subtraction problem 81 − 54 can be illustrated using a scratch mark to note that one of the tens in 81 is being exchanged for 10 ones, leaving 7 tens and making a total of 11 units in the ones column.

3.7.3
Notation for
the Subtraction
Algorithm

$$\begin{array}{r} {\scriptstyle 7\ 11} \\ 8\!\!\!/1 \\ -\ 54 \\ \hline 27 \end{array}$$

The algorithm used to subtract a two-digit whole number from a two-digit whole number involving one act of borrowing also works with more complicated problems involving multiple trades. For example, to subtract 3,456 from 5,289, we follow the traditional algorithm, recording each exchange.

$$\begin{array}{r} \overset{\scriptstyle 1\ \ 18}{5\ \cancel{2}\ \cancel{8}\ 9} \\ -\ 3\ 4\ 9\ 6 \\ \hline 1\ 7\ 9\ 3 \end{array} \qquad \begin{array}{r} \overset{\scriptstyle 11}{} \\ \overset{\scriptstyle 4\ \cancel{1}\ 18}{\cancel{5}\ \cancel{2}\ \cancel{8}\ 9} \\ -\ 3\ 4\ 9\ 6 \\ \hline 1\ 7\ 9\ 3 \end{array}$$

Exchange 1 $\longrightarrow$ Exchange 2

In this problem, as in all whole-number subtraction problems, we begin with the ones place. Because 6 can easily be subtracted from 9, the subtraction is done and we move into the tens place. In the tens place we need to subtract 9 from 8. Because this poses a problem, we exchange one set of one hundred for 10 sets of ten. We record this exchange by scratching through the 2 in the hundreds place and writing a 1 above the 2, and then by scratching through the 8 in the tens place and writing 18 above the 8. Thus, after exchange 1, there is 1 set of one hundred and 18 sets of 10. Now the subtraction of 9 tens from 18 tens can be done and the difference recorded. Next, when faced with subtracting 4 one hundreds from 1 one hundred, we must borrow again. The picture illustrates that 1 set of one thousand is exchanged for ten sets of one hundred, leaving 4 one thousands and 11 one hundreds. The subtractions in the hundreds and thousands columns are completed to then yield an overall difference of 1,793.

3.7.4
Subtraction in Base Six

The subtraction algorithm can be performed using number in other bases, for example, in base six. Note that in base six, each column represents a power of six. Therefore, an exchange of a block from one column (or place) is equal to six blocks in the next smaller column (or place).

For example, consider the steps in the subtraction of $421_{six} - 145_{six}$:

$$\begin{array}{r} \overset{\scriptstyle 1\ \ 11}{4\ \cancel{2}\ \cancel{1}_{six}} \\ -\ 1\ 4\ 5_{six} \\ \hline 2\ 3\ 2_{six} \end{array} \qquad \begin{array}{r} \overset{\scriptstyle 11_{six}}{} \\ \overset{\scriptstyle 3\ \cancel{1}\ 11_{six}}{\cancel{4}\ \cancel{2}\ \cancel{1}_{six}} \\ -\ 1\ 4\ 5_{six} \\ \hline 2\ 3\ 2_{six} \end{array}$$

Exchange 1 $\longrightarrow$ Exchange 2

Starting with the ones place, we need to subtract 5 from 1. Because this is not possible in whole-number subtraction, we borrow one set of 6 from the next higher place (the sixes place). Thus, in the first exchange we see that one set of 6 is borrowed, leaving 1 in the sixes place. That set of six is brought to the ones place, added to the 1 that is already there, and is expressed 11_{six} (note that 11_{six} is worth 7). Then the subtraction of $11_{six} - 5_{six}$ yields 2_{six} in the ones column.

Then when we move to the six's place to subtract 4 from 1, we find that we must perform another exchange. In the third column over, 1 set of 36 (or 6 squared) is borrowed from the 4 that are there, leaving 3 sets. One of these is the exchanged for 6 sets of six. Adding these 6 sets of six to the 1 that is already there yields 7 or 11_{six} in the sixes place. Subtracting we end up with a difference of 3 in the middle column. Finally, the 1 set of 36 is subtracted from the 3 sets of 36 in the third column, leaving 2 as the difference in the third column.

RELATED TOPICS   Multiplication Algorithms | Division Algorithms

TOPIC 3.8 MULTIPLICATION WITH WHOLE NUMBERS

| Addition with Whole Numbers | **CORNERSTONE** |

Multiplication of whole numbers is initially seen as a short cut to adding multiple amounts of the same number together. Thus is most often introduced as repeated addition. However, multiplication can be seen as having more than this one interpretation. In this topic, we describe three interpretations of multiplication and illustrate multiplication through various models.

INTRODUCTION

The term *multiplication* comes from the Latin phrase *numerus multiplicandus* meaning "the number to be multiplied." A few Latin writers suggested the term *muliplicate* as the process of multiplication. In the 14th century, the word *multiplier* was used to refer to the terms being multiplied together as were *multiplicans* and *mutlipliant*.

DID YOU KNOW?

The word *product* stems from the Latin word *producere* meaning "to lead forth" or "result." In the 15th century, the word *factor*, from the Latin root *factus* became the popular term as did the word *product*.

The process of multiplication was referred to in Egyptian times as *duplation*, which was the repetition of a same number over and over a given number of times. It is speculated that the Greeks multiplied on wax tables, but most evidence indicates that multiplication was done most extensively throughout history on some sort of abacus.

For More Information: Smith, D. E. (1958). *History of mathematics, Volume II.* New York: Dover Publications.

When two whole numbers a and b are multiplied together and the result is a whole number, c, this is written $a \times b = c$. The whole numbers a and b are called **factors,** and c is called the **product**. Multiplication of whole numbers builds, somewhat, upon the addition of whole numbers in that one key way to view multiplication is as **repeated addition**. Multiplication, though, can also be viewed as an **array** and as a **Cartesian product**.

3.8.1
Definition and Terminology

Multiplication is often viewed as repeated addition. We can use repeated addition to solve such problems as the following: "If Frank wants to give three pieces of candy to each of his five party guests, how many pieces of candy will he need?" We can answer this question by adding 3 together five times: $3 + 3 + 3 + 3 + 3 = 15$. See Figure 3.14. We have repeatedly added 3. Ultimately, we find that adding 3 five times can be translated to 5 times 3 or $5 \times 3 = 15$.

3.8.2
Repeated Addition Multiplication

Figure 3.14

Multiplication can often be viewed as determining the number of elements in an array. An **array** is a rectangular collection of objects placed in equal-size rows and columns. For example, if the classroom has 6 rows of desks with 4 desks in each row, the total number of desks can be found by multiplying $4 \times 6 = 24$. Note that the picture that is associated with this problem is a rectangular

3.8.3
Array Multiplication

collection of desks comprised of rows and columns. See Figure 3.15. It is valuable to be able to see multiplication in an array situation because array multiplication defined as the number of rows times number of columns is connected to finding the area of a rectangle by multiplying length × width.

Figure 3.15

Six rows with 4 desks in each
row yields 24 desks altogether.

3.8.4
Cartesian Product

Finally, multiplication can be seen as a Cartesian-product situation. A **Cartesian product** (or "cross product" as it is sometimes called) is the set of different combinations that can be created when pairing each item from one set with each item from another set. That is, if set A = {a, b, c} and set B = {x, y}, then the Cartesian product of sets A and B, written, A × B = {(a, x), (a, y), (b, x), (b, y), (c, x), (c, y)}. Notice that the size of set A, written n(A), times the size of set B, written n(B), is equal to the size of A × B, written n(A × B).

Consider this more concrete situation. Suppose the local diner offers and soup and sandwich lunch special with your choice of one of the following two soups: {onion and tomato}, combined with your choice of one of the following three sandwiches: {cheese, turkey, and veggie}, how many different lunch specials can be ordered? To solve this problem, we can pair each of the soup choices with each of the sandwich choices as follows: {(onion soup, cheese sandwich), (onion soup, turkey sandwich), (onion soup, veggie sandwich), (tomato soup, cheese sandwich), (tomato soup, turkey sandwich), (tomato soup, veggie sandwich)}. Ultimately we find that there are six possible lunch combinations, which can be seen as the product of the number of soup choices times the number of sandwich choices, or 2 × 3 = 6.

3.8.5
Tree Diagram

There are a number of ways to model multiplication. First, when illustrating the Cartesian-product situation described above, a **tree-diagram model** is quite useful. In Figure 3.16 we see the modeling of the combinations of soup-

Figure 3.16

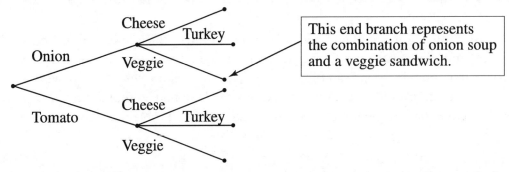

This end branch represents
the combination of onion soup
and a veggie sandwich.

and-sandwich specials using a tree diagram. Note that the number of ending branches of the tree indicate the total number of possible combinations.

As previously alluded to, multiplication is often modeled through some **array** drawing of rows and columns. For example, when determining how many flower seeds you were able to plant if you had 9 rows of seeds with 8 seeds in each row, the model in Figure 3.17a clearly illustrates this situation. However, if the rectangular region in a multiplication situation is not an arrangement of discrete objects and rather is described by some linear dimensions of measure, then a better model to represent the situation would be a rectangular **area model**. For example, if a floor tile measures 8 cm by 9 cm, the total square footage of the floor tile $8 \times 9 = 72$ sq. cm. See Figure 3.17b.

3.8.6
Array Model and Area Model

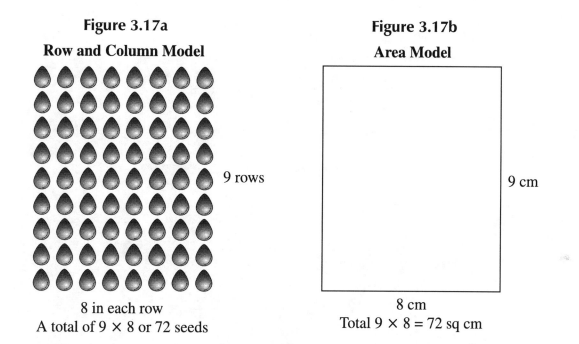

Figure 3.17a

Row and Column Model

9 rows

8 in each row
A total of 9×8 or 72 seeds

Figure 3.17b

Area Model

9 cm

8 cm
Total $9 \times 8 = 72$ sq cm

The repeated addition view of multiplication can be illustrated using a set model as was seen in Figure 3.18. However, it is also possible to illustrate repeated addition using a **number-line model.** For example, if we place six 3-inch strips of trim around a hexagonal picture frame and need to know how many inches of trim we need, we would view this as repeated addition and model this multiplication on the number line showing an arrow having started at zero and jumped three notches six times to end up on the amount 18. See Figure 3.18.

3.8.7
Number-Line Model

$3 + 3 + 3 + 3 + 3 + 3 = 18$

0   3   6   9   12   15   18   21   Figure 3.18

Multiplication Properties and Patterns (Whole Numbers)   **RELATED TOPICS**
Multiplication Algorithms

TOPIC 3.9 MULTIPLICATION PROPERTIES AND PATTERNS (WHOLE NUMBERS)

CORNERSTONE | Addition Properties and Patterns | Multiplication and Whole Numbers

INTRODUCTION | *Like properties of whole number addition, properties of whole number multiplication stem from properties associated with operations on sets. Properties of multiplication influenced the development of the multiplication table. Today's multiplication table provides a convenient summary of the basic multiplication facts and illustrates many patterns of whole number multiplication. In this topic, we describe and provide examples of the properties of whole number multiplication.*

DID YOU KNOW? The square form of the multiplication table was known as the Pythagorean Table. Many mistakenly thought Pythagoras himself created this multiplication table, but it was confirmed that later Pythagoreans were the inventors. It was found in the tenth-century work of Anicius Manlius Severinus Boethius and a work attributed to Beda Venerabilis (c. 710).

Table 3.2

1	2	3	4	5	6	7	8	9
2	4	6	8	10	12	14	16	18
3	6	9	12	15	18	21	24	27
4	8	12	16	20	24	28	32	36
5	10	15	20	25	30	35	40	45
6	12	18	24	30	36	42	48	54
7	14	21	28	35	42	49	56	63
8	16	24	32	40	48	56	64	72
9	18	27	36	45	54	63	72	81

Figure 3.19

A second standard form of the multiplication table was the triangular array (see Figure 3.19). It appeared first in a Prague manuscript in the 14th century, but several variations have been noted throughout history.

For More Information: Smith, D. E. (1958). *History of mathematics, Volume II*. New York: Dover Publications.

3.9.1 Multiplication Table

When learning basic multiplication facts, that is the set of multiplication problems involving two 1-digit factors, working with a multiplication table is quite useful. The multiplication table illustrates patterns and properties associated with the multiplication of elements within the set of whole numbers.

Table 3.3

x	0	1	2	3	4	5	6	7	8	9
0	0	0	0	0	0	0	0	0	0	0
1	0	1	2	3	4	5	6	7	8	9
2	0	2	4	6	8	10	12	14	16	18
3	0	3	6	9	12	15	18	21	24	27
4	0	4	8	12	16	20	24	28	32	36
5	0	5	10	15	20	25	30	35	40	45
6	0	6	12	18	24	30	36	42	48	54
7	0	7	14	21	28	35	42	49	56	63
8	0	8	16	24	32	40	48	56	64	72
9	0	9	18	27	36	45	54	63	72	81

Many patterns can be observed in the whole number multiplication table. For example, observe that the first row and first column of the multiplication table are all zeros. This illustrates the **Zero Property of Whole Number Multiplication** that says any whole number times zero will yield a product of zero. Formally, for any whole number, a, $a \times 0 = 0$ and $0 \times a = 0$.

3.9.2
**Zero Property
of Multiplication**

Notice that the second row and second column of the multiplication table in Table 3.3 match the set of factors that head the rows and columns of the table. This illustrates the **Identity Property of Multiplication**; that is, from the table one can see that the whole number, 1, is the **multiplicative identity** which means that for any whole number, a, $a \times 1 = a$ and $1 \times a = a$.

3.9.3
**Multiplicative
Identity**

Other properties of whole-number multiplication are evident from the multiplication table. For example, notice that when you look at the product associated with 4×3, it is the same product associated with 3×4. Thus, like with the addition of whole numbers, multiplication of whole numbers has the property of being commutative. Essentially, the **Commutative Property of Whole-number Multiplication** states that it does not matter in what order the factors appear; the product will always be the same. So, for any two whole numbers a and b, $a \times b = b \times a$.

3.9.4
**Commutative
Property**

The multiplication table illustrates a fourth property of whole number multiplication called the **Closure Property**; that is, for any two whole numbers, a and b, $a \times b = c$, where c is also a whole number. Essentially, this property says, whenever you multiply two whole numbers together, the product will also be a whole number. All of the products seen within the multiplication table are whole numbers.

3.9.5
Closure Property

Another property of whole number multiplication is the **Associative Property**. This property says that when multiplying three (or more) whole numbers together, it does not matter which pairs of numbers you multiply together first; once all three (or more) numbers are multiplied together, the product will always be the same. For example, when multiplying $4 \times 2 \times 6$, we can group the 4 and 2 together and multiply them first, taking that product, 8, and multiply it by 6 for a total product of 48. This might be written as $(4 \times 2) \times 6 = 48$ to indicate that the 4 and 2 are multiplied together first. On the other hand, we get the same product if we multiply the 2 and 6 together first and then multiply 4 times that product, again getting a total of 48. This would be written as $4 \times (2 \times 6) = 48$. In general, when multiplying any three whole numbers a, b, and c together, the associative property of whole number multiplication guarantees that $(a \times b) \times c = a \times (b \times c)$.

3.9.6
Associative Property

3.9.7
**Distributive
Property of
Multiplication
over Addition**

The final property that is associated with the multiplication of whole numbers is the **Distributive Property of Multiplication over Addition**. The property states that for any whole numbers a, b, and c, $a \times (b + c) = (a \times b) + (a \times c)$. The distributive property can be put to use to find the product of 5×14. It might be easier to view the factor 14 as $10 + 4$ because instead of performing the multiplication of 5×14, you can compute $5 \times (10 + 4) = (5 \times 10) + (5 \times 4)$. The products 5×10 and 5×4 can easily be found using mental math. The sum of the products $50 + 20 = 70$ can also be found quickly using mental math.

RELATED TOPICS   Multiplication Algorithms | Division Algorithms

TOPIC 3.10 MULTIPLICATION ALGORITHMS

CORNERSTONE

Learning the traditional multiplication algorithm proceeds through various stages. We initially learn to multiply two single-digit whole numbers together to find a product and work toward being able to multiply two multi-digited whole numbers together, performing "carrying" when necessary. In the following sections, a variety of multiplication algorithms are displayed with examples to illustrate the algorithms in use.

INTRODUCTION

Multiplication algorithms developed as the need to add similar amounts to each other repeatedly became necessary. The first real methods of multiplication started with Italian mathematician Luca Pacioli (1494 A.D.) who came up with eight plans for multiplication algorithms. Our common method of multiplying stemmed from a plan which took the form shown in Figure 3.20.

DID YOU KNOW?

Multiplicandus.				9	8	7	6
Producentes.				6	7	8	9
Multiplicans.		8	8	8	8	4	
	7	9	0	0	8		
	6	9	1	3	2	Schachieri	
5	9	2	5	6		Bericuocolo	
Summa	6	7	0	4	8	1	6	4

Figure 3.20

   Like the algorithm in Figure 3.20, our current multiplication algorithm provides a procedure for finding the product of the numbers written in columnar form with partial products written underneath the two factors and the final sum written at the very bottom.

For More Information: Smith, D. E. (1958). *History of mathematics, Volume II*. New York: Dover Publications.

   Developing the multiplication algorithm begins with working from known basic whole number multiplication facts and leads to multiplying a one-digit whole number times a two-digit whole number and beyond. As with addition and subtraction, concrete models, such as base-ten blocks, can assist the learning of such algorithms.

**3.10.1
Multiplication
Algorithm**

   The multiplication of 16 × 13 can be visualized using base ten blocks. The base-ten blocks provide a means of illustrating the array model of multiplication with 16 rows having 13 unit blocks in each row. See Figure 3.21.

**3.10.2
Base-Ten Blocks**

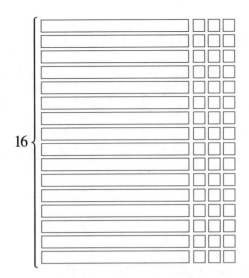

Figure 3.21

16

3.10.3
**Partial-Products
Multiplication
Algorithm**

To further develop the partial products multiplication algorithm, regroup the base-ten blocks from Figure 3.21 as seen in Figure 3.22; that is, where possible, begin with the upper left-hand corner exchange one hundred unit blocks in for a flat or "hundreds" block. Then, starting from the top to the right of the flat, in each column, trade in sets of ten units for as many longs as possible. Do the same for the rows starting with the row beneath the flat. Once all possible exchanges are complete, we can quickly count up, the total number in the product of 16 × 13.

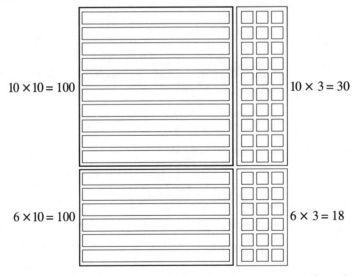

Figure 3.22

$10 \times 10 = 100$

$10 \times 3 = 30$

$6 \times 10 = 100$

$6 \times 3 = 18$

This concrete model of array multiplication lays a visual foundation for the **partial-products multiplication algorithm**. Seen within the array above are the partial products found in the traditionally-written version of partial products illustrated below.

$$
\begin{array}{r}
13 \\
\times 16 \\
\hline
18 \quad (6 \times 3) \\
60 \quad (6 \times 10) \\
30 \quad (10 \times 3) \\
\underline{100} \quad (10 \times 10) \\
208
\end{array}
$$

Note that the partial products are those found by multiplying the ones-place digit of one factor times the ones-place digit of the other factor (3×6), multiplying the ones-place digit of one factor times the value of the tens' place digit of the other factor (and vice versa) (3×10 and 10×6), and finally, multiplying the value of the tens' place digit by the value of the tens-place digit in each of the factors (10×10). Using this transitional multiplication algorithm, we see that when multiplying, for example, 3×6, the product 18 must be recorded as 8 ones in the ones column, and 1 in the tens column. Recognizing that such products have to be written in terms of tens and ones leads nicely to the carrying involved in the standard algorithm.

Using the transitional partial products algorithm, we can better understand performing multiplication using the **standard algorithm of multiplication**. Ultimately, using this algorithm, we can easily perform complex multiplications such as 23×345 doing the necessary carrying.

3.10.4
Standard
Multiplication
Algorithm

$$
\begin{array}{r}
345 \\
\times 23 \\
\hline
15 \ (3 \times 5) \\
120 \ (3 \times 40) \\
900 \ (3 \times 300) \\
100 \ (20 \times 5) \\
800 \ (20 \times 40) \\
6000 \ (20 \times 300) \\
\hline
7935
\end{array}
$$

Partial Products

$$
\begin{array}{r}
345 \\
\times 23 \\
\hline
1035 \\
6900 \\
\hline
7935
\end{array}
$$

Standard Algorithm

In the problem 23×345, the standard algorithm requires the multiplication of 3 times the number 345, carrying when necessary, and the multiplication of 20 time 345, again carrying when necessary. Then these two products are added together to yield the total product. This standard algorithm can makes good use of the distributive property of multiplication over addition in that we can the product of 23×345 as $(20 + 3) \times 345 = (20 \times 345) + (3 \times 345)$.

The details of the standard algorithm followed in the box above goes as follows. When the multiplication 3×345 is carried out, the product $3 \times 5 = 15$ is recorded with the 5 written in the ones column below the multiplication line and the set of ten is carried over to the tens column and recorded as 1 set of ten. Then the $3 \times 4 = 12$ (really representing 3×40) is found and the 1 that was carried over is added to that to make a total of 13. The 3 is recorded in the tens column and the 1 is carried over to the hundreds column. Finishing, the product 3×3 (really 3×300) is found to be 9 and the 1 that was carried over is added to that for a total of 10. The 10 is recorded with the 0 in the hundreds place and the 1 in the thousands place. A similar procedure is followed for 20×345, with the added step of putting a zero in the ones place as a place holder.

Division Algorithms

RELATED TOPICS

TOPIC 3.11 WHOLE-NUMBER DIVISION

CORNERSTONE   Multiplication with Whole Numbers

INTRODUCTION

Division can be thought of as the inverse operation to multiplication. Much of division is connected to multiplication. For example, in long division we estimate the answer to a division problem by guessing what we would have to multiply the divisor by in order to get as close to the starting dividend as possible. Although the two operations are strongly related, the properties associated with multiplication of whole numbers do not hold for the division of whole numbers. Within this topic, we will see that this division process can be interpreted in two different ways using a variety of models to illustrate the division process.

DID YOU KNOW?

Probably the oldest and most widely-accepted definition of division is *the operation of seeking a number which, multiplied by the divisor, is equal to the dividend.* Historically, division has been referred to as partitioning. However, in the Middle Ages, division performed on the abacus was often based upon the operation of subtraction.

Early mathematicians gave names only to two of the numbers used in division, the *numerus dividendus* (the number to be divided) and the *numerus divisor* (the number doing the dividing). names such as *answer* or *result* were commonly used for quotient. The name for the remainder of a division problem has varied quite a bit over time. Medieval Latin writers used *numerus residuus, residuus,* and *residua* to refer to the remainder.

Division was considered the most difficult operation. In the late 15th century, Italian mathematician Pacioli remarked, "If a man can divide well, everything else is easy, for all the rest is involved therein."

For More Information: Smith, D. E. (1958). *History of mathematics, Volume II.* New York: Dover Publications.

**3.11.1
Definition and
Terminology**

In the division of the whole number a by the whole number b, where $a \div b = c$, a is called the **dividend**, b is called the **divisor**, and c is called the **quotient**. Division is thought of as the inverse operation of multiplication. Consequently, division can be viewed as finding the **missing factor** in a multiplication problem. Generally, there are two situations in which division is found. These situations are **repeated subtraction** (sometimes called measurement division) and **sharing** (also known as partitioning).

**3.11.2
Repeated
Subtraction**

Repeated subtraction is the view of division presented in the following problem. *If the general store has 36 balloons and plans to give four balloons to as many customers as possible when they enter the store, how many lucky customers will receive balloons?* The action in solving this problem is that of starting with 36 balloons and subtracting 4 at a time until none are left. Arithmetically this can be seen as:

$36 - 4 = 32, 32 - 4 = 28, 28 - 4 = 24, 24 - 4 = 20, 20 - 4 = 16,$
$16 - 4 = 12, 12 - 2 = 8, 8 - 4 = 4, 4 - 4 = 0$

From this, we see that we can subtract 4 a total of 9 times. The conclusion, then, is that $36 \div 4 = 9$.

Division may be needed in a different type of situation. Consider this example: *If Eva has 28 marbles she wants to put in 4 different bags, having the same number in each bag, how many can she put in each bag?* This scenario presents the idea of sharing the 28 marbles equally among four different sites. This much like distributing the marbles, saying, *one in the first bag, one in the second bag, one in the third bag, one in the fourth bag, another in the first bag, another in the second bag, another in the third bag*, etc.. The image is that of doling things out one at a time to a fixed number of sets until they are all gone (See Figure 3.23).

3.11.3
Sharing

In Step 1, one marble is placed in each bag. In Step 2, a second marble is placed in each bag. Continuing in this manner of partitioning the marbles, all marbles have been distributed at the end of Step 7. Altogether, each bag received 7 marbles. Thus, $28 \div 4 = 7$.

Starting with 28 marbles, distribute them equally into 4 bags

Figure 3.23

3.11.4
Repeated Subtraction Versus Partitioning

The distinction between repeated subtraction division and sharing division can be explained in this way. When we divide, we start with an initial amount. With repeated subtraction division, we know how many items we want to have in each set, we simply do not know how many sets we will have. On the other hand, with partitioning division, we know how many sets we want to divide our items among. We simply do not know how many items will be in each set.

Initial Amount ÷ the number in each set = the number of sets (repeated subtraction)

Initial Amount ÷ the number of sets = the number in each set (partitioning)

3.11.5
Discrete Models of Division

We can model whole number division using any kind of counters or set of objects (like counting chips) and physically dividing a total number of chips into a certain number of piles, determining how many in each pile. This type of division was modeled with marbles in Figure 3.23. Likewise, we can take away a fixed number of chips from a larger pile, determining how many of these fixed-size sets we can create from the original set. In Figure 3.24 the division problem $15 \div 5 = 3$ is modeled using chips to represent the problem.

Start with 15 chips.

Figure 3.24

Place 5 chips at a time in as many piles as possible.
We find we can make a total of 3 equal-sized piles.

3.11.6
The Array Model

The division problem $15 \div 5 = 3$ can also be modeled in an array. In Figure 3.25 we see that given the task of placing 15 chips in equal-sized rows, we find that if there are 5 chips in each row, there must be 3 rows. This model is very useful when solving a division problem viewing it from the missing-factor approach.

Start with 15 chips.

Figure 3.25

You can form 3 rows with 5 in each row.

We can also illustrate division using a number-line model. For example, we can show the problem $24 \div 4 = 6$ on a number line. The picture in Figure 3.26 shows that if you take a section of a number line that is 24 units in length and divide it into 4 equal lengths, each of these smaller lengths is 6 units long.

Figure 3.26

One key issue to note with division is that division by zero is undefined. That is, you cannot solve a division problem where the divisor is zero. We can understand why this is so by thinking about division as finding a missing factor. For example, when we solve the problem $14 \div 7 = ?$, we can ask, "What can I multiply 7 times to get a product of 14?" The answer would be 2 because $2 \times 7 = 14$. Thus, $14 \div 7 = 2$.

If we have a situation where the divisor is 0, such as in the problem $10 \div 0 = ?$, restating the problem as a missing factor situation makes no sense; that is, we ask the question, "What number times zero yields a product of 10?" There is no such number because according to the Zero Property of whole-number multiplication, zero times any whole number is zero. Therefore, there is no logical solution to this problem. Hence, division by zero is not defined.

Division Algorithms

RELATED TOPICS

TOPIC 3.12 DIVISION ALGORITHMS

| **CORNERSTONE** | Whole Number Division |

INTRODUCTION   *The traditional division algorithm builds upon the other operations. We first learn to divide with a single-digit divisor and work toward begin able to divide a multi-digited whole number by a multi-digited divisor. In the following sections, we explore the division algorithm by looking at concrete models and various transitional division algorithms.*

DID YOU KNOW?   Division algorithms developed as the need to break amounts into smaller same-sized amounts became necessary. The oldest form of division is the one used by the Egyptians, which was a process based upon what they termed *duplation* and *mediation*. See the table below, which is used for division by 8. For example, to divide 19 by 8, we can arrange the division as followed. Take $2 \times 8 = 16$, $\frac{1}{2}$ of $8 = 4$, and so on, and select the numbers in the right-hand column of the table which have 19 for their sum. For this example, $16 + 2 + 1 = 19$. The quotient, then, is $2 + \frac{1}{4} + \frac{1}{8} = 2\frac{3}{8}$.

1	8
2	16
$\frac{1}{2}$	4
$\frac{1}{4}$	2
$\frac{1}{8}$	1

Note that the left column consists of numbrs that represent the result when the numbers in the right column are divided by 8. Thus, this duplation and mediation table is designed specifically for division by 8.

In the late Middle Ages, a method of division that consisted of using the factors of the divisor was developed and known as *per repiego*. For example, the problem $216 \div 24$ reduces to $216 \div 8 \div 3$. The goal was to reduce the problem to 1-digit divisors that could be found more easily.

In the middle 16th century, an algorithm called the *English short division* was developed. It was based upon recognizing products in the columns of the multiplication table and working backward to find the related factors. This method is also known as *division by the column*. The division-by-column method is not unlike our traditional algorithm that relies upon estimation of products to find the quotient.

For More Information: Smith, D. E. (1958). *History of mathematics, Volume II*. New York: Dover Publications.

**3.12.1
Concrete
Models of the
Algorithm**

   The division algorithms help us divide a 2-digit dividend by single-digit divisor as well as to perform more complicated division problems such as dividing a 4-digit dividend by a 3-digit divisor. Initially, it is best to introduce the division algorithms using concrete models such as the base ten blocks. For example, $369 \div 3$ can be modeled using base ten blocks as seen in Figure 3.27.

Start with 369 represented in base-ten blocks.
Divide the blocks into 3 equal-sized groups.

There are 123 in each group

We can readily connect the modeled division to the traditional written representation of the long division algorithm. The problem $369 \div 3 = 123$ can be recorded in this manner:

$$
\begin{array}{r}
3 \\
20 \\
100
\end{array} \Big\} 123
$$

$$
\begin{array}{r}
3\overline{)369} \\
-300 \\
\hline
69 \\
-60 \\
\hline
9 \\
-9 \\
\hline
0
\end{array}
$$

Starting with the 369 in the form of base-ten blocks, we first ask how many flats can we put in each of the three groups? The answer is 1, and is recorded above the hundreds column of the number 369. Then the question is asked, "When we put one hundred in each of the three groups, how much did we put out altogether?" The answer is 300. The 300 is written under the 369 and is subtracted to leave a difference of 69.

Next we ask the question, "How many longs can we put in each of the three groups?" The answer is 2, and it is recorded above the tens column of the number 369. Then the question is asked, "When we put 2 tens in each of the three groups, how much did we put out altogether?" The answer is 60. The 60 is written under the 69 and subtracted to leave a difference of 9.

We then ask, "How many units can we put in each of the three groups?" The answer is 3, and is recorded above the ones column of the number 369. Then the question is asked, "When we put 3 units in each of the three groups, how much did we put out altogether?" The answer is 9. The 9 is written under the 9 and subtracted to leave a difference of 0.

Figure 3.27

3.12.2
Scaffolding

There are transitional division algorithms that help students build toward the traditional algorithm. **Scaffolding** is a means of writing the solution to a long division problem in stages, almost like finding "partial quotients." We then add those partial quotients together. For example, when computing $1284 \div 4 = 321$, we can illustrate the division using scaffolding as follows:

$$
\begin{array}{r}
321 \\
1 \\
20 \\
300 \\
4\overline{)1284} \\
-1200 \\
\hline
84 \\
-80 \\
\hline
4 \\
-4 \\
\hline
0
\end{array}
$$

3.12.3
Another
Transitional
Algorithm

We may also use variations of another transitional division algorithm. For example, we may develop the ability to "guess" the correct number of times a divisor goes into a dividend. See the example below of another transitional algorithm illustrating the problem $681 \div 21$:

$$
\begin{array}{r}
\text{Guess} \\
\downarrow \\
21\overline{)681} \\
-420 \quad (20 \times 21) \\
\hline
261 \\
-210 \quad (10 \times 21) \quad \Big\} 20 + 10 + 2 \\
\hline
51 \\
-42 \quad (2 \times 21) \\
\hline
9
\end{array}
$$

So,

$$
\begin{array}{r}
32\,\text{R}\,9 \\
21\overline{)681}
\end{array}
$$

3.12.4
Links to Estimating
Products

One thing to note about performing the division algorithm is the strong connection to multiplication estimation. In the long run, to perform long division we need to have developed a keen ability to estimate how many times a divisor goes into a dividend to find the quotient.

We can use any number of estimation techniques to determine the quotient. One useful technique is front-end estimation where we consider only the left-most digit (or the two left-most digits) of the dividend and divisors, making all other digits zero. For example, when performing the long division $4568 \div 13$, we can use front-end estimation and think of the problem $4000 \div 10$ and make a guess at the first number in the divisor by asking, how many times does 10 go into 4? Once we determines that it will not go into 4 a whole-number amount of times, we continue asking next, "How many times does 10 go into 40?" We see that 4 might be a good guess for the left-most digit of the quotient. We check our guess and adjust if necessary.

RELATED TOPICS   Rational Numbers

TOPIC 3.13 INTRODUCTION TO INTEGERS

INTRODUCTION

The integers is the set of numbers that include positive numbers, negative numbers, and zero. They allow us to represent arithmetic situations where a negative amount occurs, such as a negative bank account balance or temperatures below zero. In this section, we examine the relationship between integers and other sets of numbers.

DID YOU KNOW?

Julia Bowman Robinson, born in 1919, made considerable contributions to the field of mathematical research called number theory. In particular, she dedicated much of her research life to solving a problem about a particular *Diophantine Equation*, a type of equation with only integer solutions. Julia Bowman Robinson became the first female mathematician to be elected to the National Academy of Sciences and the first woman nominated for the presidency of the American Mathematical Society.

For More Information: Cooney, M. P. (Ed.) (1996). *Celebrating Women in Mathematics and Science.* Reston, VA: National Council of Teachers of Mathematics.

3.13.1
Natural Numbers and Whole Numbers

Natural Numbers are the numbers 1, 2, 3, 4, 5,…that we use to count objects. Thus, these numbers are also called **counting numbers**. When we add the number zero (0), to this group of natural numbers, we have the group of numbers 0, 1, 2, 3, 4, 5, ... which we call the **whole numbers**.

3.13.2
Positive and Negative Numbers

The Natural Numbers are all **positive numbers**; that is, they can be represented on a number line as greater than, or to the right of, zero. **Negative numbers**, on the other hand, are numbers that are less than, or to the left of zero on a number line. See Figure 3.28.

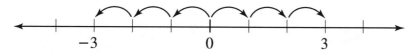

Negative numbers   Positive numbers

Figure 3.28

Notice that if we move three units to the right of zero, we can represent the distance away from zero with the positive number, 3. If we move three units to the left of zero, the distance away from zero is still a distance of three, however we indicate that we are to the left of zero using the negative number −3.

3.13.3
Notation for Positive and Negative Numbers

Positive numbers are represented simply by using the number that represents how far to the right of zero that number is; that is, the positive number six is represented with the symbol 6. Negative numbers, on the other hand, are represented using a negative sign (−) preceding the number to indicate that the amount is negative, or represents an amount to the left (or less than) zero. For example, negative 8 is represented as −8. In some situations, you might see a positive number represented with a positive sign (+) in front of the number, such as + 4 to represent positive 4. However, in most cases, numbers are assumed to be positive when no preceding sign is used.

3.13.4
Opposites

We say that two numbers are **opposites** if they have different signs associated with them. For example, 4 and −4 are opposites because there is a minus sign associated with −4 and an implied plus sign associated with 4. In general the numbers n and $-n$ are opposites of each other. The negative sign itself is sometimes expressed as *the opposite*; that is, $-n$ might be read as *the opposite of n*. Thus, $-(-n)$ could be read as *the opposite of negative n*. Therefore, $-(-n) = n$.

3.13.5
Absolute Value

The **absolute value** of a number is the number of units the number is from zero, no matter whether it is to the right or to the left of zero on a number line. For example, the absolute value of 5 is 5 because it is five units away from zero. On the other hand, the absolute value of −5 is also 5 because −5 is five units away from zero. The **notation for the absolute value of a number, n, is $|n|$**.

In general, if n is a positive number, then $|n| = n$ and $|-n|$ is n. A different way of saying this is, for any number, n, $|n| = n$ when n is positive, and $|n| = -n$ when n is negative. For example, suppose $n = -3$. Then $|-3| = -(-3)$, that is, the negative or opposite of negative three, which is 3. Yet another way to think of the absolute value of a number, n, is $|n| =$ maximum of n and $-n$. So, $|-3| =$ maximum of −3 and $-(-3)$ or 3.

3.13.6
Integers and the Set of Integers

Integers are numbers that include all natural numbers, all negatives of natural numbers (the opposites of the positive natural numbers), and the number zero; that is, **the set of integers** $= \{..., -4, -3, -2, -1, 0, 1, 2, 3, 4, ...\}$. The set of integers is denoted, I. As indicated by the ellipses (...), there is an infinite number of integers. Often, we refer to special subsets of the integers, such as the **set of positive integers** $= \{1, 2, 3, 4, 5, ...\}$, (denoted I^+), and the **set of negative integers** $= \{..., -4, -3, -2, -1\}$, (denoted I^-).

RELATED TOPICS   Rational Numbers | The Set of Rational Numbers

TOPIC 3.14 INTEGER ADDITION

Whole-Number Addition Properties and Patterns | Whole-Number Addtion Integers	**CORNERSTONE**

Integer addition involves adding positive integers to positive integers, negative integers to negative integers, and combining positive and negative integers. Performing addition with integers presents interesting and varied mathematical algorithms and models. In this section we will learn traditional integer addition formulas and will illustrate why these procedures make sense.

INTRODUCTION

When mathematician Carl Friedrich Gauss was just ten years old, his teacher wanted to keep the unruly boy busy. He asked Gauss to find the sum of the integers from 1 to 100. Gauss completed the task in a few minutes. Astounded, the teacher asked how he found the sum so quickly. Gauss explained that when if he added 1 + 100 the sum was 101. He found the same sum when adding 2 + 99, 3 + 98, 4 + 97, and so on. Thus, with the 100 numbers, there would be 50 pairs that would sum to 101. So the total sum would be 50 times 101 or 5,050. Gauss's observation led to a formula for finding the sum of the first n positive integers: $Sum = \frac{n(n+1)}{2}$.

For More Information: Reimer, L., & Reimer W. (1990). *Mathematicians Are People, Too: Stories from the Lives of Great Mathematicians, Volume 1.* Palo Alto, CA: Dale Seymour Publications.

DID YOU KNOW?

The addition of integers has a number of properties. Most of these properties correspond directly to the properties of whole-number addition; that is, like in the addition of whole numbers, the addition of integers has (1) an additive identity of zero, (2) the Commutative Property that says the order of the addends does not affect the sum, (3) the Associative Property that says when adding three or more integers the way you choose to group numbers to add two at a time does not affect the sum, and (4) the Closure Property that says whenever you add two integers, the sum is also an integer. (See Addition Properties and Patterns (Whole Numbers) for illustrative examples of these properties.)

3.14.1 Properties of Integer Addition

The set of integers has an additional property that the set of whole numbers does not have. The set of integers has the **Additive Inverse Property** that says, for any integer, a, and its **inverse** (or opposite), $-a$, $a + -a = 0$ and $-a + a = 0$. For example, given the integer, 5, and its inverse, -5, it is true that $5 + (-5) = 0$ and $-5 + 5 = 0$.

3.14.2 The Additive Inverse Property

When adding integers, there are several addition rules that can be used. These rules apply when adding two positive integers, when adding a positive integer to a negative integer and when adding two negative integers.

Rule for Adding Two Positive Integers. Because the set of positive integers is essentially the set of natural numbers, adding two positive integers is the same as adding two natural numbers; that is, for two positive integers a and b, the sum is found by computing $a + b$. For example, $3 + 6 = 9$.

3.14.3 Addition Rules for Integers

Rule for Adding a Positive Integer to a Negative Integer. To add a positive integer to a negative integer, let's first suppose that a and b are positive integers. Then we can let $-b$ represent a negative integer. To find the sum of $a + (-b)$, there are two cases to consider.

In the first case, $|a| > |-b|$. Then the rule for integer addition says, $a + (-b) = a - b$. For example, $5 + (-2) = 5 - 2 = 3$.

In the second case, $|a| < |-b|$. In this situation, the rule for integer addition says, $a + (-b) = -(|-b| - a)$. For example, $4 + (-7) = -(7 - 4) = -3$.

Rule for Adding Two Negative Integers. Given a and b are positive integers, we can let $-a$ and $-b$ represent negative integers. The rule for adding two negative integers says $-a + (-b) = -(|a| + |b|)$. For example, $-3 + (-6) = -(3 + 6) - 9$.

**3.14.4
Models of
Integer Addition**

Because the rules for integer addition can seem somewhat complicated, it is helpful to see how integer addition can be modeled. Two models that are useful are the set model and the number line model.

Set Model of Integer Addition. Suppose we want to illustrate integer addition using the Set Model. We can use two-color counters—chips that are white on one side and black on the other—to illustrate examples of integer addition. In all examples, let the white chips represent positive numbers and the black chips represent negative numbers. See Figure 3.29 for examples of integer representations using two-color counters.

Figure 3.29

Example 1: To illustrate the addition of $4 + (-5)$, we can combine the representations of the integers shown in Figure 3.29 as done in Figure 3.30.

When we combine 4 white counters with 5 black counters, we next observe that we can pair up black counters with white counters (See Figure 3.31); that is, using the Additive Inverse Property of integer addition, we note that because $1 + (-1) = 0$, then each pairing of a black counter with a white counter represents a sum of zero. Thus, removing these sets of zero from the collection of counters does not affect the total value represented by the counters. Therefore, once all pairs of counters representing zero are removed, we find that one black counter remains. So, the sum $4 + (-5) = -1$.

Figure 3.30   **Figure 3.31**

Example 2: When adding two negative integers, the two-color counters are also useful for modeling the addition. Adding $-2 + (-3)$, we demonstrate the addition combining 2 black counters with 3 more black counters for a total of 5 black counters (See Figure 3.32). Thus, the sum is -5.

Figure 3.32

The Number-Line Model of Integer Addition. Integer addition can be clearly modeled on a number line. The rules involved in using the number line to illustrate integer addition are: (1) Always start with your arrow on zero; (2) your arrow always the positive direction (to the right); (3) positive-integer addends tell you to move your arrow forward; and (4) negative integers tell you to move backward.

Example 1: Illustrating the addition problem $6 + (-4)$ on the number line, we begin with our arrow on zero, facing right as shown in Figure 3.33.

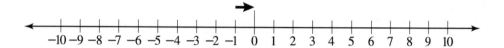

Figure 3.33

Show the first addend by advancing the arrow forward 6 units. Then show the second addend by moving the arrow backward 4 units. The arrow stops at 2. (See Figure 3.34) Therefore, $6 + (-4) = 2$.

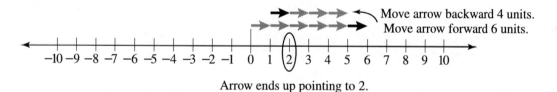

Move arrow backward 4 units.
Move arrow forward 6 units.

Arrow ends up pointing to 2.

Figure 3.34

Example 2: Next we illustrate the problem $-8 + 3$. Beginning with our arrow on zero facing toward the right, we show the first addend by moving the arrow backward 8 units. Then show the second addend by moving the arrow forward 3 units. The arrow stops at -5. (See Figure 3.35.) Therefore, $-8 + 3 = -5$.

Move arrow forward 3 units so that it points to -5.
Move arrow backward 8 units so that it points to -8.
Start with arrow pointing to zero facing right.

Figure 3.35

Example 3: We can illustrate the addition of two negative integers on the number line. Showing $-3 + (-5)$, we begin with our arrow pointing to zero facing toward the right. We represent the first addend by moving our arrow backward 3 units. We represent our second addend by moving the arrow backward another 5 units. The arrow lands on -8, showing that $-3 + (-5) = -8$. See Figure 3.36.

Figure 3.36

Move arrow backward another 5 units so that it points to -8.
Move arrow backward 3 units so that it points to -3.
Start with arrow pointing to zero facing right.

RELATED TOPICS   Order of Operations | Integer Subtraction | Integer Multiplication
                      Integer Division

TOPIC 3.15 INTEGER SUBTRACTION

Integers | Integer Addition | Whole-Number Subtraction   **CORNERSTONE**

Integer subtraction involves finding the difference between combinations of positive and negative integers. To some, the idea of subtracting a negative amount makes little sense, particularly when we are told that subtracting a negative number is like adding a positive number. In this section, models such as the number-line model and the set model help to explain this abstract notion.   **INTRODUCTION**

The use of negative numbers has not been found in the writings of ancient Egyptians, Babylonians, Hindus, or Greeks. The Chinese, however, in as early as 200 B.C. made the first distinction and use of negative numbers as subtrahends in subtraction problems. Centuries later, the Chinese began to show more distinction between positive and negative numbers by writing positive numbers in red and negative numbers in black.   **DID YOU KNOW?**

For More Information: Smith, D. E. (1958). *History of mathematics, Volume II.* New York: Dover Publications.

Most of the properties that hold for integer addition do not hold for integer subtraction; that is, integer subtraction is not commutative, is not associative, does not have an identity, and does not have an inverse feature. (See Integer Addition and Properties of Whole-Number Addition for more details about these properties.) However, integer subtraction does have the property of being closed. The **Closure Property of integer subtraction** states that the difference $a - b$ between any two integers, a and b, is also an integer. For example, the difference between the integers 7 and -9, $7 - (-9) = 2$, where 2 is also an integer.   **3.15.1**
Closure Property
for Integer
Subtraction

When subtracting an integer from another integer, there are rules to follow depending on whether the minuend (starting amount) and subtrahend (amount being subtracted) are positive or negative integers.   **3.15.2**
Rules for Integer
Subtraction

Rules for Subtraction Involving Two Positive Integers. When both the minuend and subtrahend (see Subtraction With Whole Numbers for more details) are positive, then there are two cases to consider. First, when the minuend is greater than the subtrahend, then positive integer subtraction works the same as the subtraction of whole numbers. For example, $7 > 5$, thus, $7 - 5 = 2$.

When the subtrahend is greater than the minuend, the difference is found by subtracting the minuend from the subtrahend and applying a negative sign to that answer; that is, for two positive integers a and b where $a < b$, $a - b = -(b - a)$. For example, given the integers 3 and 8, the difference $3 - 8 = -(8 - 3) = -5$.

Rules for Subtraction Involving Two Negative Integers. When finding the difference between two negative integers, there is a specific rule we can use to re-write the subtraction problem as an integer addition problem. The rule states that given any two negative integers expressed as $-a$ and $-b$, $-a - (-b) = -a + b$. Essentially, the rule says that subtracting a negative number is equivalent to adding the (positive) opposite of that number. For example, $-5 - (-6) = -5 + 6$. Likewise, $-7 - (-4) = -7 + 4$. To compute the answers, then, to these problems, we can use the rules for integer addition that apply when one addend is positive and one addend is negative (See Integer Addition for details). Thus, $-5 - (-6) = -5 + 6 = 1$ and $-7 - (-4) = -7 + 4 = -3$.

Rules for Subtracting a Negative Integer from a Positive Integer. When subtracting a negative integer from a positive integer, we can use essentially the same method described above for re-writing the subtraction problem as an integer addition problem; that is, given a positive integer, a, and a negative integer, $-b$, $a - (-b) = a + b$. Thus, when subtracting -7 from 4, we can re-write the subtraction problem as $4 - (-7) = 4 + 7$. To complete the computation we can simply add the two positive integers to find the answer $4 - (-7) = 4 + 7 = 11$.

Rules for Subtracting a Positive Integer from a Negative Integer. When subtracting a positive integer from a negative integer, we can re-write the subtraction problem as an integer addition problem and then follow the rules for integer addition. The rule for re-writing such a subtraction statement says, given a positive integer, a, and a negative integer, $-b$, $-b - a = -b + -a$; that is, subtracting a positive integer is equivalent to adding the (negative) opposite of that integer. For example, given the integers -7 and 9, $-7 - 9 = -7 + -9$. To determine the final computational answer, we can use the rule for adding two negative integers (See Integer Addition for details and examples). Thus, $-7 - 9 = -7 + -9 = -16$.

3.15.3
Models of Integer Subtraction

The rules for integer subtraction are closely related to rules for integer addition. When we model integer subtraction using the set model and the number line model, we can begin to see the connections and to better understand the integer subtraction processes.

The Set Model of Integer Subtraction. Suppose we want to illustrate integer subtraction using the Set Model. We can use two-color counters, chips that are white on one side and black on the other, to illustrate examples of integer subtraction. In all examples, let the white chips represent positive numbers and the black chips represent negative numbers. See Figure 3.37 for examples of integer representations using two-color counters.

Figure 3.37

Example 1: Suppose we want to first model the subtraction problem $-6 - (-4)$. We can begin by placing 6 black chips out to represent the beginning amount or minuend. We can then take away 4 black chips to model the subtraction of the -4. See Figure 3.38.

Figure 3.38

Step 1: Start with -6.   **Step 2:** Take away -4.   **Step 3:** Determine that -2 remains.

Example 2: A more complicated example arises when we subtract $-7 - 3$. To model this problem, we begin with seven black chips to represent -7. However, there are no white chips that we can remove to model the subtraction of positive 3. To work with this model, we must make use of the Additive Inverse Property (see Integer Addition); that is, if we simultaneously add one white chip and one black chip to the set of chips, we are essentially adding "zero" because an integer plus its opposite equal zero. Therefore, we can model the subtraction problem −7 − 3 as seen in Figure 3.39.

Step 1: Start with −7.   **Step 2:** Add 3 white and 3 black chips.

Figure 3.39

Step 3: Take away 3 white chips.   **Step 4:** Determine that 10 black chips or −10 remains.

The model of integer subtraction in Figure 3.37 suggests a relationship between integer subtraction and integer addition. The rule for subtracting −7 − 3 tells us to re-write the subtraction problem as the addition problem −7 + −3 and then add the negative integers. The set model allows us to see the conversion of the subtraction problem to an integer addition problem; that is, we ultimately add the 3 new black chips to the original seven black chips to find a total of 10 black chips or an answer of −10.

Example 3: A similar result happens when we subtract a negative integer from a positive one. In the problem 2 − (−4), we can model the problem with chips (see Figure 3.40) and find that in the end we have 6 white chips, or 6 as an answer.

Step 1: Start with 2.   **Step 2:** Add 4 white and 4 black chips.

Figure 3.40

Step 3: Take away 4 black chips.   **Step 4:** Find that 6 white chips remain.

The Number-Line Model of Integer Subtraction. Integer subtraction can be clearly modeled on a number line. The rules involved in using the number line to illustrate integer subtraction are: (1) always start with your arrow on zero; (2) your arrow points to the negative (left) direction when subtracting; (3) a positive integer tells you to move your arrow forward; and (4) a negative integers tell you to move backward.

Example 1: To illustrate the subtraction 5 − 7, we begin with our arrow on zero facing forward. (See Figure 3.41.) We move forward to positive 5. We then

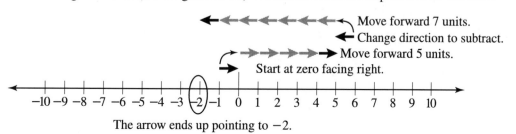

Move forward 7 units.
Change direction to subtract.
Move forward 5 units.
Start at zero facing right.

The arrow ends up pointing to −2.

Figure 3.41

turn the arrow to face the negative direction because we are about to subtract. We finally move the arrow forward seven because seven is positive. The result shows that the arrow ends at −2.

Example 2: Illustrating the subtraction of a negative number can be done by following the same rules. Subtracting 3 − (−2), we begin at zero and facing right and move forward 3 units. We then change directions to prepare to subtract. Finally we move backward 2 units because the integer subtracted is negative. (See Figure 3.42) The arrow ends pointing to positive 5, and this is our answer.

Figure 3.42

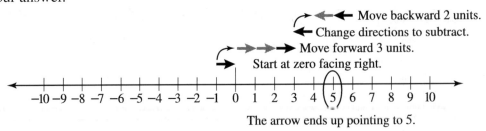

Example 3: We can illustrate −8 − (−3) on the number line. Figure 3.43 shows the arrow beginning on zero facing right and then moving backward 8 units to show −8. Then the arrow changes directions for subtraction and moves backward 3 units for the −3. Then end result is a difference of −5.

Figure 3.43

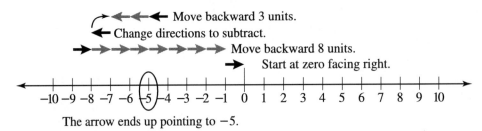

RELATED TOPICS   Order of Operations | Integer Multiplication | Integer Division

TOPIC 3.16 INTEGER MULTIPLICATION

CORNERSTONE

Multiplying integers together combine the basic fundamental steps of multiplying whole numbers with the interesting addition of having negative factors. People know the basic rule that a negative number times a negative number is a positive numbers. In this section, models are used to bring understanding to this and other rules for the multiplication of integers.

INTRODUCTION

The rules for multiplying by negative numbers times negative numbers makes sense when you analyze the pattern of product found by multiplying a given integer by a series of positive and negative integers. Observe:

DID YOU KNOW?

$$4 \times -3 = -12$$
$$3 \times -3 = -9$$
$$2 \times -3 = -6$$
$$1 \times -3 = -3$$
$$0 \times -3 = 0$$
$$-1 \times -3 = 3$$
$$-2 \times -3 = 6$$
$$-3 \times -3 = 9$$
$$etc. \ldots$$

As the first factor decreases by 1, the product of the first factor and -3 increases by 3. Thus, the pattern suggests that a negative times a negative should yield a positive number to continue the pattern.

The multiplication of integers has a number of properties. These properties correspond directly to the Properties of Whole Number Multiplication; that is, as in the multiplication of whole numbers, the multiplication of integers has (1) a multiplicative identity of one, (2) the Commutative Property that says the order of the factors does not affect the product, (3) the Associative Property that says when multiplying three or more integers the way you choose to group numbers to multiply two at a time does not affect the product, (4) the Closure Property that says whenever you multiply two integers, the product is also an integer, (5) the Zero Property of Multiplication which says that zero times any integer yields a product of zero, and (6) the Distributive Property of Multiplication over Addition, which shows us two ways to view the multiplication of an integer by the sum of two integers (See Multiplication Properties and Patterns [Whole Numbers] for illustrative examples of these properties.)

3.16.1
Properties of Integer Multiplication

When multiplying integers, there are several multiplication rules that can be used. These rules apply when multiplying two positive integers, when multiplying a positive integer by a negative integer and when multiplying two negative integers.

3.16.2
Multiplication Rules for Integers

Rule for Multiplying Two Positive Integers. Because the set of positive integers is the set of whole numbers (less zero), the rule for multiplying two positive integers is to perform the multiplication like whole number multiplication. Thus, choosing the positive integers, 6 and 8, we find $6 \times 8 = 48$.

Rule for Multiplying a Positive Integer by a Negative Integer. When multiplying a positive integer by a negative integer, the product is always the negative (opposite) of the product of the absolute values of the two factors; that is, given a positive integer, a, and a negative integer $-b$, the product $a \times -b = -(|a| \times |-b|) = -(a \times b)$. For example, given -5 and 4, we find $5 \times (-4) = -(5 \times 4) = -20$.

Rule for Multiplying Two Negative Integers. When multiplying two negative integers, the product will always be positive. The rule for multiplying negative integers states that the product of two negative integers is the product of the absolute values of each integer; that is, given two negative integers expressed as $-a$ and $-b$, the product $-a \times (-b) = |-a| \times |-b| = a \times b$. For example, the product of -6 and -12 is found by $-6 \times (-12) = |-6| \times |-12| = 6 \times 12 = 72$.

**3.16.3
Models of Integer
Multiplication**

Multiplication of integers can be modeled using a set model and a number line model. These models help provide a visual means of understanding the processes used in integer multiplication.

The Set Model of Integer Multiplication. Suppose we want to illustrate integer multiplication using the set model. We can use two-color counters, chips that are white on one side and black on the other, to illustrate examples of integer multiplication. In all examples, let the white chips represent positive numbers and the black chips represent negative numbers. See Figure 3.44 for examples of integer representations using two-color counters.

Figure 3.44

Rules for Working with the Set Model for Multiplication. The rules for working with the two-colored counters are as follows: (1) the absolute value of the first factor tells you how many chips to put out at a time (in one set); (2) the absolute value of the second factor tells you how many sets of counters to put out at a time; (3) the sign of the first factor tells you which side of the counter to have face up (white for positive, black for negative); and (4) the sign of the second factor tells you whether to maintain the face-up color determined by the first factor (if a positive sign) or change the face-up color to its opposite (if a negative sign).

Example 1: To illustrate the multiplication $3 \times (-4)$, we know that we will put down 3 counters (chips) at a time and we will put down 4 sets of three chips. Because 3 is positive, those chips will be placed white-side up. (See Figure 3.45.) Because the second factor is negative, we then know to flip the chips to their opposite side. The end result is 12 black chips representing the product -12.

Figure 3.45

Step 1: Show 3 sets of 4 white chips.

Step 2: Flip the 12 chips to their opposite sides.

Example 2: To show the product $-2 \times (-5)$, we would illustrate two sets of five starting out black-side up because of the negativity of the first factor. (See Figure 3.46.) Then we flip the counters to their opposite side because of the negativity of the second factor. The result is 10 white chips or positive 10.

Step 1: Show 2 sets of 5 black chips.

Figure 3.46

Step 2: Flip the 10 chips to their opposite sides.

This model provides a frame of reference for see how a negative times a negative yields a positive. In essence, it shows that multiplying by a second factor that is negative causes you to "flip" or change the sign, regardless of whether you start with a positive or negative first factor.

Example 3: If your first factor is negative and your second factor is positive, then you would start with counters black side up, and would not flip them because the second factor would not change the sign. See Figure 3.47 for a depiction of the product $-3 \times 5 = -15$.

Step 1: Show 3 sets of 5 black chips.

Figure 3.47

Step 2: Leave the 15 chips on the black side.

The Number-Line Model of Integer Multiplication. Integer multiplication can be clearly modeled on a number line. The rules involved in using the number line to illustrate integer multiplication are: (1) always start with your arrow on zero (2) your arrow points in the positive direction (to the right) if the first factor is positive and in the negative direction (to the left) if the first factor is negative, (3) the arrow moves forward if the second factor is positive and moves backward if the second factor is negative, (4) the absolute value of the first factor tells you how many units to move your arrow each time, and (5) the absolute value of the second factor tells you how many times to move your arrow.

Example 1: To illustrate -3×6 on the number line, we begin with our arrow pointing left because the first factor, -3, is negative. We will move our arrow forward because the second factor, 6, is positive. We will move our arrow 3 units six times. See Figure 3.48.

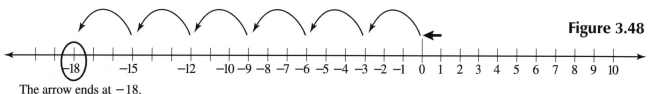

Figure 3.48

The arrow ends at -18.

Example 2: To show the product $4 \times (-3)$ on the number line, begin with the arrow facing right because 4 is positive and move the arrow backward because -3 is negative. We will move the arrow 4 units at a time, moving the arrow 4 times. This shows a product of -12. See Figure 3.49.

Figure 3.49

The arrow ends pointing to -12.

Example 3: The product $-2 \times (-3) = 6$ can also be shown on the number line. Figure 3.50 illustrates that we begin with the arrow at zero facing left because -2 is negative. We will move the arrow backward because -3 is negative. We will move the arrow 2 units at a time, moving it 3 times.

Figure 3.50

The arrow ends pointing to 6.

RELATED TOPICS   Integer Division

TOPIC 3.17 INTEGER DIVISION

Integers | Integer Addition | Integer Subtraction | Integer Multiplication
Whole-Number Division **CORNERSTONE**

The division of integers builds from basic rubrics of division and the absolute values of integers. In this section we explore rules for dividing positive and negative dividends by positive and negative divisors. These rules are further explored through the number line and set models. **INTRODUCTION**

The concept of absolute value was given its name by a mathematician named Karl Weierstrass who did most of his mathematical work in the mid- to late-nineteenth century. The term originated from the context of imaginary numbers and complex numbers when referring to what mathematicians call the "norm." **DID YOU KNOW?**

For More Information: Smith, D. E. (1958). *History of mathematics, Volume II.* New York: Dover Publications.

**3.17.1
Rules for Dividing
Integers**

When we divide an integer by an integer, the answer, or quotient, is sometimes an integer. Other times, the answer comes out with a remainder or fractional part. To understand basic integer division and rules for integer division, we will look solely at examples where the quotients are also integers. See Whole-Number Division for a review the terms quotient, divisor, and dividend.

There are three different rules that we can use when dividing integers. They are closely related to the rules for multiplication of integers. The rules pertain to cases where both the dividend and the divisor are positive, where both the dividend and divisor are negative, and where the dividend and divisor have different signs.

Rule for Dividing Integers When Both Dividend and Divisor are Positive. When the dividend and divisor in a division problem are both positive, the division is computed as if the dividend and divisors were whole numbers; that is, for integers, 40 and 5, the quotient of $40 \div 5 = 8$.

Rule for Dividing Integers When Both Dividend and Divisor are Negative. If both the dividend and divisor are negative, then the quotient will be positive; that is, a negative number divided by a negative number is equal to the quotient of the absolute values of the two numbers. Essentially, the rule says $-a \div (-b) = |-a| \div |-b| = a \div b$. For example, $-30 \div -5 = 30 \div 5 = 6$.

Rule for Dividing Integers When the Dividend and Divisor Have Opposite Signs. When the dividend and divisor have opposite signs, the quotient will always be negative. The quotient is the negative of the quotient found by dividing the absolute value of the quotient by the absolute value of the divisor. Thus, for any integers, a and b, where exactly one of a or b is negative, $a \div b = -(|a| \div |b|)$. For example, $54 \div (-9) = -(54 \div 9) = -6$. Similarly, $-72 \div 8 = -(72 \div 8) = -9$.

**3.17.2
The Set Model
for Illustrating
Integer Division**

Probably the best model for illustrating integer division is the set model. By following rules similar to those in the set model for Integer Multiplication, we can illustrate how to divide integers using two-color counters.

Rules for Working with the Set Model for Integer Division. The rules for working with the two-colored counters to illustrate division of integers are as follows: (1) the absolute value of the dividend tells you how many chips to put out at the beginning; (2) the absolute value of the divisor tells you what-sized sets to break the starting amount into; (3) the sign of the dividend tells you which side of the counter to have face up at the beginning (white for positive, black for negative); and (4) the sign of the divisor tells you whether to maintain the face-up color determined by the dividend (if a positive sign) or change the face-up color to its opposite (if a negative sign).

Example 1: To illustrate $-12 \div 4$ with the two-color counters, we start with 12 counters out facing black-side up because the dividend is a negative 12. We then break these 12 counters into groups of 4, determining how many groups we can form. Because the divisor is positive, we leave the counters facing black-side up. Thus, the quotient is shown to be negative 3 because we have 3 sets of black counters. See Figure 3.51 below.

Figure 3.51

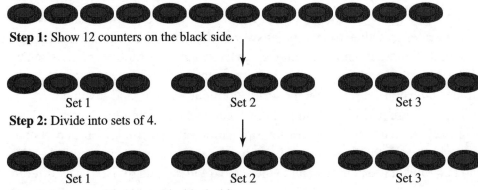

Step 1: Show 12 counters on the black side.

Set 1   Set 2   Set 3

Step 2: Divide into sets of 4.

Set 1   Set 2   Set 3

Step 3: Leave the 15 chips on the black side.

Example 2: Illustrating how to determine the quotient of $24 \div (-6)$, we begin with 24 counters facing white-side up as seen in Figure 3.52. We divide these counters into sets of 6, finding there are 4 sets. We then flip the counters

Figure 3.52

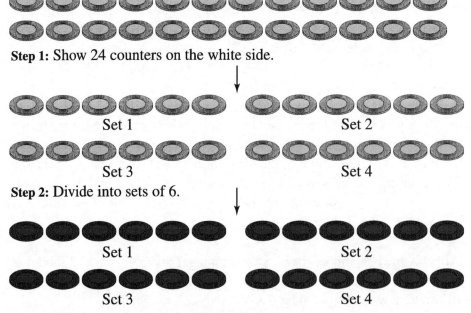

Step 1: Show 24 counters on the white side.

Set 1   Set 2
Set 3   Set 4

Step 2: Divide into sets of 6.

Set 1   Set 2
Set 3   Set 4

Step 3: Flip the counters to the black side.

to their opposite sides because the divisor is negative. Thus, the result is 4 sets of black counters, representing a quotient of negative 4.

Example 3: To find the quotient of $-21 \div (-3)$, we begin with 21 counters facing black-side up as shown in Figure 3.53. We then break the 21 counters into sets of 3. We find that there are 7 such sets. Then, because the divisor is negative, we flip the counters over to their opposite sides. Thus, we have 7 sets of white counters, so the quotient is positive 7.

Step 1: Show 21 counters on the black side.

Step 2: Divide into sets of 3.

Step 3: Flip the counters to the white side.

Figure 3.53

Order of Operations   **RELATED TOPICS**

TOPIC 3.18 ORDER OF OPERATIONS

CORNERSTONE | Integers | Integer Addition | Integer Subtraction | Integer Multiplication
Integer Division

INTRODUCTION | *Order of operations is a topic that explains which operations are computed before others. In this section we examine how agreement to this order of performing operations affords the ability to compute arithmetic problems and determine a universally-accepted answer.*

DID YOU KNOW? | Many people associate the phrase "Please Excuse My Dear Aunt Sally" with remembering that the order of operations is Parentheses, Exponents, Multiplication & Division, and Addition & Subtraction.

3.18.1
Definition of the Term Order of Operations

The phase "Order of Operations" refers to the sequence we follow when performing a series of operations in a particular computation. For example, if you were to compute the fllowing: $30 - 20 \div 2 \times 5 + 3$, you would find different answers depending on the order you performed the operations. You might think that you simply work from left to right, performing each operation as you come to it in the problem. So in the example $30 - 20 \div 2 \times 5 + 3$, you might think, $30 - 20$ is 10, then $10 \div 2$ is 5, then 5×5 is 25, and then $25 + 3$ is 28. However, this is not the case; there are specific rules we must follow.

3.18.2
The Rules of Order of Operations

There is a hierarchy of which operations should take place before others. Figure 3.54 shows a schematic design of levels of operations.

As Figure 3.54 indicates, in a series of operations, you perform any operation enclosed in parentheses first. For example, in the problem $2 + (5 \times 4)$, you find the product $5 \times 4 = 20$ first, then add 2 to 20 for an answer of 22. If the computation were $9 - 2^2 + (5 \times 4)$, you would still perform the parenthetical operation first. Next, you would find the value of $2^2 = 4$. Then, once these first two levels of computation had been performed, the problem of solving $9 - 2^2 + (5 \times 4)$ becomes $9 - 4 + 20$. Because addition and subtraction are operations on the same level, you perform the operations as you encounter them from left to right; that is, you find $9 - 4 = 5$, and then add 5 to 20 for a final answer of 25.

Some problems do not have any parentheses, such as the problem $30 - 20 \div 2 \times 5 + 3$ that was mentioned above. When faced with this, you perform higher level operations first; that is, in this problem, you perform all multiplications and divisions first (in the order in which they appear) before moving on to additions and subtractions. Thus, the solution to $30 - 20 \div 2 \times 5 + 3$ can be thought of in this way. Perform the division $20 \div 2 = 10$ first; then take that quotient of 10 and multiply by 5 for a product of 50. The problem is then reduced to $30 - 50 + 3$, which would finally be completed by performing the $30 - 50 = -20$ first, followed by $-20 + 3 = -17$.

Notice that, if when solving $30 - 20 \div 2 \times 5 + 3$ you did not follow the order of operation sequence, you could generate a variety of answers depending on the order you chose to compute each step. For example, if you simply perform the multiplication before the division—that is, you do not go in order from left to right when doing level-three operations—you would find the solution to be $30 - 20 \div 10 + 3 = 30 - 2 + 3 = 28 + 3 = 31$. Other variations from the order-of-operations rules would yield other incorrect answers to the computational problem. Thus, following the universally accepted order of operations is important so that we can all agree upon the correct answer in computational situations.

Parentheses	**Level One**
Exponential Expressions	**Level Two**
Multiplication and Division	**Level Three** (Perform in the order that they appear.)
Addition and Subtraction	**Level Four** (Perform in the order that they appear.)

Figure 3.54

Most calculators are automatically programmed to follow the correct order of operations; that is, if you punched into your calculator the problem $30 - 20 \div 2 \times 5 + 3$ that we have examined above, the calculator would perform the operations of division and multiplication, in that order, first, and then perform the subsequent subtraction and addition pieces, finding an answer of -17. Try this problem in your calculator.

3.18.3
The Calculator and Order of Operations

Exponents   **RELATED TOPICS**

IN THE CLASSROOM

Some expectations of your future students

Pre-K-2
(NCTM, 2000,
p. 78)

understand various meanings of addition and subtraction of whole numbers and the relationship between the two operations

understand situations that entail multiplication and division, such as equal grouping of objects and sharing equally

develop and use strategies for whole number computations, with a focus on addition and subtraction

Grades 3-5
(NCTM, 2000,
p. 148)

explore numbers less than 0 by extending the number line and through familiar applications

understand various meanings of multiplication and division

understand and use properties of operations, such as the distributivity of multiplication over addition

develop fluency in adding, subtracting, multiplying, and dividing whole numbers

This chapter continues to focus on the *Number and Operations Content Standard*. In its focus on the four arithmetic operations as they act on familiar sets of numbers, you will continue to construct a better understanding of number as concept. Given that "as they progress from prekindergarten through grade 12, students should attain a rich understanding of…how numbers are embedded in systems that have structures and properties" (NCTM, 2000, p. 32), we believe you must develop an understanding of (a) properties associated with a set of objects acted on by an operation within which sets of numbers acted on by familiar operations are specific examples (Activities 3.1-3.2), (b) the meanings we associate with familiar arithmetic operations and corresponding models of each (Activities 3.3-3.5), and (c) the relationship between the numerical representation of a number and the procedures used to compute familiar operations (Activities 3.6-3.12)

How Activities 3.1-3.12 help you develop an adult-level perspective on the above expectations.

- By identifying various actions associated with each arithmetic operation, you construct meaningful models of the latter. For example, comparing, taking away, and adding onto, are different ways a child might think about a problem that adults solve by subtraction.

- By exploring sets of numbers and the result of familiar arithmetic operations on them, you continue to understand number as concept. For example, the set $\{0, 1, 2, 3, …\}$ of Whole Numbers is not closed under subtraction: $2 - 3 = -1$ which is not in the set. The "take away" model of subtraction may generate a need for the concept of negative numbers.

- By explaining why different algorithms for the same arithmetic operation work, you analyze strategies for computation and deepen your understanding of the numerical representation of the numbers and its composition in terms of place values. For example, you understand why multiplication is commutative and distributes over addition.

- By solving as well as creating non-routine, multi-step, multi-operation problems, you stretch your thinking about familiar operations as well as the numbers they operate on.

BIBLIOGRAPHY

Abel, J., Allinger, G. D., & Andersen, L. (1987). Popsicle Sticks, Computers, and Calculators: Important Considerations. *Arithmetic Teacher 34*, 8- 12.

Allinger, G D., & Payne, J. N. (1986). Estimation and mental arithmetic with percent. In H. L. Schoen (Ed.), *Estimation and mental computation* (pp. 141-155). Reston. VA: National Council of Teachers of Mathematics.

Baek, J. (1998). Children's invented algorithms for multidigit multiplication problems. In L. J. Morrow (Ed.), *The teaching and learning of algorithms in school mathematics* (pp. 151-160). Reston, VA: National Council of Teachers of Mathematics.

Baker, A., & Baker, J. (1991). *Math's in the mind: A process approach to mental strategies.* Portsmouth. NH Heinemann.

Baroody, A. J. (1984). Children's difficulties in subtraction: Some causes and cures. *Arithmetic Teacher, 32* (3), 14-19.

Baroody, A. J (1985). Mastery of the basic number combinations: Internalization of relationships or facts? *Journal for Research in Mathematics Education, 16*, 83-98.

Baroody, A. J, & Standifer, D. J. (1993). Addition and subtraction in the primary grades In R. J. Jensen (Ed.), *Research ideas for the classroom: Early childhood mathematics* (pp. 72-102). Old Tappan, NJ: Macmillan.

Battista, Michael T. (1983). A complete model for operations on integers. *Arithmetic Teacher, 30*, 26-31.

Beattie, Ian D. (1986). Modeling operations and algorithms. *Arithmetic Teacher, 33*, 23-28.

Bobis, J. (1991). Using a calculator to develop number sense. *Arithmetic Teacher, 38*, 42-45.

Burns, M. (1989). Teaching for understanding: A focus on multiplication. In P. R. Trafton (Ed.), *New directions for elementary school mathematics* (pp. 123-133). Reston, VA: National Council of Teachers of Mathematics.

Bums, M. (1991). Introducing division through problem-solving experiences. *Arithmetic Teacher, 38* (8), 14-18.

Burns, M. (1992). *About teaching mathematics: A K-8 resource.* Sausalito, CA: Math Solutions Publications.

Burns, M. (1995). *Math by all means: Multiplication, grade 3.* Sausalito, CA: Math Solutions Publications.

Carpenter, T. P., Carey, D. A, & Kouba, V. L. (1990). A problem-solving approach to the operations. In J. N. Payne (Ed.). *Mathematics for the young child* (pp. 111-131). Reston, VA: National Council of Teachers of Mathematics.

Carroll, W. M., & Porter, D. (1997). Invented strategies can develop meaningful mathematical procedures. *Teaching Children Mathematics, 3*, 370-374.

Cemen, P. B. (1993). Teacher to teacher: Adding and subtracting integers on the number line. *Arithmetic Teacher, 40, 388-389.*

Chang, L. (1985). Multiple methods of teaching the addition and subtraction of integers. *Arithmetic Teacher, 33*, 14-19.

Clark, F. B., & Kamii, C. (1996). Identification of multiplicative thinking in children in grades 1-5. *Journal for Research in Mathematics Education, 27*, 41-51.

Corwin, R. B. (1989). Multiplication as original sin. *Journal of Mathematical Behavior, 8*, 223-225.

Crowley, M. L., & Dunn, M. L. (1985). On multiplying negative numbers. *Mathematics Teacher 78*, 252-256.

Curcio, F. R., Sicklick, F, & Turkel, S. B. (1987). Divide and conquer: Unit strips to the rescue. *Arithmetic Teacher, 35*, 6- 12.

Feinberg, M. M. (1990). Using patterns to practice basic facts. Arithmetic Teacher/(8), 38-41.

Graeber, A. O., & Tanenhaus. E. (1993). Multiplication and division: From whole-numbers to rational numbers. In D. T. Owens (Ed.*)*, *Research ideas for the classroom: Middle grades mathematics* (pp. 99-117) Old Tappan, N]: Macmillan.

Graeber. A. O., & Baker, K. M. (1992). Little into big is the way it always is. *Arithmetic Teacher, 39, 18-21.*

Gutstein, E, & Romberg, T A. (1995). Teaching children to add and subtract. *Journal of Mathematical Behavior, 14*, 283-324.

Hall, W. D. (1983). Division with base-ten blocks. *Arithmetic Teacher , 31*, 21-23.

Hankes, J. E. (1996). An alternative to basic-skills remediation. *Teaching Children Mathematics, 2*, 452-457.

Hendrickson, A. D. (1986). Verbal multiplication and division problems: Some difficulties and some solutions. *Arithmetic Teacher , 33*, 26-33.

Hopkins, M. H. (1987). Number facts—or fantasy. *Arithmetic Teacher, 34*, 38-42.

Huinker, D. M (1989). Multiplication and division word problems: Improving students' understanding. *Arithmetic Teacher 37*(2), 8-12.

Kamii, C. (1994). *Young children continue to reinvent arithmetic: 3rd grade.* New York: Teachers College Press.

Kamii, C., & Joseph, L. (1988). Teaching place value and double column addition. *Arithmetic Teacher, 35*(6), 48-52.

Kamii, C., & Lewis, B. A. (1993). The harmful effects of algorithms in primary arithmetic. *Teaching K-8, 23*(5), 36-38.

Kamii, C., Lewis, B. A., & Booker, B. M. (1998). Instead of teaching missing addends. *Teaching Children Mathematics, 4*, 458-461.

Kamii, C., Lewis, B. A., & Livingston, S. (1993). Primary arithmetic: Children inventing their own procedures. *Arithmetic Teacher, 41*, 200-203.

Kouba, V. L., & Franklin, K. (1993). Multiplication and division: Sense making and meaning. In R. J. Jensen (Ed.), *Research ideas for the classroom Early childhood mathematics* (pp. 103-126). Old Tappan, NJ: Macmillan.

Leutzinger, L. P. (1999). Developing thinking strategies for addition facts. *Teaching Children Mathematics, 6*, 14-18.

Leutzinger, L. P. (1999). *Facts that last: A balanced approach to memorization* [one volume for each operation]. Chicago, IL: Creative Publications.

Lindquist, M. M. (1987). Estimation and mental computation: Measurement. *Arithmetic Teacher, 34, 16- 18.*

Lobato, J. E. (1993). Making connections with estimation. *Arithmetic Teacher, 40*, 347-351.

Mahlios, J. (1988). Word problems: Do I add or subtract? *Arithmetic Teacher, 36*, 48-52.

Meyer, R. A., & Riley, J. E. 91986). Multiplication Games. *Arithmetic Teacher, 33, 22-25.*

Ohanian, S., & Burns, M. (1995). *Math by all means: Division, grades 3-4.* Sausalito, CA: Math Solutions Publications.

Pearson, E. S. (1986). Summing it all up: Pre-1900 algorithms. *Arithmetic Teacher, 33, 38-41.*

Quintero, A. H. (1986). Children's conceptual understanding of situations involving multiplication. *Arithmetic Teacher, 33* (3), 34-37.

Rathmell, E. C. (1978). Teaching thinking strategies to teach the basic facts. In M. N. Suydam (Ed.), *Developing computational skills* (pp. 13-38). Reston. VA: National Council of Teachers of Teachers of Mathematics.

Rathmell, E. C., & Trafton, P. R. (1990). Whole number computation. In J. N. Payne (Ed.), *Mathematics for the young child* (pp. 153-172). Reston, VA: National Council of Teachers of Mathematics.

Remington, J. (1989). Introducing multiplication. *Arithmetic Teacher, 37, 12- 14, 60.*

Reys, B. J. (1991). *Developing number sense in the middle grades: Addenda series, grades 5 - 8.* Reston, VA: National Council of Teachers of Mathematics.

BIBLIOGRAPHY

Reys, B. J. & Reys, R. E. (1990). Implementing the *Standards*: Estimation—Direction from the *Standards*. *Arithmetic Teacher, 37,* 22-25.

Reys, B. J., & Reys, R. E. (1999). Computation in the elementary curriculum: Shifting the emphasis. *Teaching Children Mathematics, 5,* 236-241.

Reys, R. E., & Nohda, N. (Eds.). (1994). *Computational alternatives for the twenty-first century: Cross-cultural perspectives from Japan and the United States* . Reston. VA: National Council of Teachers of Mathematics.

Rightsel, P. S., & Thornton, C. A. (1985). 72 addition facts can be mastered by mid-grade 1. *Arithmetic Teacher, 33,* 8-10.

Schwartz, S. L., & Curcio, F. R. (1995). Learning mathematics in meaningful contexts: An action-based approach in the primary grades. In P. A. House (Ed.), *Connecting mathematics across the curriculum* (pp. 116-123). Reston, VA: National Council of Teachers of Mathematics.

Sowder, J. T. (1990). Mental computation and number sense. *Arithmetic Teacher, 37,* 18-20.

Stanic, G. M. A., & McKillup, W. D. (1989). Developmental algorithms have a place in elementary school mathematics instruction. *Arithmetic Teacher, 36*(5), 14-16.

Sundar, V. K. (1990). Thou shalt not divide by zero. *Arithmetic Teacher, 37,* 50-51.

Thompson, C. S., & Hendrickson, A. D. (1986). Verbal addition and subtraction problems: Some difficulties and some solutions. *Arithmetic Teacher, 33* (7), 21-25.

Thompson, C. S., & Van de Walle, J. A. (1980). Transition boards: Moving from materials to symbols in addition. *Arithmetic Teacher, 28*(4), 4-8.

Thompson, C. S., & Van de Walle, J. A. (1981). Transition boards: Moving from materials to symbols in subtraction. *Arithmetic Teacher, 28*(5), 4-9.

Thompson, F. (1991). Two-digit addition and subtraction: What works? *Arithmetic Teacher, 38,* 10-13.

Thornton, C A., & Toohey, M. A. (1984). *A matter of facts: Addition, subtraction. multiplication, division.* Palo Alto, CA: Creative Publications.

Thornton, C. A. (1990). Strategies for the basic facts. In J. N. Payne (Ed), *Mathematics for the young child* (pp. 133-151). Reston, VA: National Council of Teachers of Mathematics.

Thornton. C A., & Smith, P. (1988). Action research: Strategies for learning subtraction facts *Arithmetic Teacher, 35*(8), 9-12.

Trafton, P. R., & Zawojewski, J. S. (1990). Implementing the *Standards*: Meaning of operations. *Arithmetic Teacher, 38,* 18-22.

Tucker, B. F. (1989). Seeing addition: A diagnosis-remediation case study. *Arithmetic Teacher 36*(5), 10-11.

Van de Walle, J. A., & Thompson, C. S. (1985). Partitioning sets for number concepts, place value, and long division. *Arithmetic Teacher, 32*(5), 6-11.

Van de Walle, J. A. (1991). Redefining computation. *Arithmetic Teacher, 38*(5), 46-51.

Van Lehn, L. (1986). Arithmetic procedures are induced from examples. In J. Hiebert (Ed.), *Conceptual and procedural knowledge: The case of mathematics* (pp. 133-179). Hillsdale, NJ: Erlbaum.

Weiland, L. (1985) Matching instruction to children's thinking about division. *Arithmetic Teacher, 33*(4), 34-45.

Whitin, D. J. (1994). Exploring estimation through children's literature. Arithmetic Teacher, *41,* 436-441.

Whitman, N. C. (1992). Activities: Multiplying integers. *Mathematics Teacher, 85,* 34-38, 45-51.

NUMBER THEORY 4

TOPIC

4.1 Prime and Composite Numbers

4.2 Prime Factorization and Tree Diagrams

4.3 Fundamental Theorem of Arithmetic

4.4 Divisibility

4.5 Greatest Common Divisor

4.6 Least Common Multiple

4.7 Clock Arithmetic & Modular Arithmetic

4.8 Patterns

In the Classroom

Bibliography

CHAPTER OVERVIEW

Number theory is a branch of mathematics that involves the study of numbers and, in particular, the natural numbers. In this chapter you can learn interesting facts related to number theory, and examine some concepts and procedures involving number theory ideas.

BIG MATHEMATICAL IDEAS

- Conjecturing
- Decomposing
- Verifying
- Problem-solving Strategies
- Multiple Representations

NCTM PRINCIPLES & STANDARDS LINKS

Number and Operation
Problem Solving
Reasoning
Communication
Connections
Representation

TOPIC 4.1 PRIME AND COMPOSITE NUMBERS

CORNERSTONE	Integer Division	Divisibility

INTRODUCTION

There are many interesting theorems associated with prime numbers and composite numbers. Learning to distinguish between prime and composite integers requires determining divisors associated with an integer. In this section we explain the definitions of prime and composite and examine a method for finding prime numbers.

DID YOU KNOW?

There are a number of interesting conjectures involving prime numbers. One such conjecture is **Goldbach's conjecture** which states that any even number greater than 4 can be expressed as the sum of two odd prime numbers. For example, $6 = 3 + 3$, $8 = 3 + 5$, and $10 = 5 + 5$. See if you can find how to write the even numbers from 12 to 20 as the sum of two odd prime numbers! This conjecture has never been proven, so it cannot be called a theorem.

For More Information: Smith, D. E. (1958). *History of mathematics, Volume II*. New York: Dover Publications.

4.1.1
Definitions of Prime and Composite

Every positive integer greater than 1 is designated as either prime or composite. A **prime number** is a positive integer that has exactly two unique factors—the number 1 and the number itself. For example, the number 7 is prime because its only factors are 1 and 7. A **composite number** is a positive integer that has more than 2 unique factors. For example, the number 12 is composite because it has as factors the numbers: 1, 2, 3, 4, 6, and 12. Note that the number 1 is considered neither prime nor composite. It has exactly 1 unique factor—itself.

4.1.2
Sieve of Eratosthenes

An interesting method of generating the set of prime numbers up through the first 100 integers is by using the **Sieve of Eratosthenes**. The idea behind the Sieve of Eratosthenes is that multiples of a given prime number will necessarily be composite because that given prime number will be a factor of that resulting multiple. Therefore, the multiple will have more than the two factors of 1 and itself. Thus, if we systematically start with the first prime number, 2, cross out all multiples of 2, then do the same for the next prime number, 3, cross out all multiples of three, and continue in this fashion, we will ultimately cross out all composite numbers and leave only the prime numbers. In this sense, we "sift out" the prime numbers. Figure 4.1 shows all the multiples of 2 crossed out.

Figure 4.1

```
      2   3   4   5   6   7   8   9  10
 11  12  13  14  15  16  17  18  19  20
 21  22  23  24  25  26  27  28  29  30
 31  32  33  34  35  36  37  38  39  40
 41  42  43  44  45  46  47  48  49  50
 51  52  53  54  55  56  57  58  59  60
 61  62  63  64  65  66  67  68  69  70
 71  72  73  74  75  76  77  78  79  80
 81  82  83  84  85  86  87  88  89  90
 91  92  93  94  95  96  97  98  99 100
```

Continuing the Sieve of Eratosthenes, Figure 4.2 shows all multiples of 2
and 3 crossed out.

```
    2   3   X   5   X   7   X   X   X
11  X   13  X   X   X   17  X   19  X
X   X   23  X   25  X   X   X   29  X
31  X   X   X   35  X   37  X   X   X
41  X   43  X   X   X   47  X   49  X
X   X   53  X   55  X   X   X   59  X
61  X   X   X   65  66  67  X   X   X
71  X   73  X   X   X   77  X   79  X
X   X   83  84  85  X   X   X   89  X
91  X   X   X   95  X   97  X   X   X
```

Figure 4.2

Finally, Figure 4.3 shows the Sieve of Eratosthenes completed up through
the number 100, revealing that the prime numbers less than 100 are: 2, 3, 5, 7,
11, 13, 17, 19, 23, 29, 31, 37, 41, 43, 47, 53, 59, 61, 67, 71, 73, 79, 83, 89, and
97.

```
    2   3   X   5   X   7   X   X   X
11  X   13  X   X   X   17  X   19  X
X   X   23  X   X   X   X   X   29  X
31  X   X   X   X   X   37  X   X   X
41  X   43  X   X   X   47  X   X   X
X   X   53  X   X   X   X   X   59  X
61  X   X   X   X   X   67  X   X   X
71  X   73  X   X   X   X   X   79  X
X   X   83  84  X   X   X   X   89  X
X   X   X   X   95  X   97  X   X   X
```

Figure 4.3

| Prime Factorization and Tree Diagrams | **RELATED TOPICS** |

TOPIC 4.2 PRIME FACTORIZATION AND TREE DIAGRAMS

CORNERSTONE	Divisibility | Prime and Composite Numbers

INTRODUCTION *Breaking composite integers into their prime factorizations is akin to finding the fundamental and unique composition of an integer. In this section we learn the definition of prime factorization and examine a method of finding an integer's prime factorization using a tree diagram.*

DID YOU KNOW? We can determine the number of divisors that an integer has by examining the prime factorization of the number. One interesting fact about the number of divisors is this: only square numbers have an odd number of divisors. To uncover why this is the case, examine the prime factorization of these square numbers: 4, 9, 16, 25, 36, 49, 64, 81, and 100. Try to uncover a pattern and explain why square numbers are the only numbers with an odd number of divisors.

**4.2.1
Definition of Prime Factorization**

There are many ways to factor integers. *Factoring* means that we express a given integer as a product of two or more numbers. For example, 24 can be factored many ways, such as $24 = 2 \times 12$, $24 = 3 \times 8$, $24 = 2 \times 2 \times 6$. An integer can also be expressed solely as a product of prime numbers. When we express a number as a product of prime numbers, we call this expression the **prime factorization** of the number. For example, the prime factorization of 24 would be $24 = 2 \times 2 \times 2 \times 3$. As another example, the prime factorization of 30 would be $2 \times 3 \times 5$. Note that because prime numbers only have 1 and itself as factors, it makes little sense to talk about the prime factorization of prime numbers; that is, if we try to express 7 as a product of prime numbers, it is impossible because the only way to factor 7 is $7 = 1 \times 7$, and the number 1 is not prime.

**4.2.2
Tree Diagrams**

A useful means of determining the prime factorization of a number is to make a tree diagram. A tree diagram essentially starts with a number and then branches out to factors that number as the product of two other numbers. If either of these other numbers are not prime, then the tree can branch further to express those numbers as the product of two numbers. The tree continues branching in this manner until the end of all the branches are prime numbers. See how Figure 4.4 illustrates a tree diagram for finding the prime factorization of 36.

Figure 4.4

From the tree diagram, we take the prime numbers that appear at the ends of the branches and multiply them together to form the prime factorization. Thus, the prime factorization of 36 is $2 \times 2 \times 3 \times 3$.

If you begin your tree diagram with a different first factoring, your prime factorization will always end the same. For example, Figure 4.5 shows a different tree diagram for factoring the number 36, but notice that the prime numbers that result at the end of each final branch are still the same, confirming that the prime factorization of 36 is 2 × 2 × 3 × 3.

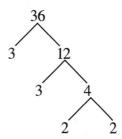

Figure 4.5

Note that order of factors does not alter the prime factorization itself; that is, expressing the prime factorization of 36 as 3 × 2 × 3 × 2 is equivalent to the prime factorization expressed by 2 2 3 3. However, it is good form to express prime factorization in ascending order of prime factors. Thus, the form 2 × 2 × 3 × 3 is preferable for the prime factorization of 36. Prime factorizations are also frequently expressed using exponential notation; that is, because 2 × 2 can be written as 2^2 and 3 × 3 can be expressed as 3^2, then the prime factorization of 36 can be expressed as $2^2 × 3^2$. This is a very useful and popularly used notation for prime factorization.

4.2.3
Notation of Prime Factorization

Fundamental Theorem of Arithmetic

RELATED TOPICS

TOPIC 4.3 FUNDAMENTAL THEOREM OF ARITHMETIC

CORNERSTONE | Prime and Composite Numbers | Prime Factorization and Tree Diagrams

INTRODUCTION | *In mathematics, two very basic premises that underlie key theorems are existence and uniqueness. The Fundamental Theorem of Arithmetic makes a claim about the existence and uniqueness of the prime factorization of integers. This very brief section describes this very important theorem in number theory.*

DID YOU KNOW? | The fact that there are an infinite number of prime numbers is an intriguing notion. A proof of this claim can be simply stated by making use of the **Fundamental Theorem of Arithmetic**. The proof is what is called an indirect proof where we assume that there is a finite number of prime numbers and show that this cannot be true. Thus, the logical conclusion will be that there must be an infinite number of primes.

Proof: Assume that there is a largest prime and call it p_n. Then, using all primes less than p_n, p_1, p_2, p_3,...p_{n-1}, we can look at the composite integer, n, that is one more than the product of all the primes: $n = (p_1 \times p_2 \times p_3 \times ... \times p_{n-1} \times p_n) + 1$.

We know that $p_1 | (p_1 \times p_2 \times p_3 \times ... \times p_{n-1} \times p_n)$. Therefore p_1 cannot divide $(p_1 \times p_2 \times p_3 \times ... \times p_{n-1} \times p_n) + 1$. Similar arguments can be made for why none of the other primes p_2, p_3, ... p_{n-1}, p_n can be divisors of n. Therefore, none of the prime numbers are divisors of n. However, the Fundamental Theorem of Arithmetic assures us that every composite integer has a unique prime factorization. If none of the primes p_1, p_2, p_3, ... p_{n-1}, p_n are factors of n, then this conflicts with the Fundamental Theorem of Arithmetic. Therefore, there must be an infinite number of prime numbers.

For More Information: Bunt, L. N. H., Jones, P. S., & Bedient, J. D. (1988). *The historical roots of elementary mathematics*. New York: Dover Publications.

The Fundamental Theorem of Arithmetic states that every composite integer has a unique prime factorization, without considering order of factors or notational style as changing the prime factorization itself. Thus, for example, the prime factorization of 20 is $2 \times 2 \times 5$. Although you can rearrange the order of factors, such as $2 \times 5 \times 2$, or write the factorization in exponential form, such as $2^2 \times 5$, the primes involved, and the number of each prime involved, remains the same. Thus, the prime factorization is unique in this sense.

This theorem is important because the prime factorization of a number can help generate a complete list of factors for a number, determine the number of factors for a number, help determine the least common multiple of two numbers and the greatest common divisor of two numbers. Take, for example, the integer 90. It's unique prime factorization is $2 \times 3^2 \times 5$. We can use the prime factorization to help uncover all the factors of 90. The factors of 90 would include 1, each of the primes in the prime factorization, and all product combinations of 2 or more of the prime factors in the prime factorization. So, for 90 the factors would be: 1, 2, 3, 5, 2×3, 3^2, 2×5, 3×5, 2×3^2, $2 \times 3 \times 5$, $3^2 \times 5$, and $2 \times 3^2 \times 5$; that is, the factors of 90 are: 1, 2, 3, 5, 6, 9, 10, 15, 18, 30, 45, and 90. Because the prime factorization of 90 is unique, we can be certain that we are generating all of the factors of 90 because no other combinations of the prime factors is possible.

RELATED TOPICS | Greatest Common Divisor | Least Common Multiple

TOPIC 4.4 DIVISIBILITY

| Integer Division | **CORNERSTONE** |

The concept of divisibility centers around determining which integers divide into other integers evenly with no remainder. In this section, we are introduced to the formal definition of divisibility, to concepts related to divisibility, and to several theorems of divisibility. We also explore a variety of divisibility tests that allow us to quickly and accurately determine which integers are divisors of other integers.

INTRODUCTION

Euclid of Alexandria (330–275 B.C.) did most of his mathematical work in the area of number theory. One of his most interesting findings was a means of classifying numbers by the number of proper divisors they had. He said that an integer is considered **perfect** it is equal to the sum of its proper divisors. Note that a **proper divisor** of a given integer is any divisor except for the integer itself. Thus, the number, 6, is perfect because the sum of its proper divisors, 1 + 2 + 3 is 6. Integers that are not perfect are classified as either deficient or abundant. An integer is considered **deficient** if the sum of its proper divisors is less than the integer, and an integer is **abundant** if the sum of its proper divisors is greater than the integer itself. so, 8 (8 < 1 + 2 + 4) is deficient, but 12 (12 > 1 + 2 + 3 + 4 + 6) is abundant.

For More Information: Reimer, L., & Reimer W. (1995). *Mathematicians are people, too: Stories from the lives of great mathematicians, Volume 2.* Palo Alto, CA: Dale Seymour Publications.

DID YOU KNOW?

When we say that an integer a is **divisible** by an integer b, this means that there is some other integer, c, such that $a \div b = c$ with no remainder. In other words a is divisible by b if there is some other integer, c, such that $c \times b = a$. For example, we can say that 24 is divisible by 8 because $24 \div 8 = 3$ or $3 \times 8 = 24$. On the other hand, we say 10 is not divisible by 3 because there is no integer, c, such that $c \times 3 = 10$.

4.4.1
Definition of Divisibility

When we talk about divisibility, instead of saying that a is divisible by b, we often use the expression, b divides a. The notation for divisibility mirrors this expression; that is, we use the notation $b\,|\,a$, which is read "b divides a" to suggest that a is divisible by b. Thus, it would be appropriate to write $3\,|\,27$, which reads "3 divides 27," meaning that 27 is divisible by 3. If a number is not divisible by another number, we use the symbol to read "does not divide." For example, we can say that $3\nmid14$.

4.4.2
Divisibility Notation

There are several theorems that stem from the definition of divisibility. Given integers a, b, c, and k:

4.4.3
Divisibility Theorems

Theorem 1: If $a\,|\,b$, then $a\,|\,k \times b$. Essentially, this theorem says that if an integer divides another integer, then it will divide any multiple of that integer, too. For example, because $3\,|\,6$, then $3\,|\,2 \times 6$, $3\,|\,4 \times 6$, $3\,|\,10 \times 6$, etc.

Theorem 2: If $a\,|\,b$ and $a\,|\,c$, then $a\,|\,(b + c)$. This theorem states that if an integer divides two separate integers, then it will also divide the sum of those two integers. For example, because $4\,|\,12$ and $4\,|\,16$, then $4\,|\,(12 + 16)$.

Theorem 3: If a|b and a|c, then a|(b – c). Like Theorem 2, this theorem states that if an integer divides two separate integers, then it will also divide the difference between those two integers. For example, because $5|35$ and $5|20$, then $5|(35-20)$.

4.4.4
False, But Often Believed Divisibility Theorems

There are also false theorems that people often mistakenly believe are true; that is, people tend to believe that the reverse argument of the theorems above are also true even though this is not always the case. Given integers a, b, c, and k:

False Theorem 1: If a|k × b, then a|k and a|b. This false theorem is the converse of theorem 1 above. Although an integer divides the product of two integers, it may not divide each integer individually. For example, $6|(4 \times 9)$, but $6\nmid 4$ and $6\nmid 9$.

False Theorem 2: If a|(b + c), then a|b and a|c. Many people assume this is true because it is the converse of theorem 2. However, consider this example. We know that $3|(4+8)$, but $3\nmid 4$ and $3\nmid 8$.

False Theorem 3: If a|(b – c), then a|b and a|c. This is the inverse of Theorem 3 and is not necessarily true. For example, $8|(70-6)$, but $8\nmid 70$ and $8\nmid 6$.

4.4.5
Related Terms

We can use the notion of divisibility to describe sets of numbers. For example, we can describe the set of **even numbers** this way. An integer, a, is even if a is divisible by 2 (that is, $2|a$). Similarly, we can describe **odd numbers** by saying that an integer, a, is odd if it is not divisible by 2 (that is, $2\nmid a$). For example, 8 is even because 8 is divisible by 2. On the other hand, 7 is odd because 7 is not divisible by 2.

The concept of divisibility also suggests a number of related mathematical vocabulary. For example, if $b|a$, then we say that b is a **divisor** of a. This makes sense because one way of defining divisibility is to say that $b|a$ if there is some integer c, such that $a \div b = c$. We clearly see b acting as a divisor, particularly where b divides evenly with no remainder. If $b|a$, we can also refer to b as a **factor** of a. When we consider the alternative way of describing divisibility, that is, a is divisible by b if there is some other integer, c, such that , $c \times b = a$, b acts as a factor. Thus, the words *divisor* and *factor* can be used interchangeably when talking about divisibility.

The concept of divisibility is also related to the concept of **multiple**. We say a is a multiple of b if there is some whole number, c, such that $c \times b = a$. For example, 30 is a multiple of 6 because we can identify the whole number 5 such that $5 \times 6 = 30$. So, when we know that $b|a$, that is, b divides a, we can also claim that a is a multiple of b.

4.4.6
Divisibility Tests

There are some divisibility tests that are designed to be an efficient means of determining whether or not a given integer is divisible by a particular number without having to perform long division to check. What follows are the descriptions of divisibility tests for divisibility by 2, 3, 4, 5, 6, 7, 8, 9, 10, 11, and 12.

Divisibility Test for 2. The test for divisibility by 2 states that a number is divisible by 2 if the digit in the ones place is 0, 2, 4, 6, or 8. For example, the number 6,598 is divisible by 2 because the one's place digit is an 8. Therefore it passes the test for divisibility by 2. On the other hand, the number 309 is not divisible by 2 because the one's place digit is a 9. Thus, it fails the divisibility test for 2.

Divisibility Test for 5. The test for divisibility by 5 states that a number is divisible by 5 if the digit in the ones place is 0 or 5. For example, at a glance we can tell that the number 324,880 is divisible by 5 because the one's place digit is a 0. Similarly, we say that the number 7,899 fails the divisibility test for 5 because the ones place is neither 5 or a 0. Thus, 7889 is not divisible by 5.

Divisibility Test for 10. The test for divisibility by 10 states that a number is divisible by 10 if the digit in the ones place is a zero. For example, we can easily tell that 956 is not divisible by 10 but that 74,330 is divisible by 10 by checking to see whether or not the digit in the one's place is a zero.

There is another way we can think about devising a test for divisibility by 10. Because $10 = 2 \times 5$, both 2 and 5 are divisors of 10. We could say that if a number passes both the tests for divisibility by 2 and divisibility by 5, then it should be divisible by ten. Recall that to be divisible by 2, the ones place must be 0, 2, 4, 6, or 8. To be divisible by 5, the ones place must be or 0 or 5. To pass both tests simultaneously (see Figure 4.6), we can see that the overlap between the two tests would be having a zero in the ones place, which is the originally stated divisibility test for 10. This alternative way of thinking about the divisibility test for 10 as being a combination of passing the tests for 2 and 5 will be crucial in developing divisibility tests for other numbers such as for 6 and 12 (see these explained further in this section).

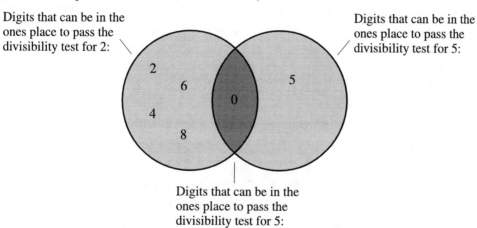

Digits that can be in the ones place to pass the divisibility test for 2:

Digits that can be in the ones place to pass the divisibility test for 5:

Digits that can be in the ones place to pass the divisibility test for 5:

Figure 4.6

Divisibility Test for 3. The test for divisibility by 3 states that a number is divisible by 3 if the sum of the digit in the number is divisible by 3. For example, the number 786 is divisible by 3 because $7 + 8 + 6 = 21$, and 21 is a number that is divisible by 3. Using the test we can confirm that 1255 is not divisible by 3 because $1 + 2 + 5 + 5 = 13$, and 13 is not divisible by 3.

Divisibility Test for 9. The test for divisibility by 9, which is very similar to the test for divisibility by 3, states that a number is divisible by 9 if the sum of the digit in the number is divisible by 9. For example, the number 22,356 is divisible by 9 because $2 + 2 + 3 + 5 + 6 = 18$, and 18 is a number that is divisible by 9. On the other hand, 8991 is not divisible by 9 because $8 + 9 + 9 + 2 = 28$, and 28 is not divisible by 9.

Divisibility Test for 4. The test for divisibility by 4 states that a number is divisible by 4 if the number formed by the two right-most digits is divisible by 4; then the entire number is divisible by 4. For example, in the number 78,924, the number formed by the two right-most digits, 24, is divisible by 4. Therefore, the number 78,924 is also divisible by 4. However, the number 44,433 is not divisible by 4 because the number 33 is not divisible by 4.

Divisibility Test for 8. The test for divisibility by 8 is similar to the test for divisibility by 4. The test for divisibility by 8 states that a number is divisible by 8 if the number formed by the three right-most digits is divisible by 8. For example, because the number 568 is divisible by 8, then the number 123,568 is divisible by 8. Further, the number 6,790 is not divisible by 8 because 790 is not divisible by 8.

Divisibility Test for 6. The test for divisibility by 6 states that a number is divisible by 6 if it passes the divisibility tests for 3 and 2. In other words, a number is divisible by 6 if the sum of the digits is divisible by 3 AND if the digit in the ones place is a 0, 2, 4, 6, or 8. For example, the number 777 is not divisible by 6 because even though the sum of the digits, $7 + 7 + 7 = 21$, is divisible by 3 (that is, it passes the test for divisibility by 3), the digit in the ones place is a 7. Therefore it is not divisible by 2. Consequently, 777 is not divisible by 6 because it did not pass both tests. On the other hand, the number 516 is divisible by 6 because the sum of the digits $5 + 1 + 6 = 12$ is divisible by 3 and the digit in the ones place is a 6.

Divisibility Test for 12. The divisibility test for 12 states that a number is divisible by 12 if it passes the divisibility tests for 3 and 4; that is, a number is divisible by 12 if the sum of the digits is divisible by 3 and the number formed by the two right-most digits is divisible by 4. To verify, we find that for the number 912, the sum of the digits, $9 + 1 + 2 = 12$, is divisible by 3 and the number formed by the two right-most digits, 12, is divisible by 4. Therefore, because 912 passes both the test for divisibility by 3 and the test for divisibility by 4, then 912 is divisible by 12.

You might be tempted to say that another test for divisibility by 12 might be passing the divisibility tests for 2 and for 6. This does not work, however, because the numbers 2 and 6 are not relatively prime. For two integers, a and b, we say that a and b are **relatively prime** if the only factor they have in common is 1. When we develop new tests for divisibility, we can create new tests by combining other tests as long as (a) the product of the numbers associated with each divisibility test equals the number for which we are designing a new test, and (b) the numbers associated with each of the combined divisibility tests are relatively prime. Thus, because $4 \times 3 = 12$, and 4 and 3 are relatively prime, a possible divisibility test for divisibility by 12 would be passing the tests for divisibility by 3 and by 4. On the other hand, even though $2 \times 6 = 12$, because 2 and 6 are not relatively prime—that is, they not only share 1 as a common factor, but also 2 as a common factor—passing the tests for 2 and 6 would not be sufficient to say that a number passes the divisibility test for 12. Note that the number 6 is divisible by 2 and is also divisible by 6, but it is not divisible by 12. Therefore, this counterexample shows that the only viable test for divisibility by 12 is the one involving the tests for divisibility by 3 and 4.

Divisibility Test for 7. The test for divisibility by 7 states that a number is divisible by 7 if the number found by taking the difference between the number formed by all the digits except the digit in the one's place, and twice the digit in the one's place, is divisible by 7, then the original number is divisible by 7. For example, given the number 791, we first find the number formed by all the digits except the digit in the one's place: 79. Then we subtract twice the digit in the one's place from this number: $79 - (2 \cdot 1) = 79 - 2 = 77$. Because 77 is divisible by 7, then the original number, 791, is divisible by 7. Looking to another example, the number 1,235 is not divisible by 7 because when we take 123 and subtract $(2 \cdot 5)$, we get $123 - 10 = 113$. Because 113 is not divisible by 7, then 1,235 is not divisible by 7.

Divisibility Test for 11. The test for divisibility by 11 states that a number is divisible by 11 if the difference found by subtracting the sum of all the digits in the even-powered places from the sum of the digits in all the odd-powered places is divisible by 11. Recall that because the Hindu-Arabic Number System is a base-ten system, then each place can be expressed as a power of ten (the hundreds place is 10^2, the thousands place is 10^3, etc.). For all the places where the exponent (power) is odd, as in the thousands place, we add the digits to find the sum of those digits. We do the same for digits in even-powered places. So, for example, given the number 128,457, we add the digits in the odd-powered places: $5 + 8 + 1 = 14$, and then add the digits in the even-numbered places: $7 + 4 + 2 = 13$. We then find the difference between those sums: $14 - 13 = 1$. Because the number 1 is not divisible by 11, then the number 128,457 is not divisible by 11. On the other hand, checking the number 837,298, because $(9 + 7 + 8) - (3 + 2 + 8) = 11$, and 11 is divisible by 11, then the number 837,298 is also divisible by 11.

Prime and Composite Numbers | Greatest Common Divisor
Least Common Multiple   **RELATED TOPICS**

TOPIC 4.5 GREATEST COMMON DIVISOR

CORNERSTONE Prime and Composite Numbers | Prime Factorization and Tree Diagrams
Fundamental Theorem of Arithmetic

INTRODUCTION *The Greatest Common Divisor is a key concept that lays the foundation for meaningful work with fractions. In particular, the greatest common divisor, is useful in reducing fractions to their simplest form. In this section we define and illustrate notation for the Greatest Common Divisor. We also illustrate two methods for determining the Greatest Common Divisor of two or more integers.*

DID YOU KNOW? Mathematician Euclid of Alexandria's work in number theory included the development of an algorithm for finding the Greatest Common Divisor. In fact, the algorithm is referred to as the Euclidean Algorithm in his honor.

For More Information: Reimer, L., & Reimer W. (1995). *Mathematicians are people, too: Stories from the lives of great mathematicians, Volume 2.* Palo Alto, CA: Dale Seymour Publications.

4.5.1
Definition of Greatest Common Divisor

The **greatest common divisor** (GCD) of two or more integers is the largest divisor that is shared by each of the numbers. Because the words *divisor* and *factor* can be used interchangeably, the greatest common divisor is often referred to as the **greatest common factor** (GCF). So, given the numbers 24 and 30, we can see that they have several factors in common: 1, 2, 3, and 6. Because the largest divisor that they both have is 6, we say the greatest common divisor of 24 and 30 is 6.

4.5.2
Relatively Prime

For two integers, *a* and *b*, we say *a* and *b* are **relatively prime** if the only factor they have in common is 1; that is, *a* and *b* are relatively prime if the GCD $(a, b) = 1$. For example, GCD $(4, 9) = 1$ because they have no divisors in common other than 1.

4.5.3
Notation for GCD

The notation GCD (a, b) is read "the greatest common divisor of *a* and *b*." Thus, using the example above, we can say the GCD $(24, 30) = 6$. We can find the greatest common divisor that more than two number share. To find GCD $(12, 30, 45)$, we look for the largest factor shared by all three integers. Looking at factors of each number and finding the ones they have in common, we can determine that GCD $(12, 30, 45) = 3$.

4.5.4
Methods for Finding the GCD

There are a number of methods for finding the GCD of two or more integers. These methods include finding the intersection of their sets of divisors, the Euclidean Algorithm, and using prime factorization.

Method 1: Finding the Intersection of Sets of Divisors. One way to find the Greatest Common Divisor of two or more numbers is to first list out the divisors of each number. Then, once you locate all the divisors they have in common, you can determine the largest from this set. For example, to find the GCD (48, 56), we can first list the divisors of 48 and the divisors of 56.

The set of divisors of 48 = {1, 2, 3, 4, 6, 8, 12, 16, 24, 48}
The set of divisors of 56 = {1, 2, 4, 7, 8, 14, 28, 56}

Now we can determine the set of divisors that they have in common = {1, 2, 4, 8}. From this set we determine that 8 is the largest divisor they share. Therefore, GCD (48, 56) = 8.

Method 2: The Euclidean Algorithm. A second means of determining the greatest common divisor is the **Euclidean algorithm**. The algorithm is based on the division algorithm that says that the GCD of two positive integers, a and b, will be the same as the GCD of b and the remainder found when a is divided by b; that is, given any two positive integers, a and b, a can be expressed as $a = bq + r$, where $0 \leq r < b$. Then it follows that the GCD (a, b) = GCD (b, r). The Euclidean algorithm builds on this division algorithm and suggests a set of repetitive steps that lead to the identification of the GCD (a, b):

Let a and b be any two positive integers. Then using the division algorithm, we can find a series of natural numbers $q_1, q_2, q_3, \ldots q_n$ and $r_1, r_2, r_3, \ldots r_{n-1}$ such that $r_{i+1} < r_i$ and:

$$a = bq_1 + r_1$$
$$b = r_1q_2 + r_2$$
$$r_1 = r_2q_3 + r_3$$
$$\bullet$$
$$\bullet$$
$$\bullet$$
$$r_{n-3} = r_{n-2}q_{n-1} + r_{n-1}$$
$$r_{n-2} = r_{n-1}q_n$$

Then GCD (a, b) = r_{n-1}.

For example, to find the GCD (672, 456) using the Euclidean Algorithm:

$$672 = 456 \times 1 + 216$$
$$456 = 216 \times 2 + 24$$
$$216 = 24 \times 9$$

Now that we have reached a point where there is no remainder, we can determine that the GCD (672, 456) is the remainder in the second-to-last step; that is, GCD (672, 456) = 24. Note that this algorithm allows us to determine the GCD of only two integers at a time.

For a second example, find the GCD (20,753, 2136)

$$20{,}753 = 2136 \times 9 + 1529$$
$$2136 = 1529 \times 1 + 607$$
$$1529 = 607 \times 2 + 315$$
$$607 = 315 \times 1 + 292$$
$$315 = 292 \times 1 + 23$$
$$292 = 23 \times 12 + 16$$
$$23 = 16 \times 1 + 7$$
$$16 = 7 \times 2 + 2$$
$$7 = 2 \times 3 + 1$$
$$3 = 1 \times 3$$

Therefore, the GCD (20,751, 2136) = 1; that is, we can conclude that 21,751 and 2136 are relatively prime.

Method 3: Using Prime Factorizations. Another way to find the greatest common divisor of two or more numbers is, first, to find the prime factorization of each number and then to identify which prime factors and how many of each prime factor they both have. Then, the GCD will be the product of all the prime factors they share. For example, to find the GCD (72, 60), first find the prime factorizations of 72 and 60.

The prime factorization of 72 = 2 × 2 × 2 × 3 × 3.
The prime factorization of 60 = 2 × 2 × 3 × 5.

Now we determine the primes, and the number of each prime, that their factorizations have in common: 2, 2, 3. Multiplying these primes together we find 2 × 2 × 3 = 12. Therefore, GCD (72, 60) = 12.

RELATED TOPICS   Simplifying Fractions

TOPIC 4.6 LEAST COMMON MULTIPLE

CORNERSTONE

The least common multiple of two integers is a key concept in number theory. The least common multiple is often a good choice when finding a common denominator for two fractions when adding or subtracting fractions. In this section, we introduce the definition and notation for least common multiple and demonstrate two methods for the determining the least common multiple between two or more numbers. We also explore a key relationship between the least common multiple and the greatest common divisor of two or more integers.   **INTRODUCTION**

Female mathematician, Sophie Germain (1776 - 1831) began her mathematics career disguising herself as a man because women were not wholly accepted as mathematicians at that time. She initially became recognized for her work in Number Theory, particularly on the strides she made toward solving Fermat's last theorem. This theorem has fascinated mathematicians for centuries and was not completely proven until 1993 by British mathematician Andrew Wiles, a professor at Princeton University.   **DID YOU KNOW?**

For More Information: Reimer, L., & Reimer W. (1995). *Mathematicians are people, too: Stories from the lives of great mathematicians, Volume 2.* Palo Alto, CA: Dale Seymour Publications.

The **least common multiple** (LCM) of two or more positive integers is the smallest non-zero multiple that is common to each number. Every positive integer has an infinite number of multiples. The set of nonzero **multiples** of an integer, *a*, is the set of numbers found by multiplying *a* times the set of positive integers; that is, the set of multiples of *a* = {*a, 2a, 3a, 4a, 5a, 6a,…*}. Even though there is an infinite number of multiples for each number, and an infinite number of multiples that two or more numbers share, there is an identifiable smallest multiple that they share. For the numbers 6 and 10, we can find that even though they share multiples: 30, 60, 90, 120,…, the smallest multiple they have in common is 30.   **4.6.1**
Definition of Least Common Multiple

The notation LCM (*a, b*) is read the least common multiple of a and b. For the example given above, we can say that the LCM (6, 10) = 30. We can find the least common multiple that more than two number share. To find LCM (6, 8, 10), we are look for the smallest multiple shared by all three integers. Looking at multiples of each number and finding the ones they have in common, we can determine that LCM (6, 8, 10) = 120.   **4.6.2**
Notation for LCM

There are a number of methods for finding the LCM of two or more integers. These methods include finding the intersection of their sets of multiples and using prime factorization.   **4.6.3**
Methods for Finding the LCM

Method 1: Finding the Intersection of Sets of Multiples. One way to find the least common multiple of two or more numbers is to first list out the list the multiples of each number. Then, once you identify what these sets look like, you can determine what they have in common. Finally, you can determine the smallest from this set of multiples that they share. For example, to find the LCM (14, 10), we can first illustrate the set of multiples of 14 and the set of multiples of 10.

The set of multiples of 14 = {14, 28, 42, 56, 70, 84, 98, 112, 126, 140, 154,...}.
The set of multiples of 10 = {10, 20, 30, 40, 50, 60, 70, 80, 90, 100, 110, 120, 130, 140, 150, 160,...}.

Now we can observe a pattern of multiples that they share and determine the set of common multiples to be = {70, 140, 210, 280, . . . }. From this set of common multiples, we determine that 70 is the least common multiple. Therefore, LCM (14, 10) = 70.

Method 2: Using Prime Factorizations. Another way to find the least common multiple of two or more numbers is, first, to find the prime factorization of each number and then to identify both the prime factors that appear in either number and the largest number of times each prime factor appears in either number. The LCM will be the product of all the prime factors identified through this process. For example, to find the LCM (60, 72), first find the prime factorizations of 60 and 72.

The prime factorization of 60 = 2 × 2 × 3 × 5.
The prime factorization of 72 = 2 × 2 × 2 × 3 × 3.

Now, determine all the primes that appear in 2, 3, or 5. Then, determine the largest number of times each prime appears in either number (2 appears three times in 72, 3 appears twice in 72, and 5 appears once in 60). So, we take three 2s, two 3s, and one 5. Multiplying these primes together we find 2 × 2 × 2 × 3 × 3 × 5 = 360. Therefore, LCM (72, 60) = 360.

In a second example, we find the LCM (10, 45, 21):

The prime factorization of 10 = 2 × 5.
The prime factorization of 45 = 3 × 3 × 5.
The prime factorization of 21 = 3 × 7.

We find that the primes 2, 3, 5, and 7 appear in one or more of the factorizations. Looking for the highest number of times these primes appear in any one factorization, we find that 2 appears once in 10, 3 appears twice in 45, 5 appears once in both 10 and 45, and 7 appears once in 21. Multiplying these primes together the appropriate number of times, we find 2 × 3 × 3 × 5 × 7 = 630. Therefore, LCM (10, 45, 21) = 630.

4.6.4
Relationships Between the LCM and GCD

There is a strong relationship between the LCM and the GCD. Given two integers a and b, GCD (a, b) LCM (a, b) = a × b. This relationship is most easily seen if we examine the prime factorizations of two numbers, writing the prime factorizations in exponential form. Consider the numbers 24 and 40. Let us first find the prime factorization of each number.

$$24 = 2^3 \times 3$$
$$40 = 2^3 \times 5$$

Note that the GCD (24, 40) = 2^3 and the LCM (24, 40) = $2^3 \times 3 \times 5$. When we multiply the LCM × GCD we have $2^3 \times 2^3 \times 3 \times 5$ which equals 24 × 40 = 960.

RELATED TOPICS   Adding and Subtracting Fractions

TOPIC 4.7 CLOCK ARITHMETIC & MODULAR ARITHMETIC

| Integer Division | **CORNERSTONE** |

We all learned to tell time on a standard clock. Doing so, we had to, albeit most often subconsciously, perform clock arithmetic. Unlike the infinite set of integers, a clock offers a finite set of integer-numbers on which to perform operations. Like clock arithmetic, modular arithmetic deals with a finite set of numbers. In this section we explore the fundamental concepts of clock and modular arithmetic and learn to perform the four basic operations in these settings.

INTRODUCTION

One of the greatest names in the history of mathematics come from the area of number theory. German mathematician, Carl Friedrich Gauss (1777–1855) is a noted number theorist and is often called the "Prince of Mathematicians." Much of his work in number theory was published in *Disquisitiones Arithmeticae* when he was only 24 years old. In this publication, his work with the congruence of numbers and modular arithmetic is highlighted.

DID YOU KNOW?

Modular arithmetic has used by mathematicians working for national security groups such as the National Security Agency (NSA) in developing and interpreting secret codes. As a result, many secret messages could be sent and received safely because of codes that involved various congruence sequences for equating and unraveling information presented in disguised form.

For More Information: Reimer, L., & Reimer W. (1995). *Mathematicians are people, too: Stories from the lives of great mathematicians, Volume 2.* Palo Alto, CA: Dale Seymour Publications.

**4.7.1
Telling Time**

When we tell time, we usually refer to the hours of 1 o'clock, 2 o'clock, 3 o'clock,…, 12 o'clock, and then we start over again at 1 o'clock differentiating morning and afternoon times using A.M. and P.M. If it is 8 o'clock in the morning and someone tells you to meet them in six hours, we know that the time to meet is 2:00 PM. How do we figure out the time to meet? Some people might simply count up six hours from 8 A.M., counting: 9 o'clock, 10 o'clock, 11 o'clock, 12 o'clock, 1 o'clock, 2 o'clock, knowing that once you reach 12 o'clock, you loop back, starting again at 1 o'clock.

**4.7.2
Clock Arithmetic**

Rather than counting up to find a time, we can perform **clock arithmetic**. The key behind clock arithmetic is that time is **cyclic** in nature; that is, the clock itself is fixed, and there is a finite set of times on the clock that loop around in cycles. Because the clock is cyclic, another way of finding out what time it is 6 hours after 8 o'clock is simply to add the 6 and 8 for a sum of 14. Knowing that 12 is the highest hour on the clock, we can determine the "real time" associated with 14. To do this, answer the question, "How much more than 12 did I go?" In essence, in doing so, we are finding, after we divide out a set of 12 hours, the amount that remains. Thus, to find what 10 o'clock plus 10 more hours is, we find the sum, $10 + 10 = 20$. Dividing 20 by 12, we find a remainder of 8. Therefore, $10 + 10$ in clock arithmetic is 8.

**4.7.3
Modular Arithmetic**

Modular arithmetic works much like the way clock arithmetic works. In modular arithmetic, we say that integers that have the same remainders when divided by an integer, m, are congruent in that modulo. Formally, we say for integers a, b, and m, a and b are *congruent modulo m*, written $a \equiv b \bmod m$, if a and b have the same remainders when divided by m. Another way of stating this definition is as follows: a is congruent to b (mod m) if m divides $(a - b)$. Let us check both versions of this definition. For example, in mod 5, the numbers 6 and 11 are congruent because $6 \div 5 = 1$ *with a remainder of 1* and $11 \div 5 = 2$ *with a remainder of 1*. Usually, given an integer, we like to identify to which of the remainders in the modulo that integer is congruent. Thus, we can say $6 \equiv 1$ (mod 5) and $11 \equiv 1$ (mod 5) because 1 is the common remainder. We can also check that 11 and 6 are congruent (mod 5) by checking that 5 does divide the difference $(11 - 6)$ or that $5 \mid 5$.

Modulo. When performing modular arithmetic, the **modulus** you are working within, say *modulo m*, defines a fixed set of numbers that comprise the set of possible remainders when you divide by m. For example, in modulo 5, written mod 5, the set of possible remainders when you divide any integer by 5 are the integers: 0, 1, 2, 3, and 4.

Addition in Modular Arithmetic. To add numbers in a particular modulo, you simply find the sum and then translate that sum to the appropriate remainder in that modulo. For example, in mod 4, adding $9 + 8$, we get 17. However, dividing by 4 and finding the remainder, we determine that $17 \equiv 1$ (mod 4). Note that because $9 \equiv 1$ (mod 4) and $8 \equiv 0$ (mod 4), it is clear that adding $9 + 8$ in mod 4 is equivalent to adding $1 + 0$ in mod 4, which equals 1.

Subtraction in Modular Arithmetic. To find $2 - 4$ in mod 5, we might use the missing-addend approach for subtraction; that is, we can ask, "$4 + x = 2$ (mod 5)?" Because we know that 7 has a remainder of 2 when divided by 5, we can try to form a sum of 7 and conclude that $x = 3$, because $4 + 3 = 7$, and $7 \equiv 2 \bmod (5)$.

An Addition Table for Mod 5. We can create an addition table for mod 5 using the remainders 0, 1, 2, 3, and 4 as the potential addends (See Table 4.1). All sums are written as 0, 1, 2, 3, and 4, having reduced each sum to its "simplest" congruent form.

Note that the addition table for mod 5 can assist in finding a missing sum when solving a subtraction problem in mod 5. For example, to find $1 - 2$ in mod 5, look for a sum of 1 within the table that is associated with an addend of 2. Trace along the table to find the missing addend of 4, showing that $4 + 2 = 1$ mod 5.

Table 4.1

+	0	1	2	3	4
0	0	1	2	3	4
1	1	2	3	4	0
2	2	3	4	0	1
3	3	4	0	1	2
4	4	0	1	2	3

Multiplication in Modular Arithmetic. We can multiply numbers in modulo. For example, 4×8 in mod 6 is 2 because $32 \div 6 = 5$ with a remainder of 2. Similarly, 79 in mod 6 is 3 because $63 \div 6 = 10$ with a remainder of 3.

Division in Modular Arithmetic. Division in modular arithmetic can be viewed as a missing-factor problem. For example, to solve $3 \div 4$ in mod 5, we can seek the missing factor, x, such that $4 \times x = 3$ in mod 5. Because $8 \equiv 3$ (mod 5), we can say that $x = 2$ because $4 \times 2 = 8$.

A Multiplication Table for Mod 5. We can create a multiplication table for mod 5 using the remainders 0, 1, 2, 3, and 4 as the potential factors (See Table 4.2). All products are written as 0, 1, 2, 3, and 4, having reduced each product to its "simplest" congruent form.

Note that solving division problems using the missing-factor approach is made easier using the multiplication table. For example, to solve $1 \div 4$ in mod 5, look for the product 1 within the table; then find where a factor of 4 is associated with that product. Then, tracing along the table, locate the other missing factor of 4. Thus, $1 \div 4 = 4$ (mod 5).

×	0	1	2	3	4
0	0	0	0	0	0
1	0	1	2	3	4
2	0	2	4	1	3
3	0	3	1	4	2
4	0	4	3	2	1

Table 4.2

Divisibility

RELATED TOPICS

TOPIC 4.8 PATTERNS

INTRODUCTION

Patterns exist all around us. From the musical rhythms we hear, the days of the week that we follow, to the designs in sunflowers and pinecones, we observe and feel comfort in patterns on a daily basis. Some mathematicians define mathematics as the science of patterns. Mathematical patterns describe much of the work around us, providing a means of predicting and generalizing from a fixed set of examples. In this section, we explore types of patterns and the process of generalizing a pattern.

DID YOU KNOW?

Leonard of Pisa, better known as Fibonacci (c. 1170–after 1240) introduced a mathematical pattern that describes many phenomena in nature. This type of pattern has become known as the Fibonacci sequence. Many have been fascinated by Fibonacci sequences, and over time, many applications of the sequence have been uncovered. For example, botanists have found that the patterns of leaf buds on many stems, the spirals of seeds in the heads of sunflowers, the petals on artichokes, and the scales on pineapples all follow the sequence. (The Fibonacci sequence is discussed later in this section.)

For More Information: Reimer, L., & Reimer W. (1995). *Mathematicians are people, too: Stories from the lives of great mathematicians, Volume 2.* Palo Alto, CA: Dale Seymour Publications.

4.8.1
Definition of a Pattern

A **pattern** is a design or relationship that is predictable in some manner or a schematic that can be followed. In mathematics, we can observe a wide range of number patterns and geometric patterns. For example, a number pattern might be 1, 2, 3, 1, 2, 3, 1, 2 , 3,…which is a sequence of numbers that follow the same scheme: they follow an ordering that repeats so that we can predict subsequent numbers by observing previous numbers.

An example of a geometric pattern is:

Because there is an identifiable relationship among the shapes in succession, we can describe how the pattern of shapes would continue; that is, we predict that following the last circle would be six squares, which would be followed by one circle, followed by seven squares, etc..

4.8.2
Arithmetic Sequences

A *sequence* is a listing of numbers, separated by commas. An **arithmetic sequence** is a pattern of numbers where the difference between any two terms of the sequence is the same amount; that is, we can determine some amount, *a*, such that the *(n + 1)st* term is found by finding the sum of the *nth* term and *a*. Examples of arithmetic sequences include:

$$1, 3, 5, 7, 9, \ldots$$
$$3, 6, 9, 12, 15, \ldots$$
$$40, 30, 20, 10, 0, -10, \ldots$$

Notice that in each of the examples, the difference between any two successive terms is constant. In the first example, the difference is always 2; in the second example is always 3; and in the last example, the difference is always 10.

A geometric sequence is a pattern of numbers where each term is a constant multiple of the preceding term; that is, we can determine some amount, *a*, such that the *(n + 1)st* term is found by multiplying the *nth* term by *a*. Examples of geometric sequences include:

$$1, 2, 4, 8, 16, 32, \ldots$$
$$3, 9, 27, 81, \ldots$$
$$1, .1, .01, .001, .0001, \ldots$$

In every example, each term differs from the next by the same factor. In the first example, each successive term is found by multiplying the previous term by 2; in the second example, each successive term is found by multiplying the previous term by 3; and in the last example, each successive term is found by multiplying the previous term by 0.1.

4.8.3
Geometric Sequences

Many patterns are **growing patterns** where each successive term changes from the previous term, but the change differs with each term. For example, consider the pattern: 1, 3, 6, 10, 15, 21,.... Notice that the difference between the first two terms is 2, the difference between the next two terms is 3, the difference between the next two terms is 4, and so on. Thus, there is an identifiable pattern among the series of numbers, and that pattern grows from term to term.

Consider another growing pattern: 1, 3, 12, 60,..., where each successive term is found by multiplying the previous term by an amount that changes with each term. The second term is found by multiplying the first term by 3; the third term is found by multiplying the second term by 4; the fourth term is found by multiplying the third term by 5; and so on.

4.8.4
Growing Patterns

A **Fibonacci sequence** is a sequence where each successive term is found by summing the two previous terms. An example of a Fibonacci Sequence is 1, 1, 2, 3, 5, 8, 13, 21, 34,.... Notice that adding $1 + 1 = 2$, adding $1 + 2 = 3$, adding $2 + 3 = 5$, $3 + 5 = 8$, and so on.

4.8.5
Fibonacci Sequences

When we generate a sequence of numbers in a mathematical problem, we often strive to explain the pattern by describing the **nth term**, that is, the **general term**. In describing the nth term, we provide a generalization for the pattern. Finding the nth term is strongly related to inductive reasoning (refer to the topic on Logic).

Consider this mathematical problem and how finding a generalization of a pattern of numbers can help solve the problem:

4.8.6
Finding the nth Term

> One day I called two friends and invited them to a party. The next day, each of my two friends called and invited two more friends to the party. The next day, each of the people who had been invited thus far called and invited two more friends to the party. If this went on for 15 days, how many people were actually called and invited to the party on the 15th day?

To solve this problem, we can try to establish a pattern of how many people were invited on the nth day. We can use a table to help facilitate this pattern (see Table 4.3).

Table 4.3

Day	Number Invited
1	2
2	4
3	8
4	16
5	32
•	•
•	•
n	2^n

From the table, we observe the pattern that each day, the number of people invited on that day increased by a multiple of 2. Thus, we note that on the nth day, the number of people invited can be expressed as 2^n. Therefore, we can find that on the 15th day, 2^{15}, or 32,768, people were called and invited. What a party this is going to be!

4.8.7
Figurate Numbers

Figurate numbers are numbers that are associated with polygons such as triangles, squares, pentagons, etc.. Figurate numbers generate a pattern related to the "size" of the shape. **Triangular numbers** are found by examining the triangular shapes shown in Figure 4.7.

Figure 4.7

Notice that the first "triangle" is formed with 1 dot, the second triangle is formed with 3 dots, the third triangle is formed with 6 dots, the fourth with 10 dots, and so on. Thus, we say that the sequence of triangular numbers is 1, 3, 6, 10, 15,.... As we examine the number of dots in each row of a given triangle, we observe that the number in each row increases by one as we move from top to bottom. The third triangular number is found by adding $1 + 2 + 3 = 6$. The fourth triangular is found by adding $1 + 2 + 3 = 4$. Thus, the nth triangular number will be found by adding $1 + 2 + 3 + ... + n = \frac{n(n+1)}{2}$.

Square numbers are found by examining the "size" of square shapes as shown in Figure 4.8.

Figure 4.8

Looking at the square shapes, and the total number of dots required to make each square, we generate the list of square numbers: 1, 4, 9, 16,.... The first square number is 1^2 or 1, the second square number is 2^2 or 4, the third square number is 3^2 or 9, and so on. Thus, the *nth* square number is n^2 .

Pentagonal numbers are found by examining the pentagonal shapes found in Figure 4.9.

Pentagonal numbers include the numbers 1, 5, 12, 22, 35,.... We can exam-

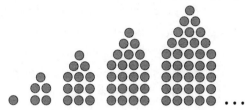

Figure 4.9

ine the fourth pentagon and notice that it can be described as the combination of the fourth square figure and the third triangular figure (See Figure 4.10).

Thus, we can generalize and describe the nth pentagonal figure as the com-

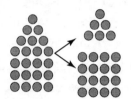

Figure 4.10

bination of the nth square figure and the (n − 1)st triangular figure. Therefore, in general, the *n*th pentagonal figure can be found by $n^2 + \frac{(n-1)n}{2}$.

Logic | Problem Solving   **RELATED TOPICS**

IN THE CLASSROOM

Some expectations of your future students

**Pre-K-2
(NCTM, 2000,
p. 78)**

develop understanding of the relative position and magnitude of whole numbers and of ordinal and cardinal numbers and their connections

develop a sense of whole numbers and represent and use them in flexible ways, including relating, composing, and decomposing numbers

develop fluency with basic number combinations for addition and subtraction

**Grades 3-5
(NCTM, 2000,
p. 148)**

describe classes of numbers according to characteristics such as the nature of their factors

identify and use relationships between operations, such as division as the inverse of multiplication, to solve problems

develop fluency with basic number combinations for multiplication and division

While the focus on the *Number and Operations Content Standard* continues, this chapter also begins to emphasize the *Reasoning and Proof Process Standard*. "By developing ideas, … justifying results, and using mathematical conjectures … with different expectations of sophistication—at all grade levels, students should see and expect that mathematics makes sense" (NCTM, 2000, p. 56). We believe that you should make such mathematical sense of (a) natural numbers by analyzing their factors and developing and justifying conjectures (Activities 4.1– 4.9), and (b) patterns that build on the theories that you have developed and whose formalization requires your creative use of operations with natural numbers (Activities 4.10 – 4.16).

How Activities 4.1-4.16 help you develop an adult-level perspective on the above expectations.

- By developing and organizing your knowledge of the factors of natural numbers, you learn to classify numbers according to their possible factorizations.

- By seeing common patterns in examples of composite numbers that have structurally similar prime factorization, you begin to generalize the idea of prime numbers to other more abstrac t ways of composing and decomposing numbers.

- By working with the concept of the uniqueness of the prime factorization of a composite number, you construct ways to determine both the greatest common factor and the least common multiple of two numbers.

- By creating tests for determining divisibility in different bases and by exploring modular arithmetic, you continue to develop your sense of numeration systems and the additive and multiplicative structures embedded in them. You begin to use the inverse operations of addition (or multiplication) to solve problems involving subtraction (or division) in modular arithmetic thus becoming more flexible in your thinking of each operation.

- By analyzing different number patterns you continue to develop ways of composing and decomposing numbers using the four operations. You learn to identify the common pattern and construct the general form of the nth number.

BIBLIOGRAPHY

Bezuszka, S. J. (1985). A test for divisibility by primes. *Arithmetic Teacher, 33,* 36-38.

Brown, G. W. (1984). Searching for patterns of divisors. *Arithmetic Teacher, 32,* 32-34.

Dearing, S. A., & Holtan, B. (1987). Factors and primes with a T square. *Arithmetic Teacher, 34,* 34.

Dockweiler, C. J. (1985). Palindromes and the "Law of 11." *Arithmetic Teacher , 33,* 46-47.

Eisen, A. P. (1999). Exploring factor sets with a graphing calculator. *Mathematics Teaching in the Middle School, 5,* 78-82.

Graviss, T., & Greaver, J. (1992). Extending the number line to make connections with number theory. *Mathematics Teacher, 85,* 418-420.

Hudson, F. M. (1990). Are the primes really infinite? *Mathematics Teacher 83,* 660.

Lamb, C. E., & Hutcherson, L. R. (1984). Greatest common factor and least common multiple. *Arithmetic Teacher, 31,* 43-44.

Lefton, P. (1991). Number theory and public-key cryptography. *Mathematics Teacher, 84,* 54-62.

Martinez, J. G. R. (1988). Helping students understand factors and terms. *Mathematics Teacher, 81,* 747-751.

Olson, M. (1991). Activities: A geometric look at greatest common divisor. *Mathematics Teacher, 84,* 202-208.

5 DATA & CHANCE

CHAPTER OVERVIEW

A great many events in the world around us involve uncertainty and chance. It is easy to find examples from business, education, law, medicine, and everyday experience. Two examples come readily to mind: (1) the weather forecaster on TV says, "There is a 70% chance of rain tomorrow"; (2) sometimes with only a small portion of votes counted, newscasters are able to project winners of political elections and final percentages of votes with considerable accuracy. How was the 70% figure obtained? How can newscasters attain such accuracy with so little information? The branches of mathematics called probability and statistics were developed to help us deal with situations involving uncertainty and chance in a precise and objective manner. In this chapter you can learn interesting facts about probability and statistics and will examine some concepts and procedures involving probability and statistics ideas.

TOPIC

5.1 Probability Notions

5.2 Equally Likely Outcomes

5.3 Mutually Exclusive and Complementary Events

5.4 Multistep Experiments

5.5 Counting Principles

5.6 Statistics Notions

5.7 Measures of Central Tendency

5.8 Data Dispersion

5.9 Representing Data

In the Classroom

Bibliography

BIG MATHEMATICAL IDEAS

- Data and Chance
- Independence/ Dependence
- Multiple Representations
- Mathematical Modeling

NCTM PRINCIPLES & STANDARDS LINKS

Data Analysis, Statistics, and Probability

Problem Solving

Reasoning

Communication

Connections

Representation

TOPIC 5.1 PROBABILITY NOTIONS

| Fractions | **CORNERSTONE** |

Probability situations are all around us. Whether we are listening to the weather report explaining the chances of it raining that day or whether we play the lottery hoping to win, even though we know we are not likely to win, probabilities influence the decisions we make. In this section, we examine probability terms and introduce a formula for computing simple probabilities. We also see several examples of how a simulation of a given experiment helps to model a situation and facilitate finding the probability of certain outcomes from the experiment.

INTRODUCTION

Mathematician Pierre de Fermat is credited for fully developing the study of probability. He corresponded often with mathematician Blaise Pascal in the mid–1600's to test his theories and to compare results of probability experiments.

DID YOU KNOW?

For More Information: Reimer, L., & Reimer W. (1995). *Mathematicians are people, too: Stories from the lives of great mathematicians, Volume 2.* Palo Alto, CA: Dale Seymour Publications.

Probability is about degrees of uncertainty and chance. An **experiment** is any activity in which different results can occur. These results are called **outcomes**. There is a numerical chance (probability) associated with each outcome. The list of all possible outcomes is considered the **sample space** of an experiment. Any subset of the sample space is considered an **event**.

For example, suppose we have a hat containing 5 yellow marbles, 6 blue marbles, 3 white marbles, and 4 red marbles. An experiment associated with the hat and marbles is drawing a marble out of the hat and noting the color of the marble. The possible outcomes associated with the experiment are: drawing a yellow marble, drawing a blue marble, drawing a white marble, and drawing a red marble. Thus, the sample space is yellow, blue, white, and red. We can consider possible events as being: drawing either a red or a blue marble, or drawing anything but a white marble.

5.1.1
Probability Terminology

A **probability** is the computed likeliness tha a given event will happen. Probabilities can be expressed as fractions between 0 and 1, as decimals between 0.00 and 1.00, or percentages between 0% and 100%. To compute the probability of a particular event occurring, we usually create a fraction where the numerator depicts the number of ways the event can occur and the denominator represents the total number of ways any outcome in the sample space can occur; that is, given an event, A, the probability of event A occurring, denoted P(A) is found by:

5.1.2
Computing a Simple Probability

$$P(A) = \frac{\text{number of ways A can occur}}{\text{total number of outcomes}}$$

As you can see, the numerator is always ≥ 0, the denominator is always > 0, and the numerator is always $\leq$ denominator.

For example, in the marble experiment where there are 5 yellow marbles, 6 blue marbles, 3 white marbles, and 4 red marbles in a hat and a marble is drawn from the hat, we can compute the probability of drawing a blue marble by:

$$P(\text{drawing a blue marble}) = \frac{\text{number of blue marbles}}{\text{total number of marbles}} = \frac{6}{18} = \frac{1}{3}$$

In a given experiment, we can determine a **probability distribution**, which is a list of all possible outcomes to the experiment along with the probabilities associated with each outcome. For example, in the marble experiment previously described, we can form the probability distribution illustrated in Table 5.1.

Note that each of the probabilities listed in the probability distribution in Table 5.1 are fractions between 0 and 1 and that the sum of all the probabilities listed in the probability distribution is 1. In general, the probability of an event is between 0 and 1 (inclusive) and the sum of all the probabilities in the probability distribution is 1.

Table 5.1

Outcomes	Probability
yellow	$\frac{5}{18}$
blue	$\frac{6}{18}$
white	$\frac{3}{18}$
red	$\frac{4}{18}$
	1

Table 5.2

Outcomes	Probability
yellow	$\frac{5}{18}$
blue	$\frac{6}{18}$
white	$\frac{3}{18}$
red	$\frac{4}{18}$
	1

5.1.3
Simulation with a Spinner

Figure 5.1

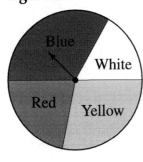

Because probabilities describe what could happen in an experiment, it is often useful to act out or model the experiment with what we call a **simulation** of the experiment. Let us imagine a simulation of the probabilities of outcomes associated with spinning a spinner as shown in Figure 5.1. By spinning the spinner in Figure 5.1 many times (e.g. 100 times, or 1000 times, or even 10,000 times), we can approximate, that is simulate, an experiment involving drawing marbles from a hat. Note that the probability distribution of the spinner in Figure 5.1 is the same as that shown in Table 5.1. (See Table 5.2 for the probability distribution associated with the spinner.)

The probabilities for each outcome on the spinner are determined by figuring what part of the whole each outcome represents. For example, because one-sixth of the circle is white, then the probability of spinning the arrow and having it land on a white section is one-sixth. Likewise, because the blue section of the spinner is twice as large as the white section, the blue section is two-sixths (or one-third) of the spinner. Therefore, the probability of spinning blue is one-third. Finally, because the red and yellow sections on the spinner are four-eighteenths and five-eighteenths of the whole circle, respectively, the probabilities of spinning red and yellow are four-eighteenths and five-eighteenths, respectively.

RELATED TOPICS   Equally Likely Outcomes | Mutually Exclusive and Complementary Events
Multistep Experiments

TOPIC 5.2 EQUALLY LIKELY OUTCOMES

Fractions | Decimals | Decimals and Fractions | Probability Notions **CORNERSTONE**

INTRODUCTION

Sometimes, the chance of some outcome occurring is very high and other times very low. However, in some settings, the chances of different outcomes occurring are equal. For example, whenever we flip a coin before a game to decide who goes first, we find this a fair method to decide because the coin is just as likely to land on heads as it is on tails. Thus, one person does not have a better chance than the other to win. In this section, we explore situations where different outcomes are equally likely and how to determine the probabilities for equally likely outcomes. We also compare theoretical versus empirical probabilities.

DID YOU KNOW?

Jakob Bernoulli was a Swiss mathematician from a family of mathematicians. The Bernoulli family made many contributions to the theory of probability in the mid- to late 1600's. Jakob Bernoulli is most noted for being the first person to develop the fundamental concept behind empirical probability. This concept grew into a theory known as the theory of large numbers which states that when you conduct an experiment a large number of times, the data gathered from outcomes of the experiment begin to stabilize as the number of times the experiment is conducted gets larger and larger.

For More Information: Reimer, L., & Reimer W. (1995). *Mathematicians are people, too: Stories from the lives of great mathematicians, Volume 2.* Palo Alto, CA: Dale Seymour Publications.

5.2.1
Equally Likely

In probability experiments, the probability assigned to each outcome provides a numerical expression of how **likely** the outcome is to occur. For example, if, in an experiment, there are two outcomes, "Yes and No", and the probability of the outcome being Yes is $\frac{4}{5}$ and the probability of the outcome being No is $\frac{1}{5}$, then we say that the outcome Yes is more likely to occur than No because the probability is higher.

In some experiments, all outcomes are **equally likely**; that is, they have the same probability of occurring. For example, when rolling a single die (where the numbers rolled represent the number of dots on the top face), the sample space associated with the experiment is: 1, 2, 3, 4, 5, and 6. In a fair die, each outcome is equally likely because you are just as likely to roll a 1 as a 2, as a 3, as a 4, as a 5, or as a 6. Because there are six possible outcomes and each outcome is equally likely, then the probability associated with each outcome is $\frac{1}{6}$.

5.2.2
Certain and Impossible Events

A **certain event**, E, is an event which must occur; that is, every element of the sample space satisfies E. A certain event has probability equal to 1. For example, suppose you flip a regular coin. What is the probability of the coin landing on heads or tails. Clearly, both of the outcomes are in the sample space, and one of the outcomes must occur. Thus, the probability of a coin landing on heads or tails is 1.

On the other hand, in a given experiment, we can describe events that are considered **impossible events**. Impossible events are events that are not part of the sample space, and therefore, the probability of an impossible event is not defined. For example, if you have 5 red marbles and 5 blue marbles in a hat, we might ask the question, "What is the probability of drawing a green marble?" You may be tempted to claim that the probability of drawing a green marble in this situation is zero. However, because there are no green marbles, green will not be a part of the sample space, and thus, the probability of this event is not defined.

5.2.3
Theoretical
Probability

When we consider an experiment and determine the probabilities associated with each outcome based on how likely the outcome is to occur, we are determining a theoretical probability. For example, when rolling a single die, each of the outcomes 1, 2, 3, 4, 5, and 6, has a chance of occurring because there are six possible outcomes and they are all equally likely. The probability is a **theoretical probability** because it is the probability associated with what should happen given the nature of the experiment of rolling a die.

5.2.4
Empirical
Probability

An **empirical probability** is a probability that is determined from data collected by conducting multiple rounds of an experiment; that is, given an experiment, if the experiment is conducted and data from the experiment are collected, we can use that data to determine the probability of the different outcomes occurring.

For example, suppose we actually roll a single die 100 times, given the results: the number one occurs 11 times, the number two occurs 24 times, the number three occurs 14 times, the number four occurs 13 times, roll the number five occurs 26 times, and the number six occurs 12 times. From this experiment, we determine the empirical probabilities associated with the each roll of that single die as shown in Figure 5.2.

In the experiment, the probabilities of each roll have been determined by actually rolling the die. Notice that these **experimental probabilities** vary from the theoretical probabilities. Comparing empirical and theoretical probabilities, we can confirm the fundamental notion behind probability: probability is all about chance and what **should** happen, not necessarily about what **does** actually happen.

Figure 5.2

Outcomes	Probability
1	$\frac{11}{100}$
2	$\frac{24}{100}$
3	$\frac{14}{100}$
4	$\frac{13}{100}$
5	$\frac{26}{100}$
6	$\frac{12}{100}$

Note that the empirical probabilities determined in the experiment of rolling a die were based on only 100 rolls of a die. If we were to actually roll a die 1,000 times, 100,000 times, or even 1,000,000 times, we would likely produce data that determined empirical probabilities that were more closely matched to the theoretical probability associated with this experiment; that is, as the number of times, n, that we conduct an experiment gets large, the closer empirical probabilities mirror theoretical probabilities. In fact, as n becomes so large as to approach infinity, empirical probabilities will equal theoretical probabilities.

Once we have a probability distribution of numerical outcomes and related probabilities, whether theoretical or empirical probabilities, we can compute the **expected value** of an experiment. The expected value of an experiment is essentially what the *average outcome* of an experiment would be over time where the outcomes are number values.

To compute the expected value of an experiment with outcomes O_1, O_2, O_3, O_4, ... O_n and respective probabilities, p_1, p_2, p_3, p_4, ... p_n, we determine the expected value, E,

$$E = (O_1 \times p_1) + (O_2 \times p_2) + (O_3 \times p_3) + (O_4 \times p_4) + \cdots + (O_n \times p_n)$$

For example, consider the probability distribution associated with spinning a spinner where the possible outcomes are 2, 4, 6, 8, and 10 and the probabilities associated with each outcome are those listed in Table 5.3.

Outcomes	Probability
2	0.125
4	0.25
6	0.30
8	0.20
10	0.125

Table 5.3

Given this probability distribution, we can compute the expected value:

E = (2 × 0.125) + (4 × 0.25) + (6 × 0.30) + (8 × 0.20) + (10 × 0.125)
  = 0.25 + 1 + 1.8 + 1.6 + 1.25
  = 5.93

What this expected value tells us is that if we spin the spinner over and over again for a large number of times, the overall average of the outcomes we generate should be close to 5.93.

Mutually Exclusive and Complementary Events | Multistep Experiments   **RELATED TOPICS**

TOPIC 5.3 MUTUALLY EXCLUSIVE AND COMPLEMENTARY EVENTS

CORNERSTONE | Probability Notions | Equally Likely Outcomes | Adding Rational Numbers
Sets | Set Notation

INTRODUCTION

If two friends each enter a contest, they may wonder what the chances are that one of them will win. Thus, they are not just interested in how likely it is for one of them to win, but want to know what the chances of one or the other winning. Intuitively, we understand that the chance of one or the other winning is greater than the chance of exactly or only one of them winning. In this section, we compute the probability of one event or another occurring. We explain how to distinguish between mutually exclusive events and non-mutually exclusive events. Further, given an event, we describe what the complement of that event is.

DID YOU KNOW?

Many people like to play the lottery. They hold onto the hope that one day might be their lucky day and they will win. In reality, in a lottery where you are to choose six numbers from a set of 45 numbers, the chance that your set of six numbers will be the winning set is approximately 1 in 8 million!

5.3.1
Mutually Exclusive Events

Two events, A and B, are said to be **mutually exclusive events** if they cannot occur at the same time. For example, when rolling a die, let us consider the events A and B where A = rolling a 4 and B = rolling a 3. Events A and B are mutually exclusive because it is impossible to roll a 4 and a 3 at the same time in rolling a single ordinary die.

5.3.2
Non-Mutually Exclusive Events

Two events, A and B are said to be **non-mutually exclusive events** if they can occur at the same time. For example, when drawing a card from ordinary deck of 52 cards, consider two events A and B where event A = drawing an ace and event B = drawing a diamond. Events A and B are non-mutually exclusive because it is possible, when drawing a card, to draw both an ace and a diamond at the same time; that is, if we draw the ace of diamonds, both events A and B have occurred simultaneously.

5.3.3
Understanding "Or" Probability Situations

In some cases, we need to determine the probability of either one or another outcome occurring. Given two events, A and B, the probability of event A or event B occurring, denoted P(A or B) or P(A $\cup$ B), is:

P(A or B) = P(A) + P(B), when A and B are mutually exclusive events.
P(A or B) = P(A) + P(B) − P(both A and B), when A and B are not mutually exclusive events.

Example 1: When rolling a single die, we might want to find the probability of rolling either a 5 or a 2. Because the events of rolling a 5 and rolling a 2 are mutually exclusive, we compute the probability of rolling a 5 or a 2 by:

$$P(\text{rolling 5 or 2}) = P(\text{rolling 5}) + P(\text{rolling 2}) = \frac{1}{6} + \frac{1}{6} = \frac{2}{6} = \frac{1}{3}.$$

Example 2: Suppose we roll a single die and we want to find the probability of rolling an even number or rolling a number less than 3. The events A and B, where A = rolling an even number and B = rolling a number less than 3, are non-mutually exclusive because it is possible to roll a number that is both even and less 3 at the same time if you roll the number 2. Thus, when computing the probability of A or B occurring, we use the formula for non-mutually exclusive events:

P(rolling an even number or a number less than 3) = P(rolling even) + P(rolling < 3) − P(rolling an even number less than 3).

Because there are six numbers on the die and three of them are even, the probability of rolling an even number is $\frac{3}{6}$. Further, because there are two numbers on the die that are less than 3, then the probability of rolling a number less than 3 is $\frac{2}{6}$. Finally, because there is only 1 number on the die that is both even and less than 3, the probability of rolling an even number less than 3 is $\frac{1}{6}$. Therefore, P(rolling an even number or a number less than 3)

Example 3: When drawing a card from an ordinary deck of cards, what is the probability of drawing either a diamond or a club? Because the events drawing a diamond and drawing a club are mutually exclusive, computing, we find:

$$P(\text{drawing a diamond or a club}) = P(\text{drawing a diamond}) + P(\text{drawing a club})$$
$$= \frac{13}{52} + \frac{13}{52}$$
$$= \frac{26}{52} = \frac{1}{2}.$$

Example 4: When drawing a card from an ordinary deck of cards, what is the probability of drawing a heart or a Queen? Because the events drawing a heart and drawing a Queen are non-mutually exclusive, we compute:

$$P(\text{drawing a heart or Queen}) = P(\text{drawing a heart}) + P(\text{drawing a Queen})$$
$$- P(\text{drawing the Queen of hearts})$$
$$= \frac{13}{52} + \frac{4}{52} - \frac{1}{52}$$
$$= \frac{16}{52} = \frac{4}{13}.$$

A Venn Diagram representation of two events in a given experiment can help determine whether or not the two events are mutually exclusive or non-mutually exclusive. For example, consider an experiment involving spinning the following spinner (see Figure 5.3):

5.3.4
Using a Venn Diagram to Look at Mutually Exclusive Events

Figure 5.3

If we want to determine the probability of spinning an odd number or a number that is a multiple of three, we can determine if these events are mutually exclusive or not by forming the Venn Diagram shown in Figure 5.4.

Figure 5.4

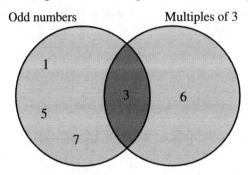

Odd numbers   Multiples of 3

The overlap in the Venn Diagram shows that the two events are not mutually exclusive. Therefore, we can determine the probability of spinning an odd number or a multiple of three by:

P(odd or multiple of 3)=P(odd)+P(multiple of 3)−P(odd and multiples of 3)

$$= \frac{4}{8} + \frac{2}{8} - \frac{1}{8} = \frac{5}{8}.$$

5.3.5
Interpreting an "Or" Situation

Figure 5.5

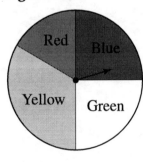

In some probability questions, it is not explicitly clear that we are dealing with an "or" situation, even when it is, in fact, an "or" situation. For example, consider the spinner shown in Figure 5.5.

If we ask the question, "What is the probability of spinning a primary color?" we can interpret the question as an "or" situation, asking instead, "What is the probability of spinning a red or a blue or a yellow?" Because these events are mutually exclusive, we can solve the problem:

P(spinning a primary color) = P(spinning red or blue or yellow)

$$= P(red) + P(blue) + P(yellow)$$

$$= \frac{1}{6} + \frac{1}{4} + \frac{1}{3} = \frac{2}{12} + \frac{3}{12} + \frac{4}{12} = \frac{9}{12} = \frac{3}{4}.$$

As another example, suppose a number x is selected at random from a set of numbers $\{1, 2, 3, ..., 8\}$. What is the probability that $x < 5$?

This question can be rephrased as an "or" situation asking, "What is the probability of selecting a 1 or 2 or 3 or 4?" Thus, because these are mutually exclusive events, we solve by finding P(1) + P2) + P(3) + (P4) = $\frac{1}{8} + \frac{1}{8} + \frac{1}{8} + \frac{1}{8} = \frac{4}{8} = \frac{1}{2}$.

5.3.6
Table of Data Simulation

Sometimes we are given empirical data from which to determine the answer to an "or" probability situation. Suppose we had 1000 people volunteer to participate in a study. From a questionnaire, we learn that some of the male and female participants in the study are smokers and some are non-smokers. Consider the table of data of male and female smokers and non-smokers provided in Table 5.4.

Table 5.4	Smokers	Nonsmokers	Total
Female	198	245	443
Male	310	247	557
Total	508	492	1,000

If we randomly choose one person from the pool of 1,000 volunteers to be the first person to interviewed, what is the probability that the person selected is either a female or a non-smoker? Using data from the table, and noting that the events "being a female" and "being a non-smoker" are not mutually exclusive, we compute:

$$P(\text{female or non-smoker}) = P(\text{female}) + P(\text{non-smoker}) - P(\text{non-smoking female})$$

$$= \frac{443}{1000} + \frac{492}{1000} - \frac{245}{1000}$$

$$= \frac{690}{1000}$$

$$= \frac{69}{100}.$$

A Venn diagram (see Figure 5.6) representation of the male and female smokers and non-smokers illustrates that the events "being female" and "being a non-smoker" are not mutually exclusive. The striped section indicates non-smokers and the polka-dotted section indicates females. The overlap is seen as the 245 non-smoking females (refer to Figure 5.6).

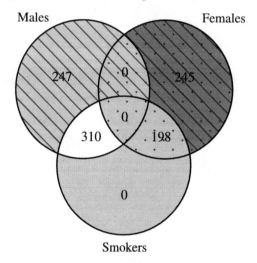

Figure 5.6

Given an event A, we say the **complement** of event A, denoted $\overline{A}$, is the sample space of an experiment less the event A. Stated another way, the complement of even A is the set of all events in the sample space *except* event A. For example, when rolling a die, if we know event A = rolling a 3, then the complement of A is $\overline{A}$ = rolling anything but 3. Note that sometimes the complement of A, $\overline{A}$, is referred to as "not A."

5.3.7 Complementary Events

The probability of a complementary event, $\overline{A}$, denoted $P(\overline{A})$, is closely related to the probability of event A, $P(A) : P(\overline{A}) + P(A) = 1$. Thus, given the probability of an event A, we can determine the probability of its complement, or vice versa, using this relationship as follows:

$$P(\overline{A}) = 1 - P(A)$$
$$P(A) = 1 - P(\overline{A})$$

For example, given a hat with 4 green marbles, 3 blue marbles, and 2 black marbles, and the experiment of drawing a marble out of the hat, suppose A is the event drawing a black marble. Then $\overline{A}$ = not drawing a black marble or $\overline{A}$ = drawing a green or blue marble. Consequently, because $P(A) = \frac{2}{9}$, then $P(\overline{A}) = 1 - \frac{2}{9} = \frac{7}{9}$.

5.3.8
**Odds In Favor and
Odds Against**

To determine the **odds in favor** of an event, E, occurring, we compute the ratio, $\frac{P(E)}{P(\overline{E})}$ [or $P(E){:}P(\overline{E})$]. To compute the **odds against** an event, E, occurring, we compute the ratio, $\frac{P(\overline{E})}{P(E)}$ [or $P(\overline{E}){:}P(E)$] .

Example 1: Leroy has a chance for 5 different summer jobs, 3 of which are at resort areas. If he selects a job at random, find the odds in favor of the job being at a resort and the odds against its being at a resort.

The event at hand is E = selecting a job at a resort. Thus, $P(E) = \frac{3}{5}$ and $P(\overline{E}) = \frac{2}{5}$. To determine the odds in favor, we find $\frac{P(E)}{P(\overline{E})} = \frac{3/5}{2/5} = \frac{3}{2}$ or 3 : 2. To determine the odds against, we compute $\frac{P(\overline{E})}{P(E)} = \frac{2/5}{3/5} = \frac{2}{3}$ or 2 : 3.

Example 2: You have a "loaded" coin where there is a two-thirds chance of flipping heads and a one-third chance of flipping tails. What are the odds in favor of flipping heads? What are the odds against flipping heads?

Odds in Favor of flipping heads $= \frac{\frac{2}{3}}{\frac{1}{3}} = \frac{2}{1}$ or 2 : 1.

Odds Against flipping heads $= \frac{\frac{2}{3}}{\frac{1}{3}} = \frac{1}{2}$ or 1 : 2.

RELATED TOPICS   Multistep Experiments

TOPIC 5.4 MULTISTEP EXPERIMENTS

Probability Notions | Equally Likely Outcomes | Mutually Exclusive and
Complementary Events | Multiplying Rational Numbers

CORNERSTONE

I flip a coin five times, and I wonder how likely it is that it will land on heads each time? Questions like this center around multistep experiments. The probability of a coin landing on heads on one flip is much different than the probability of this happening five times in a row. In this section, we examine probabilities associated with multiple events, determining when these events are independent from each other and when they are dependent in a way that affects the probability of both events occurring.

INTRODUCTION

Did you know that in a group of 15 people there's a 25% chance that at least two people will have the same birthday? Further, if you are in a group of 25 people there's almost a 60% chance that at least two people will have the same birthday. In fact, in a group of 35 people, there's more than an 80% that at least two people will have the same birthday. Next time you are in a group of 35 people, test the probability!!

DID YOU KNOW?

When an experiment involves multiple events, to compute the probability of both events occurring, we must first determine whether those events are independent or dependent. Two events, one to follow the other, are **independent** if the occurrence of the first event does not affect the probability of the occurrence of the second event. Two events, one to follow the other, are **dependent** if the occurrence of the first event affects the probability of the occurrence of the second event.

5.4.1
Independent Versus Dependent Events

For example, suppose I am going to roll a die twice. What is the probability that we will roll a 3 on the first roll and an even number on the second roll. Because the die is "fixed" that is, does not change after the first roll, then the events of rolling a 3 and then rolling an event number are independent.

On the other hand, suppose we have a hat with 6 red marbles and 4 white marbles. We are to draw two marbles out of the hat, one right after the other without replacing the first marble. What is the probability that we draw a red marble on the first draw and a white marble on the second draw? Because, after the first draw, the marble is not replaced, we have reduced the number of marbles in the hat. This will affect the probability of drawing a white marble on the second draw. Therefore, these two events, drawing a red marble followed by drawing a white marble, are dependent.

When the probability of event B is affected by the occurrence of event A, we express the probability of B, given that A has occurred, read **B given A**, using the notation P(B|A). We call a situation involving P(B|A) a **conditional probability**.

5.4.2
Conditional Probability

For example, if we have a hat with 6 red marbles and 4 white marbles as previously described, and we draw 2 marbles out, one at a time without replacing the first marble, we can determine the probability of drawing the white marble on the second draw using conditional probability. If we have drawn a red marble on the first draw and have not replaced the marble, then we are left with just 9 marbles in the hat, 5 being red and 4 being white. Thus, the probability of drawing a white marble on the second draw is affected by the fact that one red marble has been removed from the hat. Thus, the P(drawing a white | a red marble has been drawn) = $\frac{4}{9}$.

5.4.3
Understanding "And" Probability Situations

In probability situations where we determine the probability of two events, A and B, both occurring, denoted, P(A and B) or P(A ∩ B), we compute the probability of these "and" probability settings by:

P(A and B) = P(A) P(B) when A and B are independent events.

P(A and B) = P(A) P(B|A) when A and B are dependent events.

Example 1: Suppose we are experimenting with the spinner shown in Figure 5.7 and we spin the spinner twice. We may ask the question, "What is the probability of spinning red twice in a row?" This is equivalent to determining the probability of spinning a red and a red. Because what happens on the first spin does not affect the probabilities associated with the second spin, the two events are independent. Therefore, the probability of spinning a red and a then another red is found by:

$$P(\text{spinning red and red}) = P(\text{red}) \times P(\text{red}) = \frac{1}{4} \times \frac{1}{4} = \frac{1}{16}.$$

Figure 5.7

Example 2: Suppose we revisit the situation where we have a hat with 6 red marbles and 4 white marbles and we draw two marbles, without replacing the first marble drawn. What is the probability of drawing a red marble followed by a white marble. The probability of drawing a red marble on the first draw is $\frac{6}{10}$. If we draw a red marble on the first draw and do not replace the marble, then we are left with just 9 marbles in the hat, 5 being red and 4 being white. Thus, the probability of drawing a white marble on the second draw is affected by the fact that one red marble has been removed from the hat. Thus, the P(drawing a white | a red marble has been drawn) = $\frac{4}{9}$. Thus, to compute the probability of drawing the red marble and the white marble as described, we compute:

$$P(\text{red first and white second}) = P(\text{red}) \times P(\text{white}|\text{red})$$

$$= \frac{6}{10} \times \frac{4}{9}$$

$$= \frac{24}{90} = \frac{4}{15}.$$

Example 3: Suppose you are going to draw four cards from a deck of cards, one right after the other, replacing cards into the deck after each draw. What is the probability of drawing four Queens? We can think of this as an "And" the situation of finding the probability of drawing a Queen and a Queen and a Queen and a Queen. Because we are replacing the cards after each draw, then each event is independent of the others. Therefore we compute:

P(queen and queen and queen and queen)

$$= P(queen) \times P(queen) \times P(queen) \times P(queen)$$

$$= \frac{4}{52} \times \frac{4}{52} \times \frac{4}{52} \times \frac{4}{52}$$

$$= \frac{256}{7,311,616}$$

$$= \frac{1}{28,651}.$$

Example 4: We are going to draw 5 cards from a deck of cards, one right after the other without replacing cards after they have been drawn. What is the probability of drawing five hearts? As an "And" situation we must find the probability of drawing a heart and a heart and a heart and a heart and a heart. In this case, because cards are not being replaced after each draw, the events in this multistep experiment are dependent. Thus, we determine the probability by:

P(heart and heart and heart and heart and heart) =

P(heart) × P(heart | 1 heart has been drawn) × P(heart | 2 hearts have been drawn) × P(heart | 3 hearts have been drawn) × P(heart | 4 hearts have been drawn)

$$= \frac{13}{52} \times \frac{12}{51} \times \frac{11}{50} \times \frac{10}{49} \times \frac{9}{48}$$

$$= \frac{33}{66,640}.$$

Notice that the conditional probability associated with the second draw indicates that after the first card has been drawn, there are only 51 cards left. Also, because we're assuming the first card drawn was a heart, then only 12 hearts remain after the first draw. Thus, the probability for drawing a heart, given that one heart has already been drawn is $\frac{12}{51}$. The determination of the conditional probabilities for the third, fourth, and fifth draws follow a similar process.

Tree diagrams can illustrate probabilities associated multistep experiments by showing the possible combination of outcomes at each step of multistep experiments. For example, suppose we are working with the spinner in Figure 5.8.

As seen in the spinner, P(Yes) = $\frac{1}{4}$, and P(No) = $\frac{3}{4}$. If we spin the spinner three times, we can illustrate the various probabilities associated with the three spins and the different combinations of outcomes using a **tree diagram**. Note that the events associated with each spin of this multistep experiment are independent because the spinner is not altered from spin to spin.

5.4.4
Tree Diagrams

Figure 5.8

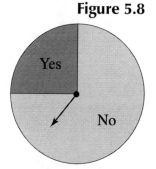

Figure 5.9 illustrates the tree diagram for the probabilities of three spins of this spinner. Highlighted in the diagram is the path that we could follow to determine the probability of spinning a "Yes" followed by a "No" followed by a "Yes." We would compute the probability:

$$P(\text{Yes and No and Yes}) = P(\text{Yes}) \times P(\text{No}) \times P(\text{Yes})$$

$$= \frac{1}{4} \times \frac{3}{4} \times \frac{1}{4}$$

$$= \frac{3}{64}$$

Figure 5.9

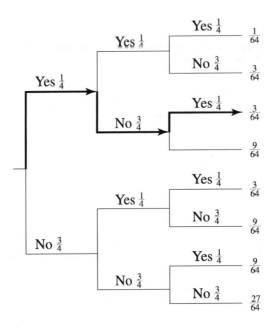

TOPIC 5.5 COUNTING PRINCIPLES

CORNERSTONE

INTRODUCTION

When it comes to determining how many ways to arrange books on a shelf or how many ways to put people into groups, we can use counting techniques that make the counting process simpler and easier. In this section, we examine ways to compute combinations, permutations, and basic counting principles.

DID YOU KNOW?

Mathematician Blaise Pascal is known for developing Pascal's Triangle, a triangular arrangement of numbers that has many interesting patterns. One notable pattern in the triangle is the row-by-row pattern of numbers that show the number of combinations you can make from n items selecting r at a time. For example, looking at row 4 of Pascal's Triangle shown in Figure 5.10, the numbers across represent, in order, the number of combinations you can make (1) choosing 0 from a set of 3 objects, (2) choosing 1 from a set of 3 objects, (3) choosing 2 from a set of 3 objects, and (4) choosing 3 from a set of 3 objects. Those possible combinations, in order are 1, 3, 3, 1.

```
              1
            1   1
          1   2   1  ←——— Third row
        1   3   3   1  ←——— Fourth row
      1   4   6   4   1
    1   5  10  10   5   1
                :
                :
```

Figure 5.10

Row 3 of Pascal's Triangle shows the combinations you can make with 2 objects; that is, the first number, 1, is the number of combinations you can create with 2 objects selecting 0 at a time. The second number, 2, is the number of combinations you can create with 2 objects selecting 1 at a time. Finally, the last number, 1, is the number of combinations you can create with 2 objects selecting 2 at a time. In general, the nth row in Pascal's Triangle represents the number of combinations you can make with $n - 1$ objects selecting 0 at a time, 1 at a time, 2 at a time, ..., $3n - 1$ at a time. For more information on determining combinations, see the section entitled Computing Combinations in this topic.

For More Information: Reimer, L., & Reimer W. (1990). *Mathematicians are people, too: Stories from the lives of great mathematicians, Volume 1.* Palo Alto, CA: Dale Seymour Publications.

5.5.1
Factorial

Given a whole number, n, we compute the factorial of n, read ***n* factorial** and denoted ***n!***, by multiplying n times all the non-zero whole numbers less than n; that is:

$$n! = n \times (n - 1) \times (n - 2) \times (n - 3) \times \cdots \times 3 \times 2 \times 1.$$

For example, $4! = 4 \times 3 \times 2 \times 1 = 24$. Likewise, $10! = 10 \times 9 \times 8 \times 7 \times 6 \times 5 \times 4 \times 3 \times 2 \times 1 = 3,628,800$. Note that $0!$ is defined to be equal to 1. Note that most calculators have a factorial button, often labeled $n!$, that compute the factorial value for the value of n that is input into the calculator.

5.5.2
Definition of Permutations

Given a set of objects, we can compute the number of unique ways to arrange those objects in different orders. The arrangements of a set of objects are called the **permutations** of the objects. For example, given the set of objects = {a, b, c}, we can determine six permutations of these objects: abc, acb, bac, bca, cab, cba.

Suppose we have the set of objects = {a, b, c, d} and, selecting two at a time, we want to determine all the permutations of two items from the set. There are twelve such permutations: ab, ba, ac, ca, ad, da, bc, cb, bd, db, cd, dc.

5.5.3
Computing Permutations

Given whole numbers n and r, where $n \geq r$, we can determine the number of permutations of n thing taken r at a time, denoted $P(n, r)$, by the formula:

$$P(n, r) = \frac{n!}{(n - r)!} .$$

For example, how many permutation of 6 objects, taken 2 at a time, are there? We compute: $P(6, 2) = \frac{6!}{(6-2)!} = \frac{6!}{4!} = \frac{6 \times 5 \times 4 \times 3 \times 2 \times 1}{4 \times 3 \times 2 \times 1} = \frac{30}{1} = 30$.

Note that $P(n, n) = n!$ For example, the number of permutation of 5 objects selected 5 at a time is found by $P(5, 5) = 5! = 720$.

5.5.4
Permutation Notation and the Calculator

Many calculators have the capability of computing permutations given your input values for n and r. Some calculators will have a button labeled $P(n, r)$ or $_nP_r$. Although each calculator works in its own way, most calculators require that you input the value for n, punch the button and then wait for you to input the r value. Once the r value is input, you then punch the "equal to" button and the calculator will display the result.

5.5.5
Definition of Combinations

Given a set of objects, we can compute the number of unique ways to group those objects into certain-sized sets. These groupings of a set of objects are called the **combinations** of the objects. For example, given the set of objects = {x, y, z}, we can determine three ways to combine two of the objects at a time: xy, xz, yz. When we are finding the combinations of objects, we are not concerned with the different orderings or permutations of the groups of objects, simply the different groupings.

Suppose we have the set of objects = {w, x, y, z} and we want to determine all the different combinations we can form taking three objects at a time. There are four such combinations: wxy, wxz, wyz, xyz.

5.5.6
Computing Combinations

Given whole numbers n and r, where $n \geq r$, we can determine the number of combinations of n things taken r at a time, denoted $C(n, r)$, by the formula:

$$C(n, r) = \frac{n!}{r!(n - r)!} .$$

For example, how many combinations of 8 objects, taken 3 at a time, are there? We compute: $C(8, 3) = \frac{8!}{3!(8-3)!} = \frac{8!}{3!\,5!} = \frac{8 \times 7 \times 6 \times 5 \times 4 \times 3 \times 2 \times 1}{3 \times 2 \times 1 \times 5 \times 4 \times 3 \times 2 \times 1} = \frac{56}{1} = 56$.

Note that $C(n, n) = 1$. For example, the number of combinations of 5 objects selected 5 at a time is 1.

Many calculators have the capability of computing combinations given your input values for *n* and *r*. Some calculators will have a button labeled $C(n, r)$ or $_nC_r$. Although each calculator works in its own way, most calculators require that you input the value for *n*, and then punch the $_nC_r$ button and then will then wait for you to input the *r* value. Once the *r* value is input, you then punch the "equal to" button and the calculator will display the result.

5.5.7
Combination Notation and the Calculator

In some cases, we need to count the number of ways that a certain situation can occur, and the method required does not involve permutations or combinations. For these types of problems, we can create a solution using the Fundamental Counting Principle.

5.5.8
Fundamental Counting Principle

The **Fundamental Counting Principle** says that given events A and B, and letting n(A) represent the number of ways for A to occur and n(B|A) represent *the number of ways for B to occur, given that A has occurred*, then the number of ways for A and B to both occur, denoted n(A and B) is found by:

$$n(A \text{ and } B) = n(A) \times n(B|A)$$

Example 1: Suppose we are creating license plate codes that are comprised of three letters of the alphabet, with no letter being used more than once in a given code. To count the number of different license plate codes we can develop, we can use the Fundamental Counting Principle. We can compute the number of codes by:

n(codes) = n(choices for first letter)
   × n(choices for second letter | one letter has already been selected)
   × n(choices for third letter | two letters have already been selected).
   = 26 × 25 × 24 = 15,600.

Note that there are 26 letters in the alphabet, so there are 26 possible choices for the first letter in the code. Once one letter has been used, there are only 25 letters left to choose from for the second letter in the code. Finally, once the first two letters have been chosen, only 24 letters remain to choose for the third letter in the code. Thus, we find the total number of possible codes by multiplying these numbers together.

Example 2: Within a certain area code, we want to figure out all of the 7-digit phone numbers the phone company can distribute in a certain town where phone numbers all begin with the prefix 358. Thus, phone numbers in that area would all look like: 358 - _ _ _ _. We essentially need to determine the number of ways to fill in the last four digits of the phone number.

Thinking in terms of the Fundamental Counting Principle, to solve this problem we need to find the number of ways to create the first missing digit *and* the number of ways to create the second missing digit *and* the number of ways to create the third missing digit *and* the number of ways to create the fourth missing digit. Note that in this scenario, it is okay to use the same digit more than once in the last four digits in a given phone number. Because we have 10 digits (0, 1, 2, 3, 4, 5, 6, 7, 8, 9) to choose from for each of the four digits, we can conclude that we have 10 × 10 × 10 × 10 or 10,000 different phone numbers to create.

Multistep Experiments

RELATED TOPICS

TOPIC 5.6 STATISTICS NOTIONS

| **CORNERSTONE** | Percents | Fractions | Decimals |

INTRODUCTION

Of all the branches of mathematics, statistics is probably the most visible one in the everyday world. If you pick up any newspaper or magazine today, you are likely to come across various surveys done on different categories of population or data records such as those in sports, medicine, or the corporate world. In this section, we define statistics and terms associated with statistical studies including hypotheses, populations, and random sampling.

DID YOU KNOW?

The beginning of the modern theory of statistics and statistical analysis can be traced back to the time of the Industrial Revolution. Statistical analysis began at this time for practical reasons. It was at this time that mass production through large factories began. This created urban populations with all the attendant problems of overpopulation, disease, unemployment, and large population changes. Social scientists of that time were searching for tools to study these changes, and were unable to come to grips with the fast changing social scenario. Then two 17th-century Englishmen, John Graunt and William Petty, studying the death records of English cities, came across surprising patterns of these data. Based on these data, the two made some startling observations. These observations laid the foundations of the study of statistics in the modern sense.

For More Information: Reimer, L., & Reimer W. (1995). *Mathematicians are people, too: Stories from the lives of great mathematicians, Volume 2.* Palo Alto, CA: Dale Seymour Publications.

5.6.1
Statitics and Statistical Data

Statistics is a collection of methods for planning experiments, gathering data, and then organizing, analyzing, interpreting and representing data with the intent of drawing conclusions and making decisions based on the data.

A piece of **data** is a fact or figure that provides some information, usually gathered to support a position or for some sort of decision-making purpose. **Statistical data** is usually numerical information that can be presented in a variety of forms including whole numbers, a fractions, a decimal numbers, or a percents. Examples of data in use are seen in the following statements:

More than 50% of all marriages end in divorce.

The Dow Jones Average went up 15 points today.

Four-fifths of college students own their own cars.

The government spends an average of $1.5 million per year on miscellaneous expenditures.

5.6.2
Hypotheses

A **hypothesis** is a statement that is used a premise for investigating and proving whether something is true or false. Investigating a hypothesis involves gathering and analyzing data. Examples of hypotheses are the statements, "Most American college students who own their own cars, own domestic cars," "Smoking causes cancer," and "The average family has 1.5 pets." Each of these statements is stated as if it is true. However, to prove their truth or falseness, we must gather information. For example, to determine whether or not most American college students own domestic cars, the investigator would have to survey a sample of college students and use this data to determine whether or not it is appropriate to conclude that most American college students own domestic cars.

In a statistical study, the **population** is the complete collection of items (whether people, test scores, etc.) to be studied. For example, in studying the hypothesis, "Most American college students who own their own cars, own domestic cars," the population for the study would be all American college students who own their own car.

Because it would be impossible to contact each and every American college student to ask him (or her) if he owns his own car and whether or not the car is domestic, we would probably draw upon a subgroup of college students to survey who would be representative of the entire population. This group of items drawn from a population is called a **sample**.

Samples can be determined in a variety of ways. In **random sampling**, a subset of the population is selected in a way that each member of the population has an equal chance of being selected. For example, when you are called on the telephone to be polled about your choice of presidential candidates, your phone number was selected randomly by a computer-generated program. Thus, anyone with a phone number on the computer's list had a chance of being called.

In some instances, when sampling from a population, we need to subdivide that population into at least two different subgroups that share the same characteristics. In this situation we are engaged in **stratified sampling**. For example, suppose we are studying the number of hours that college students prepare for exams. We may want to make sure we include or differentiate between freshmen, sophomores, juniors, and seniors. Thus, the population of college students is stratified into four categories, and samples are drawn, proportionally, from each of the categories. Within each category, random sampling can be applied so that each freshmen, each sophomore, each junior, and each senior have an equal chance of being selected. Note that in this particular stratified sampling, we are guaranteeing that the sample we select will include students from each class.

Systematic sampling is a method of sampling where we identify a starting point and then select every *kth* element in the population. For example, in a graduating class, you might select every fourth graduate exiting the graduation ceremony to survey about a current event issue.

In **cluster sampling**, we divide a population area into sections and then randomly select a few of those sections. Then we choose all the members from the selected sections. For example, if we want to survey high school students about school lunches, we can randomly select certain tables in the cafeteria and survey all the students sitting at those tables.

Finally, there is **convenience sampling** where we simply use the sample that is available to us. For example, if a veterinarian wants to study the effectiveness of a new type of flea collar, she might use her own patients to test the flea collar because these pets are readily available.

**5.6.3
Populations,
Samples
and Types of
Sampling**

TOPIC 5.7 MEASURES OF CENTRAL TENDENCY

CORNERSTONE	Statistics Concepts

INTRODUCTION

In many statistical situations, we want to know what happens in general, or on average. For example, we might want to know the average income of women in the United States as compared to the average income of men. Or we might want to know the most popularly-selling car over the last five years. Both of these situations are asking to find some sort of measure of central tendency or sense of what is happening on average. In the following sections, we explore a variety of ways of determining a measure of central tendency including finding the mean, median, and mode of a set of data.

DID YOU KNOW?

Two important early instances of the use of statistics are provided by Florence Nightingale and Gregor Mendel. Florence Nightingale (1820–1910), the famous English nurse, who worked with death records in hospitals during the Crimean War, used statistics in order to show that change was desperately needed in the conditions of the hospitals. The Austrian monk, Gregor Mendel (1822–1911), maintained records of his botany experiments, and from the results laid the foundations of the science of genetics.

For More Information: Smith, D. E. (1958). *History of mathematics, Volume II.* New York: Dover Publications.

5.7.1 Mean

In statistical studies we often want to determine the mean of the data. The **mean** is one way of determining what the data imply on average. To compute the mean, denoted, $\bar{x}$, we divide the sum of individual numerical data items, x_1, x_2, x_3, ... x_n, by the total number of data items, n; that is:

$$\text{Mean} = \bar{x} = \frac{x_1 + x_2 + x_3 + \cdots + x_n}{n}$$

For example, we might want to determine the mean test score on a final exam in a history course. Thirty students took the final exam and the scores earned were the following:

44, 51, 60, 61, 62, 66, 66, 68, 70, 71,
71, 71, 74, 75, 78, 79, 79, 80, 81, 82,
83, 83, 84, 84, 85, 85, 87, 88, 90, 93

To determine the mean, we find the sum of the test scores and divide by 30:

$$\bar{x} = \frac{44 + 51 + 60 + \cdots + 90 + 93}{30} = \frac{2183}{30} = 72.8 \ .$$

Notice that even though the raw scores were given as whole numbers, the mean shown is a decimal number.

In some statistical situations, you may not have the raw data itself, but may have the data presented in a table such as a frequency table (refer to the section on Frequency Tables in the Representing Data topic for more details on developing frequency tables). We can compute the mean of the data presented in a frequency table.

Suppose, instead of raw data form, the data on history final exam scores are presented in a frequency table as shown in Table 5.5. The class column indicates how scores were classed or categorized as scores between 40 and 49, between 50 and 59, etc. and the frequency column depicts how many test scores fell within that categorization with the total frequency being 30, the total number of test scores.

Because we do not know, for example, the exact scores in the 60–69 category, we can determine a representative score for that category by computing the mean of the high and low score represented by the category; that is, finding the mean of 60 and 69, $\frac{60+69}{2} = \frac{129}{2} = 64.5$, we can let the score 64.5 represent the average score earned within that category. We call this representative score for the class the **class mark**. Using the class marks and the frequency of each class, we can approximate the sum of test scores in class and the sum of the all test scores as shown in Table 5.6.

We then compute the mean from the frequency table by dividing the sum of the scores determined in the last column by the total frequency. Computing, we find: $\frac{2275}{30} = 75.8$. You may note that the mean determined using raw data scores, 72.8, differs from the mean determined using the frequency table, 75.8. Of course, the mean from the frequency table is an approximation. However, if raw data are not available, but a frequency table is, the mean from the frequency table usually provides a reasonable representation of the true mean.

Table 5.5

Class	Frequency
40-49	1
50-59	1
60-69	6
70-79	9
80-89	11
90-99	2
	30

Table 5.6

Class	Frequency	Class Mark	Class Mark × Frequency
40-49	1	44.5	44.5
50-59	1	54.5	54.5
60-69	6	64.5	387.0
70-79	9	74.5	670.5
80-89	11	84.5	929.5
90-99	2	94.5	189.0
	30		Sum of All Scores 2,275.0

5.7.2 Mode

Another way to examine data and determine what occurs on average is to find the mode of the data. The **mode** of a set of data is the score, or item, that occurs most often. For example, consider the thirty test scores from the history final discussed:

44, 51, 60, 61, 62, 66, 66, 68, 70, 71,
71, 71, 74, 75, 78, 79, 79, 80, 81, 82,
83, 83, 84, 84, 85, 85, 87, 88, 90, 93

We look at the scores and notice that 71 occurred most often. Therefore, 71 is mode of this data set. In some data sets, there may be more than one mode. If there are two scores that occur the same number of times and more than any others, we say the data set is **bimodal**. If there are more than two modes, we say the data is **multimodal**. Finally, if no score occurs more than any others, we say there is **no mode**.

If raw data are not available, but we have a frequency table of data, we can approximate the mode. Recall the frequency table for the history final exam scores (see Table 5.7).

Table 5.7

Class	Frequency
40-49	1
50-59	1
60-69	6
70-79	9
80-89	11
90-99	2
	30

We look to the frequency table and note the class that has the highest frequency. In this example, the class 80–89 has the highest frequency. We then find the class mark, 84.5, of that class and let that class mark represent the mode of the data in this frequency table. As in the case where the mean of raw scores and the mean found in a frequency table differ, so do the modes found from raw data and from frequency tables.

5.7.3
Median

The **median** of a set of data is the middle score or the data item when data items are written in increasing order. Determining the median differs depending on whether there is an even or odd number of data items. Suppose, for example, we have 15 quiz scores:

$$39, 42, 59, 64, 66, 70, 77, \mathbf{80}, 81, 82, 83, 83, 86, 90, 99$$

Because the scores are already written in increasing order, the middle score can be identified within the data set as the eighth score in the list, or 80.

Suppose instead of 15 scores, we have the following 16 scores:

$$39, 42, 59, 64, 66, 70, 77, \mathbf{80, 81}, 82, 83, 83, 86, 90, 99, 100$$

There is no single middle score among this data set because there is an even number of scores. Thus, to determine the median, we find the middle two scores and determine the average of those two scores. In this example, the middle two scores are 80 and 81. So, the median is $\frac{80+81}{2} = \frac{161}{2} = 80.5$.

When data are provided in a frequency table, instead of in raw data form, we can determine the median. For example, consider the data in the frequency table of history test scores as revisited in Table 5.8.

To determine the median, because there is an even number of scores, we need to average the middle two scores—that is the class marks associated with the 15th and 16th scores. Using the frequency column, beginning at the top, we can add the frequencies until we get a sum of 15 and a sum of 16 to find which classes the 15th and 16th scores fall into. Adding we find that both the 15th and 16th scores fall within the class 70–79. Therefore, the average of the class marks for the 15th and 16th scores would be 74.5 ($\frac{70+79}{2} = 74.5$). Thus, the median for the data in this frequency table is 74.5.

Table 5.8

Class	Frequency
40-49	1
50-59	1
60-69	6
70-79	9
80-89	11
90-99	2
	30

5.7.4
Range and Midrange

Given a set of raw data, we can determine the range of scores. The **range** is computed by subtracting the high score from the low score; that is, range = high − low. Thus, given the following set of data scores:

$$44, 51, 60, 61, 62, 66, 66, 68, 70, 71,$$
$$71, 71, 74, 75, 78, 79, 79, 80, 81, 82,$$
$$83, 83, 84, 84, 85, 85, 87, 88, 90, 93$$

we compute the range: Range = 93 − 44 = 49. Thus, the data scores in this example have a range of 49.

The **midrange** of a data set can be found by finding the average of the high and low scores. That is, Midrange = $\frac{high + low}{2}$. Using the same data set used to compute the range, we find that the midrange = $\frac{93+44}{2} = \frac{137}{2} = 68.5$.

Both the range and midrange can be approximated from a frequency table. Given a frequency table, such as the one shown in Table 5.9, we can assume the

Table 5.9

Class	Frequency
40-49	1
50-59	1
60-69	6
70-79	9
80-89	11
90-99	2
	30

low score to be the low number in the range of the first class and the high score to be the highest number in the range of the last class. In this example, the low score would be 40 and the high score would be 99. Computing the range and midrange with these scores, we find, range $= 99 - 40 = 49$ and the Midrange $= \frac{93 + 44}{2} = \frac{139}{2} = 69.5$.

With some data, we can compute an average where different data items are given different weights or values. Given data items , with their corresponding weights $w_1, w_2, w_3, \ldots w_n$, we can compute the weighted average of these n data items by:

5.7.5
Weighted Average

$$\text{Weighted Average} = \frac{(w_1 \times x_1) + (w_2 \times x_2) + (w_3 \times x_3) \cdots (w_n \times x_n)}{(w_1 + w_2 + w_3 + \cdots + w_n)}$$

For example, suppose a student's grade is based on quizzes, exam 1, exam 2, a project, a portfolio, a reflective writing journal, and a final exam. Joan's score on each item and the weight that each item will have on the overall grade determination are shown in Table 5.10.

Assessment Item	Score	Weight on Grade
Quiz average	77	14
Exam 1	76	15
Exam 2	65	15
Project	86	13
Portfolio	89	13
Reflective Writing	95	10
Final Exam	79	20

Table 5.10

To determine Joan's grade, or weighted average, we compute:

Weighted Average $= [(77 \times 14) + (76 \times 15) + (65 \times 15) + (86 \times 13) +$
$(89 \times 13) + (95 \times 10) + (79 \times 20)] / (14 + 15 +$
$15 + 13 + 13 + 10 + 20)$
$= (1078 + 114 + 975 + 1118 + 1157 + 95 + 158) / 100$
$= 7998 / 100$
$= 79.98$

Data Dispersion | Representing Data

RELATED TOPICS

TOPIC 5.8 DATA DISPERSION

CORNERSTONE	Statistics Concepts	Measures of Central Tendency

INTRODUCTION

Statistics provide a means not only of determining what happens on average, but also of determining how an individual score compares to the average score or to the rest of the data scores. For example, when students receive their SAT scores, they are told their individual score as well as what percentile their score represents. This percentile score explains how high their score was compared to the other students who took the SAT's. In the following sections, we explore how to compute percentile scores as well as other ways of showing how data scores are dispersed including finding the variance and standard deviation.

DID YOU KNOW?

One of the most common concepts in statistics is the normal distribution curve. This curve, often called the normal curve, or Gaussian curve (after Carl Friedrich Gauss who found a large number of uses for it) occurs in a large number of real life situations. In 1833, a Belgian astronomer and statistician, Adolph Quetelet, made a startling discovery. In a study of the mental and physical traits of human beings, data that had been gathered in large numbers by the artists of the Renaissance period, Quetelet found that almost all these traits were distributed along a normal curve. Height, the size of the brain or the head, intelligence, the sizes of different limbs, were all distributed normally in any one national type. In fact, the same is true for many plant and animal groups as well. What is disturbing for modern social scientists are the data that are not normally distributed such as the records for income, higher education, and access to such facilities as proper medical care. Instead of being normally distributed, these situations will follow skewed curves, reflecting the fact that in most societies, the benefits of prosperity are often limited to a select few.

For More Information: Smith, D. E. (1958). *History of mathematics, Volume II*. New York: Dover Publications.

5.8.1 Variance and Standard Deviation

Beyond needing to know the mean of data, we often want to know how the complete set of data varies about the mean. Two measures that provide such information about how data are dispersed around the mean are variance and standard deviation. In short, the **variance** is the mean of the squared deviation from the mean. Because the variance is determined by the square of the deviation, it is measured in units that are the square of the original units. To make the measure of deviation from the mean expressed in the same units as the original data, we often use the **standard deviation**, which is the square root of the variance. The standard deviation measures the average amount by which data items vary from the mean.

Given a set of data items, $x_1, x_2, x_3, \ldots x_n$, with a mean of $\bar{x}$, we compute the variance of the data, denoted s^2, by:

$$s^2 = \frac{(x_1 - \bar{x})^2 + (x_2 - \bar{x})^2 + (x_3 - \bar{x})^2 + \cdots + (x_n - \bar{x})^2}{n}$$

The standard deviation of the data, denoted s, is the square root of the variance; that is:

$$s = \sqrt{\frac{(x_1 - \bar{x})^2 + (x_2 - \bar{x})^2 + (x_3 - \bar{x})^2 + \cdots + (x_n - \bar{x})^2}{n}}$$

To illustrate, suppose we have the following set of high daily temperatures for 5 different cities: 20°, 35°, 70°, 77°, 80°. To find the variance and standard deviation, we first must determine the mean:

$$\bar{x} = \frac{20° + 35° + 70° + 77° + 80°}{5} = \frac{282}{5} = 56.4°.$$

Then, using the mean, we compute the variance:

$$s^2 = \frac{(20-56.4)^2 + (35-56.4)^2 + (70-56.4)^2 + (77-56.4)^2 + (80-56.4)^2}{5}$$

$$= \frac{(-36.4)^2 + (-21.4)^2 + (13.6)^2 + (20.6)^2 + (23.6)^2}{5}$$

$$= \frac{1324.96 + 457.96 + 184.96 + 424.36 + 556.96}{5}$$

$$= \frac{2949.2}{5}$$

$$= 589.8 \text{ sq degrees.}$$

From the variance we compute the standard deviation:

$$s = \sqrt{589.8} = 24.3 \text{ degrees.}$$

5.8.2
Z-Scores

For any individual data item in a data set, we can determine how much that item varies from the mean by computing its z-score. A **z-score** is the number of standard deviations that a given data value, x, is above or below the mean. We compute a z-score, denoted z, by:

$$z = \frac{x - \bar{x}}{30}$$

where $\bar{x}$ is the mean and s is the standard deviation. Thus, using the data scores 20°, 35°, 70°, 77°, 80° with mean $\bar{x} = 56.4°$, standard deviation s=24.3°, we can find the z-scores associated with each of the data values:

The z-score for 20° $= \dfrac{20 - 56.4}{24.3} = \dfrac{-36.4}{24.3} = -1.50°.$

The z-score for 35° $= \dfrac{35 - 56.4}{24.3} = \dfrac{-21.4}{24.3} = -0.88°.$

The z-score for 70° $= \dfrac{70 - 56.4}{24.3} = \dfrac{13.6}{24.3} = 0.56°.$

The z-score for 77° $= \dfrac{77 - 56.4}{24.3} = \dfrac{20.6}{24.3} = 0.85°.$

The z-score for 80° $= \dfrac{80 - 56.4}{24.3} = \dfrac{23.6}{24.3} = 0.97°.$

The negative z-score indicates that the given score is so many standard deviations below the mean and positive z-scores indicate that a given score is so many standard deviations above the mean. For example, the score 20 is one-and-one-half standard deviations below the mean and the score 77 is 0.85 standard deviations above the mean.

5.8.3
Normal Distribution
of Data

If we have a set of data and form a graphical representation of the data using two axes where the horizontal axis represents the data scores and the vertical axis represents the frequency of those scores, we form what is called a **distribution curve** (see Figure 5.11). When the distribution curve is a smooth bell-shaped curve, we say the data has a **normal distribution**.

Figure 5.11

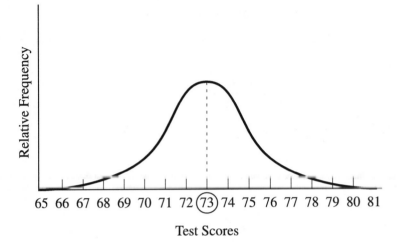

When a data set has a normal distribution, the mean, median, and mode are all the same. In a normal distribution, about 68% of the data scores will fall within 1 standard deviation of the mean, about 95% of the data scores will fall within 2 standard deviation of the mean, and about 99.7% of the data scores will fall within 3 standard deviations of the mean. See Figure 5.12.

Figure 5.12

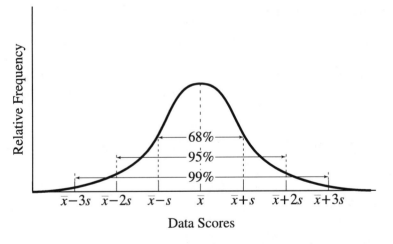

5.8.4
Skewed and
Bimodal Data
Distributions

A distribution of data is **skewed** if it is not symmetric (like the normal distribution) and it extends to one side more than the other. Data that are skewed to the left are said to be **negatively skewed** and data that is skewed to the right are said to be **positively skewed**. See Figure 5.13 for a comparison of normal and skewed data.

When a set of data is negatively skewed, the mean and median are to the left of the mode. Thus, the phrase *skewed to the left*. When a set of data is positively skewed, the mean and median are to the right of the mode, matching the phrase *skewed to the right*.

In some situations, the data are bimodal. In such cases, the data distribution curve would appear somewhat as in Figure 5.14, showing two points where the curve peaks to its highest position.

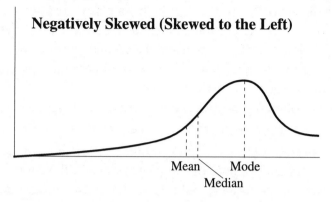

Negatively Skewed (Skewed to the Left)

Mean Mode
Median

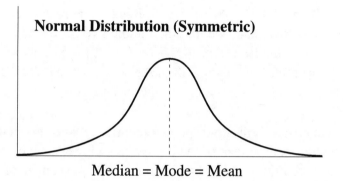

Normal Distribution (Symmetric)

Median = Mode = Mean

Figure 5.13

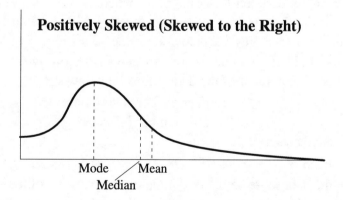

Positively Skewed (Skewed to the Right)

Mode Mean
Median

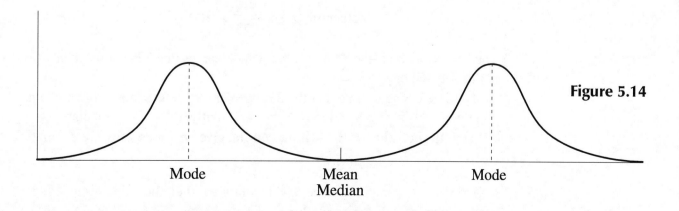

Mode   Mean   Mode
              Median

Figure 5.14

5.8.5
Quartiles

One way of showing how data are dispersed is to break the data into four equal parts called quartiles. The first quartile, denoted Q_1, represents the point in a collection of data scores listed in increasing order that separates the bottom one-fourth of the scores from the top three-fourths of the scores. The second quartile, denoted Q_2, is the point that separates the top half of the scores from the bottom half. Note that the median and the second quartile are the same number. Finally, the third quartile, denoted Q_3, is the point that separates the bottom three-fourths of the scores from the top one-fourth.

Consider the following 25 data scores presented in increasing order:

20, 29, 30, 46, 48, 55, 60, 67, 68, 70, 77, 77, 78, 79, 80, 81, 84, 84, 85, 86, 87, 88, 90, 96, 97

To identify the quartiles, we begin by finding the median, or second quartile. Because there is an odd number of scores, Q_2 is the 13th score in the order, or the value 78. Now, just considering the 12 scores below the second quartile, we identify the first quartile by finding the median of the bottom half of the scores: 20, 29, 30, 46, 48, 55, 60, 67, 68, 70, 77, 77. Because there is an even number of data items in the bottom half, we find the middle two scores and average them to determine the first quartile. Thus, $Q_1 = \frac{55+60}{2} = \frac{115}{2} = 57.5$.

To find Q_3, we focus on the top half of the scores: 79, 80, 81, 84, 84, 85, 86, 87, 88, 90, 96, 97 and find the median of these. Thus, Q_3 .

5.8.6
Percentiles

Related to quartiles, is the concept of percentiles; that is, given the whole set of data, or one hundred percent of the data, we can look to each data point and determine the percentile score of that data item. The **percentile** of a data score depicts what percent of the data scores lie below that data score. In general, the kth percentile value, denoted P_k, is the point where k% of the data scores are less than that value. For example, the 10th percentile, P_{10}, would be the value where 10% of the data scores fall below the value.

Given a particular data value, x, **we can determine the percentile of that score x,** that is what percent of the data values lie below x, by:

$$\text{percentile of score } x = \frac{\text{number of scores less than } x}{\text{total number of scores}} \times 100.$$

Consider the data set of 25 scores:

20, 29, 30, 46, 48, 55, 60, 67, 68, 70, 77, 77, 78, 79, 80, 81, 84, 84, 85, 86, 87, 88, 90, 96, 97

Selecting the data score 85, let us compute the percentile of the score 85. To compute, we count the number of scores less than 84, there are 18 such scores, and use the formula:

$$\text{percentile of } 85 = \frac{18}{25} \times 100 = 72.$$

Thus, the score 85 is the 72 percentile, which means that 72% of the data scores in this set are below 85.

It is interesting to note that the 25th percentile is the same as the first quartile; that is, $P_{25} = Q_1$. Similarly, $P_{75} = Q_3$. Finally, $P_{50} = Q_2 = $ median.
To find the value of the kth percentile, given n data scores, we compute:

$$V = \frac{k}{100} \times n.$$

Now if V is computed to be a whole number, then the value of the *kth* percentile is half way between the *Vth* data element and $(V+1)$st element in the sequence of the original data set. If the V is not a whole number when computed, then we round V up to the next larger whole number to find the position of the kth percentile.

For example, using the 25 data scores:

20, 29, 30, 46, 48, 55, 60, 67, 68, 70, 77, 77, 78, 79, 80, 81, 84, 84, 85, 86, 87, 88, 90, 96, 97

we might want to determine the 80th percentile of the data. To do so, we compute: $V = \frac{80}{100} \times 25 = 20$. Because 20 is a whole number, we find the 20th and 21st data scores in the list of data and find the average of those scores. Finding the scores 86 and 87, we conclude that 86.5 is the 80th percentile.

In a second example, we find the 10th percentile. Computing $V = \frac{10}{100} \times 25 = 2.5$, we round the value 2.5 up to the next whole number, 3. Then, locating the 3rd data score, 30, we conclude that $P_{10} = 30$.

A box-and-whisker plot is a graphical means of illustrating the dispersion of data using high and low scores and quartiles. Working with the following twenty-five data scores:

20, 29, 30, 46, 48, 55, 60, 67, 68, 70, 77, 77, 78, 79, 80, 81, 84, 84, 85, 86, 87, 88, 90, 96, 97

we have found that $Q_1 = 57.5$, $Q_2 = 78$, $Q_3 = 85.5$ and we determine the high score to be 97 and the low score to be 20. We form a box-and-whisker plot as shown in Figure 5.15.

**5.8.7
Box-and-Whisker
Plots**

Figure 5.15

First, we develop a number line that is labeled spanning the scores in the data set. We form a rectangular box stretching between Q_1 and Q_3. We then divide that rectangular box in two pieces, using the point where Q_2 is located. With the box completed, we create whiskers extending from the box to the points that indicate the high score and low score. This visual display of the high and low scores combined with the quartiles provides an immediate picture of where the top one-fourth of the scores lie, the bottom one-fourth of the scores lie, and where the middle point of the scores lie.

As a second example, suppose for a given data set the following statistics are determined: low score = 10, $Q_1 = 20$, $Q_2 = 40$, $Q_3 = 70$, and high score = 90. The box-and-whisker plot for this data set is shown in Figure 5.16.

From the illustration in Figure 5.16, we can see that one-fourth of the scores fall between 40 and 70. We can also conclude that one-fourth of the scores fall between 70 and 90. We can also see that half of the scores fall below 40. Thus, even without the original data, we can draw many conclusions about the dispersion of data from a box-and-whisker plot alone.

Figure 5.16

Representing Data

RELATED TOPICS

TOPIC 5.9 REPRESENTING DATA

CORNERSTONE | Statistical Concepts | Measures of Central Tendency | Data Dispersion

INTRODUCTION

Data can be represented in a variety of ways to clearly present information discovered in a statistical study. However, sometimes statistics and the way they are represented, can be used to mislead. In the nineteenth century, English prime minister Benjamin Disraeli stated that "there are three kinds of lies: lies, damned lies, and statistics." He was alluding to the fact that sometimes statistics can be used to deceive the general population. In this section, we examine a number of means of representing data including graphs such as pictographs, bar graphs, histograms, line graphs, scatterplots, stem-and-leaf plots, and circle graphs.

DID YOU KNOW?

Sometimes, without sufficient statistics, we can draw incorrect conclusions. Take, for example, the well-known headline, "Dewey Defeats Truman," printed in the *Chicago Daily Tribune* in 1948. This announcement about the winner of the presidential election involving Harry Truman and Thomas Dewey went to press before the final votes were counted. The article mistakenly naming Dewey as the winner was based on statistics gathered from voters as they exited the voting booths that election day. Even though the exit polls indicated that Dewey would win by a reasonable margin, this sample of data proved insufficient.

**5.9.1
Pictographs**

A **pictograph** is a graph in which pictures are used to represent data. There is usually a key that accompanies a pictograph that describes what a single picture represents. For example, consider the pictograph shown in Figure 5.17.

We see from the key that each picture of a person represents 1,000 students. From the pictograph we can infer that 2,000 students participated in a summer library reading program in Indiana; 4,000 students participated in a program in Tennessee. Notice that for Kentucky, there are three full pictures of a person plus a picture of half a man. We can interpret this part of the pictograph as indicating that 3,500 students participated in the program in Kentucky.

Figure 5.17

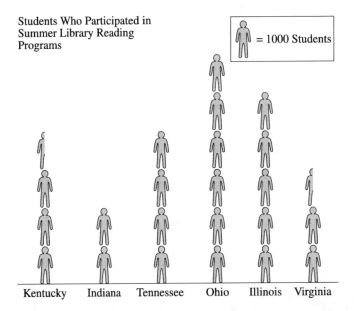

Students Who Participated in Summer Library Reading Programs

= 1000 Students

Kentucky   Indiana   Tennessee   Ohio   Illinois   Virginia

A **bar graph** provides a means of representing data that are categorized in some way. Typically, the horizontal scale represents the categories, numerical or nonnumerical, and the vertical scale represents the frequency of each category. For example, examine the bar graph depicted in Figure 5.18 that represents the favorite colors of elementary students.

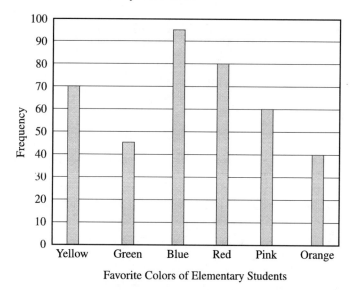

Favorite Colors of Elementary Students

Figure 5.18

From the bar graph we can see that blue is the most popular color among a sample of elementary students. From the vertical scale we can see that of the students surveyed, 95 selected blue as their favorite color.

Suppose we choose to label the vertical scale in Figure 5.18 differently. That is, instead of the scale increasing in increments of 10, the scale increases in increments of 40 (See Figure 5.19).

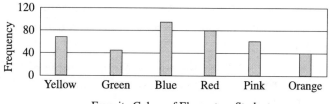

Favorite Colors of Elementary Students

Figure 5.19

Because the scale has changed, the differences in favorite color choices are not as striking. Thus, this example shows that the choice of scale can dramatically affect the appearance of a bar graph and the information you wish to display in the graph.

Bar graphs can also be presented so that the frequency is depicted along the horizontal axis. This type of graph would be referred to as a **horizontal bar graph** as opposed to the more typical **vertical bar graphs** where the frequency is shown along the vertical axis as in Figures 5.18 and 5.19. An example of a horizontal bar graph is seen in Figure 5.20 where we illustrate the same data as shown in Figures 5.18, but from the horizontal perspective.

A final possibility to consider with bar graphs are the concepts of **double bar graphs** or **triple bar graphs**. In these types of bar graphs, we can illustrate comparative data at several levels. For example, suppose we want to compare the number of alien sightings in various regions of the country across several decades. We can create a triple bar graph, like the one shown in Figure 5.21, to depict all of this information concisely.

Figure 5.20

Figure 5.21

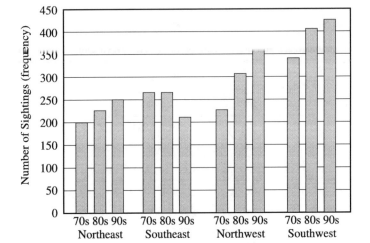

5.9.3
Frequency Tables

A way of categorizing raw data so that it is easier to interpret is to develop a **frequency table**. A basic frequency table has two columns, one denoting categories, or **classes**, of the data, and one denoting the **frequency**. The classes are most often created based on the raw data at hand and by how many categories into which you wish to break the data. For example, suppose the following set of data was gathered from 30 people surveyed about how many months they were engaged before they were married.

$$2 \quad 3 \quad 10 \quad 12 \quad 8 \quad 9 \quad 19 \quad 6 \quad 8 \quad 6$$
$$5 \quad 1 \quad 9 \quad 18 \quad 10 \quad 7 \quad 4 \quad 6 \quad 12 \quad 5$$
$$7 \quad 9 \quad 10 \quad 12 \quad 8 \quad 6 \quad 8 \quad 6 \quad 10 \quad 3$$

The data, as presented, are not very informative. However, if we break the data into categories, such as 0 – 2 months, 3 – 5 months, 6 – 8 months, etc., and then count how many responses fall into each category we can then see which category had the most responses and be better able to draw conclusions from the data. Using the categories suggested, we can form the frequency table shown in Table 5.11.

Looking at the classes, we refer to the first number in each class as the lower class limit and the last number as the upper class limit. Thus, in the class 9–11, 9 is the lower class limit and 11 is the upper class limit. Notice that the size of each class is the same. This is important when developing a frequency table. As a result, the difference between the lower class limit of one class and the lower class limit of the class that follows is always the same. The same can be said of

Table 5.11

Months Engaged	Frequency
0-2	2
3-5	5
6-8	11
9-11	7
12-14	3
15-17	0
18-20	2
	30

the difference between any two consecutive upper class limits. In this case, the difference between any two consecutive class limits is 3, indicating that each class is of size three.

Suppose you want to break the data into a particular number of, say n, classes. You can determine the size of each class by first determining the **range** of the data to be represented, and then dividing the range by n.

For example, if we decide we want to break the previous set of data into 5 classes, we first find the range, which is the high score minus the low score, in this case to be $19 - 1 = 18$. Then, we divide 18 by 5 and get 3.6. Rounding the quotient 3.6 up to the next higher whole number, 4, we then know to form classes with 4 in each class to guarantee that we will end up with 5 classes. Starting with the lowest data score, 1, we begin our first class, forming the first class 1–4 so that the class size is 4. Continuing in this manner, we form the frequency table shown in Table 5.12.

Note that no matter how many classes you break the data into, the total frequency, in this case 30, always reflects the total number of data items included in the study.

Table 5.12

Months Engaged	Frequency
1-4	5
5-8	13
9-12	10
13-16	0
17-21	2
	30

Histograms provide a means of representing data from a frequency table in a way that shows a consistent flow from one class to another. Unlike a bar graph where categories can be nonnumerical (like colors) and are shown as separate from each other along the horizontal axis, a histogram illustrates only numerical data and has a horizontal axis whose scale is not labeled by the separate categories, but by what we call the class mark. The class mark is the average of a particular class and serves as a representative of that class. To find the class mark, we compute:

$$\text{Class Mark} = \frac{\text{lower class limit} + \text{upper class limit}}{2}.$$

Table 5.13 illustrates a frequency table with a class mark column included. Notice, for example, that the first class mark was found by: $\frac{1+4}{2} = 2.5$. Also note that the difference between consecutive class marks is the same as the difference between consecutive upper class limits and lower class limits.

We will use these class marks to label the horizontal scale for our histogram. We let the vertical scale represent the frequency from the frequency table. From the frequency Table 5.13, we note that our frequency scale needs to span frequencies from 0 to 13. Thus, we can form a histogram that represents data in our frequency table as in Figure 5.22.

5.9.4
Histograms

Figure 5.22

Months Engaged	Frequency	Class Mark
1-4	5	2.5
5-8	13	6.5
9-12	10	10.5
13-16	0	14.5
17-21	2	18.5

Table 5.13

Notice that in a histogram, unlike the bar graph, the bars showing the frequency for each class are adjoining, that is, there are no gaps between the bars. This illustrates the fact that in a frequency table, one category blends naturally into the next, leaving no gaps. In a frequency table, a data item fits into one and only one category and there is no possibility that a data item will not belong in one of the categories because we have left no gap between classes.

5.9.5
Line Graphs and Frequency Polygons

Line graphs, also known as **frequency polygons**, provide a different means of representing the same type of data that you can illustrate with a histogram. Line graphs (frequency polygons) illustrate frequency across a set of continuous numerical data. Because the scale along the horizontal axis of a histogram is designed so as to show the continuity of numerical classes without gaps or breaks, we can form a line graph from any histogram.

From the histogram in Figure 5.22, we have formed a corresponding line graph in Figure 5.23. Notice that to form the line graph, we identify the midpoint of the top side of each of the rectangles in the histogram with a point and then connect the points to form the line graph.

Figure 5.23

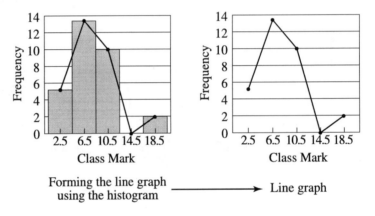

Forming the line graph using the histogram ⟶ Line graph

5.9.6
Line Graphs and Scatter Plots

A line graph does not have to be formed from a histogram. Whenever the horizontal axis represents continuous numerical data such as time, temperature, distances, etc., we can use lines to connect key data points. For example, when you have gathered **paired data**, that is, two pieces of corresponding data items from each source, we can compare those data items using a line graph. This is much like graphing coordinate points in the plane (see topics on Coordinate Graphing). For example, suppose you have gathered data on the size of the freshmen class at Jones University for the years 1990–1999 to attempt to note any trends across the decade. For each year, there is a corresponding data piece that indicates the size of the freshmen class that year. This paired data may be presented as ordered pairs (x, y) or in a table as shown in Table 5.14.

Using these paired data, we can let the horizontal axis represent the year and the vertical axis represent the sizes of the freshmen classes. Doing this, we can place points that correspond to each pair of data and then connect the points, forming the line graph as seen in Figure 5.24.

From a line graph, we can observe changes and trends quite readily. For example, we can observe that the size of the freshmen class dropped more dramatically from 1992 to 1993 than it dropped from 1990 to 1991. We can also

Table 5.14

Year	Number of Freshmen
1990	2500
1991	2480
1992	2400
1993	2200
1994	2350
1995	2600
1996	2550
1997	2700
1998	2780
1999	2900

observe that the most dramatic increase occurred between 1994 and 1995. We make this observation based on the steepness of the slope of the line connecting the points between those two years.

Scatterplots are also formed from paired data, but they are different from line graphs. A line graph is formed when you have for each numerical category that appears in the horizontal scales, exactly one corresponding numerical value along the vertical scale. Thus, when showing the points that correspond to each set of paired data, we would never have two or more points in the same row or column in the graph. For example, in the year 1995 in the data set in Table 5.14, there is only one corresponding piece of data, the 2600 students in the freshmen class.

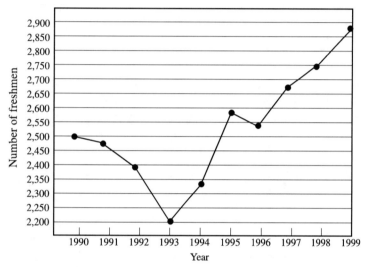

Figure 5.24

A **scatterplot** represents paired data that are collected from a number of sources through which we hope to determine whether there is some connection between the two types of data collected. For example, suppose we want to determine if there is any relationship between the number of hours a student studies for an exam and the resulting exam score. We suspect that the more students study, the higher the exam scores will be, but we need to gather data from students.

Consider the paired data shown in Table 5.15 that were gathered from 25 students. Each student provided two pieces of data, exam score and the amount of time spent studying (in hours).

Exam Score	55	60	99	87	66	88	45	77	69	81	76	75	90	92	30	78	85	96	70	25	59	92	80	84	74	Table 5.15
Study Time	2	3	6	4	3	4	1	3.5	2.5	3	2.5	2.5	7	6.5	1	3	3.5	6	2.5	2	2	6	4	1	4	

If we plot the pairs of points, labeling the horizontal axis with the range of exam scores and labeling the vertical axis with the range of study times. Plotting each point of paired data, we form the scatterplot shown in Figure 5.25.

Once we have plotted the points of our scatterplot, we try to determine if there is any relationship between time spent studying and score on the exam. Through the set of points, we draw a line that best shows the trend of the points.

We call this line the **line of best fit**. A line of best fit is determined by imposing a line through the plotted points so that most points lie on the line, just above the line, or just below the line. Figure 5.26 demonstrates a possible line of best fit for the scatterplot.

Figure 5.25

Figure 5.26

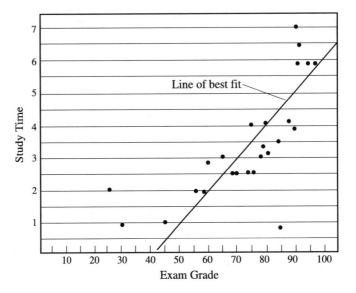

Notice while most of the points cluster around the line of best fit, either above or below the line, there are some data points that lie far away from the line. For example, notice the point that represents the student who earned a grade of 85 on the exam, but only studied 1 hour. Because this point lies far from the line of best fit, we call this point an **outlier**. There are usually some explanations as to why some points are outliers. For example, the student who only studied 1 hour but scored an 85 on the exam may have taken the course before, thus may not require as much study time before the exam.

With scatterplots, we usually try to see if there is some sort of **correlation** between the two types of data items that are being compared. We say there is a **positive correlation** if the line of best fit has a positive slope, that is if the line tends upward as we trace it from left to right.

The line of best fit in Figure 5.26 has a positive slope, therefore we can conclude from these data that there is a positive correlation between the amount of time spent studying and exam scores.

If the line of best fit has a negative slope—that is, it tends downward as we trace the line from left to right—then we say that there is a negative correlation. If we cannot identify any line of best fit among the points, then we say there is no correlation (See Figure 5.27).

Positive Correlation

Negative Correlation

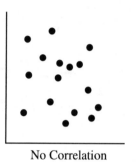
No Correlation

Figure 5.27

When we want to represent data so that we can immediately see how one category of data compares to the other categories of data, we can use a **circle graph**, also known as a **pie chart**. To form a circle graph (pie chart), we need to determine what part of the whole set of data each category represents. One way of developing a circle graph is to work from a frequency table (see Table 5.16) and develop a new column called the **relative frequency**.

5.9.7
Circle Graphs/
Pie Charts

Months Engaged	Frequency	Relative Frequency
1-4	5	5/30 = 0.17 = 17%
5-8	13	13/30 = 0.43 = 43%
9-12	10	10/30 = 0.33 = 33%
13-16	0	0/30 = 0.00 = 0%
17-21	2	2/30 = 0.07 = 7%
	30	30/30 = 1.00 = 100%

Table 5.16

The relative frequency shows how frequently that category occurs relative to all of the categories combined. The relative frequency of a category is found by dividing the frequency of that category by the total frequency. Relative frequency can be expressed as a fraction, a decimal number, or a percent. The sum of relative frequencies should be 1 or 100%.

We can use the relative frequencies to form a circle graph by breaking the circle into parts defined by the relative frequencies; that is, we want to break the circle into sections so that 33% of the circle is shown to represent the category of engagements from 9 to 12 months. To do so, we have to use the fact that the total number of degrees around the center point of a circle is 360 degrees (360°). Then, to determine the central angle of the section to represent the category 9–12 months, we would have to find 33% of 360°. Computing, we find:

$$33\% \text{ of } 360° = .33 \times 360 = 118.8°.$$

Thus, the central angle of the section representing the category of 9–12 months will be 118.8°.

Table 5.17 shows the computation of the central angles for all of the sections to be shown in the circle graph.

Table 5.17	Months Engaged	Frequency	Relative Frequency	Central Angle Measure (in degrees)
	1-4	5	5/30 = 0.17 = 17%	0.17 × 360 = 61.2
	5-8	13	13/30 = 0.43 = 43%	0.43 × 360 = 154.8
	9-12	10	10/30 = 0.33 = 33%	0.33 × 360 = 118.8
	13-16	0	0/30 = 0.00 = 0%	0.00 × 360 = 0
	17-21	2	2/30 = 0.07 = 7%	0.07 × 360 = 25.2
		30	30/30 = 1.00 = 100%	360.0

Figure 5.26

Number of Months Engaged Before Being Married

*Note: No one surveyed was engaged between 13 and 15 months before being married.

Finally, using the central angle measures from each category, we can form our circle graph with the appropriate central angle measures. We can label each section of the circle graph by its class (see Figure 5.28).

With circle graphs, it is important to indicate that a category whose frequency is 0 is not ignored. Thus, a note indicating why a region for that category is not shown is appropriate.

5.9.8
Stem-and-Leaf Plots

When you have a collection of numerical data, one way to organize the data for examination and interpretation is through a stem-and-leaf plot. A **stem-and-leaf plot** is a chart that shows two columns, the left column representing stems of data pieces and the right column representing leafs; that is, if a number of numerical data items happen to have a common first digit, or common first few digits, we can let the common digits be the stems shown in the left column. Then, the leaves, shown in the right column, show the various differentiation's among numbers with the same stem.

For example, suppose we have the following pieces of data representing test scores:

35, 79, 66, 80, 90, 91, 92, 88, 86, 46, 77, 76, 65, 70, 59, 92, 83, 61, 62, 71, 85, 89, 75, 84.

We can present these data items in a stem-and-leaf plot as shown:

Stem	Leaf
3	5
4	6
5	9
6	1, 2, 5, 6
7	0, 1, 5, 6, 7, 9
8	0, 3, 4, 5, 6, 8, 9
9	0, 1, 2, 2

In this stem-and-leaf plot, the stems represent the first digit of the test scores and the leaves represent the second digit. From this plot, it is easy to discern how many students scored in the 60's range, in the 70's range, in the 80's range, etc. We can also notice where there were two similar scores, such as the two scores of 92 as evidenced by the repeating leaves in the 9's stem row.

Stem-and-leaf plots can have more than one digit in the stem column. For example, suppose we did a survey of people at a local park, asking them what year they were born. The stem-and-leaf plot shows those years, with a stem that is 3-digits long.

From the stem-and-leaf plot we might conclude that at the time we con-

Stem	Leaf
193	0, 1, 5
194	3, 3, 5, 6
195	2, 3, 3, 4, 6, 7, 8
196	0, 1, 2, 2, 3, 6, 7, 7, 8, 8, 9
197	4, 5, 6, 6, 8
198	2, 2, 4, 7, 9
199	0, 0, 1, 1, 2, 3, 3, 3, 4, 4, 5, 6, 6, 6, 7, 8, 8

ducted the survey, there were mostly people born in the years 1990 to 1998, probably children, and then secondly people born in the years 1960 to 1969, most likely parents of some of the children.

Note that the leaves in stem-and-leaf plots do not have to be a single digit. They may be multidigited, but keep in mind that for ease of quickly reading and interpreting data in a stem-and-leaf plot, it is best not to have leaves that are too lengthy.

Coordinate Graphing | Angle Measure | Fractions | Decimals | Percents   **RELATED TOPICS**

IN THE CLASSROOM

Some expectations of your future students

**Pre-K-2
(NCTM, 2000,
p. 108)**

pose questions and gather data about themselves and their surroundings

sort and classify objects according to their attributes and organize data about the objects

represent data using concrete objects, pictures, and graphs

describe parts of the data and the set of data as a whole to determine what the data show

discuss events related to students' experiences as likely or unlikely

**Grades 3-5
(NCTM, 2000,
p. 176)**

describe the shape and important features of a set of data and compare related data sets, with an emphasis on how the data are distributed

propose and justify conclusions and predictions that are based on data and design studies to further investigate the conclusions and predictions

understand that the measure of the likelihood of an event can be represented by a number from 0 to 1

This chapter focuses on the *Data Analysis and Probability Content Standard.* "The increased curricular emphasis on data analysis proposed ... is intended to span the grades rather than be reserved for the middle grades and secondary school" (NCTM, 2000, p. 48). Given this emphasis, we believe that you should construct an understanding of some basic (a) principals underlying the concept of probability (Activities 5.1-5.5), (b) counting principals to enable efficient calculation of probability (Activity 5.6), and (c) concepts of statistics and the use of sample data (Activities 5.7-5.11).

How Activities 5.1-5.11 help you develop an adult-level perspective on the above expectations.

- By building on your current concepts of probability, you formalize a definition of probability and understand why probability values are between 0 and 1.

- By making predictions and conducting experiments to test your predictions, you construct an understanding of theoretical versus experimental probability and of sample space (what could happen) versus observed data.

- By systematizing ways of displaying the sample space, you analyze how multi-stage/step events could occur and explore the concept of independent versus dependent stages. You realize efficient techniques are essential for counting the ways such events could occur as the number of stages and options at each stage increase and you learn such techniques.

- By analyzing sample data taken from experiences you can relate to, you study important features of a sample and compare samples from the same population. You make predictions about the features of the population by building on your prior understanding of the connections between experimental and theoretical probability.

- By understanding the differences between paired and unpaired sets of data you continue to build on your concept of dependent versus independent events. You learn graphical representations suitable for displaying different kinds of data and how to interpret them.

- By discussing and studying different statistical reports—questions asked, sampling methods used, and what and how statistics are reported—you begin to develop a critical awareness of issues underlying the design of a statistical study. You learn to question and better understand reported studies as well as to justify studies you design and the conclusions you draw from sample data.

BIBLIOGRAPHY

Bryan, E. H. (1988). Exploring data with box plots. *Mathematics Teacher, 81*, 658-663.

Burrill, G., Burrill, J. C., Coffield, P., Davis, G., de Lange, J., Resnick, D., & Siegel, M. (1992). *Data analysis and statistics across the curriculum: Addenda series, grades 9-12.* Reston, VA: National Council of Teachers of Mathematics.

Corwin, R. B., & Friel, S. N. (1990). *Statistics: Prediction and sampling.* (A unit of study for grades 5-6 from *Used numbers: Real data in the classroom*). Palo Alto, CA: Dale Seymour.

Curcio, F. R., Nimerofsky, B., Perez, R., & Yaloz-Femia, S. (1998). Developing concepts in probability: Designing and analyzing games. In L. P. Leutzinger (Ed.), *Mathematics in the middle* (pp. 206-211). Reston, VA: National Council of Teachers of Mathematics.

Dessart, D. J. (1995). Randomness: A connection to reality. In P. A. House (Ed.), *Connecting mathematics across the curriculum* (pp. 177-181). Reston, VA: National Council of Teachers of Mathematics.

Elementary Quantitative Literacy Project (1998). *Exploring statistics in the elementary grades: Book 1 (K-6).* White Plains, NY: Cuisenaire-Dale Seymour.

Friel, S. N., Mokros, J. R., & Russell, S. J. (1992). *Middles, means, and in-between.* (A unit of study for grades 5 - from *Used numbers: Real data in the classroom*). Palo Alto, CA: Dale Seymour.

Friel, S. H., & Corwin, R. B. (1990). Implementing the *Standards*: The statistics standards in *K-8* mathematics. *Arithmetic Teacher 38*, 35-39.

Goldman, P. H. (1990). Teaching arithmetic averaging: An activity approach. *Arithmetic Teacher, 37*(7), 38-43.

Hatfield, L. L. (1992). Activities: Explorations with chance. *Mathematics Teacher , 85*, 280-282, 288-290.

Hollingdale, S. (1994). *Makers of mathematics.* New York: Penguin Books.

Huff, W. D. (1954). *How to lie with statistics.* New York: Norton.

Jones, G. A., Thornton, C. A., Langrall, C. W., & Tarr, J. E. (1999). Understanding students' probabilistic reasoning. In L. V. Stiff (Ed.), *Developing mathematical reasoning in grades K-12* (pp. 146-155). Reston, VA: National Council of Teachers of Mathematics.

Jones, K. S. (1993). The birthday problem again. *Mathematics Teacher, 86*, 373-377.

Landwehr, J. M., & Watkins, A. E. (1987). *Exploring data: Quantitative literacy series.* Palo Alto, CA: Dale Seymour.

Leutzinger, L. P. (1990). Graphical representation and probability. In J. N. Payne (Ed.), *Mathematics for the young child* (pp. 251-263). Reston, VA: National Council of Teachers of Mathematics.

Lindquist, M. M. (1992). *Making sense of data: Addenda series, grades K-6.* Reston, VA: National Council of Teachers of Mathematics.

Manin, H. M., & Zawojewski, J. S. (1993). Dealing with data and chance: An illustration from the middle school addendum to the *Standards. Arithmetic Teacher, 41*, 220-223.

May, E. L., Jr. (1992). Are seven-game baseball playoffs fairer? *Mathematics Teacher, 85*, 528-531.

National Council of Teachers of Mathematics. (1990). Data analysis: Focus issue. *Mathematics Teacher, 83*(2).

Newman, C. M., Obremski, T. E., & Schaeffer, R. L. (1987). *Exploring probability: Quantitative literacy series.* Palo Alto, CA: Dale Seymour.

Orkin, M. (1996). *Can you win?: The real odds for casino gambling, Sport betting, and lotteries.* New York: Freeman.

Parker, J., & Widmer, C. C. (1992). Teaching mathematics with technology: Statistics and graphing. *Arithmetic Teacher, 39*, 48-52.

Phillips, E., Lappan, G., Winter, M J., & Fitzgerald, W. (1986). *Middle grades mathematics project: Probability.* Menlo Park, CA: Addison-Wesley.

Porter, M. T. (1986). *The rise of statistical thinking 1820- 1900.* Princeton, NJ: Princeton University Press.

Richbart, L., & Richbart, C. (1992). Trading Alfs for a Bart: A simulation. *Arithmetic Teacher, 40*, 112- 114.

Russell, S. J., & Corwin, R. B. (1989). *Statistics: The shape of the data.* (A unit of study for grades 4-6 from *Used numbers: Real data in the classroom*). Palo Alto, CA: Dale Seymour.

Russell, S. J., & Friel, S. N. (1989). Collecting and analyzing real data in the elementary classroom. In P. R. Trafton (Ed.), *New directions for elementary school mathematics* (pp. 134-148) . Reston, VA: National Council of Teachers of Mathematics.

Schule, H. S., & Leonard, B. (1989). Probability and intuition. *Mathematics Teacher, 82*, 52-53.

Shaughnessy, J. M., & Dick, T. (1991). Monty's dilemma: Should you stick or switch? *Mathematics Teacher, 84*, 252-256.

Uccellini, J. C. (1996). Teaching the mean meaningfully. *Mathematics Teaching in the Middle Grades, 2*, 112-115.

Zawojewski, J. (1992). *Dealing with data and chance: Addenda series, grades 5-8.* Reston, VA: National Council of Teachers of Mathematics.

6 FRACTION MODELS & OPERATIONS

CHAPTER OVERVIEW

Many real-world situations require the use of fractions. It is important for anyone who will teach fraction concepts and procedures to children to have a deep understanding of fractions models and operations. In this chapter you can learn some interesting facts about fractions, and examine some concepts and procedures involving fraction ideas.

BIG MATHEMATICAL IDEAS

- Problem-solving Strategies
- Conjecturing
- Verifying
- Decomposing
- Generalizing
- Using Language and Symbolism
- Mathematical Structure

NCTM PRINCIPLES & STANDARDS LINKS

Number and Operation
Problem Solving
Reasoning
Communication
Connections
Representation

TOPIC

6.1 Fractions

6.2 Equivalent Fractions

6.3 Simplifying Fractions

6.4 Improper Fractions and Mixed Numbers

In the Classroom

Bibliography

TOPIC 6.1 FRACTIONS

The word **fraction** is commonly used today to denote some part of a whole. Although the idea of fractions has been known for quite awhile, it took a long time to develop the form we use today to write fractions. The word "fraction" itself comes from a Latin word, **fractus**, which means "to break." In the next few sections, we examine the meanings of fractions and their representations.

INTRODUCTION

DID YOU KNOW?

The earliest accounts of the use of fractional quantities on a wide and practical scale come from Egypt (about 1600 B.C.), where they appeared on a roll of leather that dates back to the same time as the Ahmes Papyrus, the most important source of our knowledge of Egyptian mathematics. This roll of leather is a mathematical table that consists of decompositions of fractions into unit fractions (the single exception was $\frac{2}{3}$). Unit fractions are fractions that have 1 in the numerator. The Egyptians developed a means of writing unit fractions, decomposing all other fractions into them, and developing elaborate tables that listed such decompositions.

Egyptian fractions appear in the form of hieroglyphics (pictorial symbols for numerals which we discussed in topics related to numeration) representing unit fractions. For example, we have the following unit fractions (Figure 6.1) written as hieroglyphics.

The Egyptians used fractions for very practical purposes. They did not have a monetary system, and trade was based on a barter system of exchange of goods. This probably led them into developing a system of operations with fractions. While the Egyptians did not work with the modern techniques of operations of fractions, their rather complex system of such operations worked remarkably well for them.

Later, fractions appear in the work of the Hindu mathematician, Brahmagupta, who lived around A.D. 598-c. 665. The Hindus wrote fractions by placing integers one on top of another, without a bar between them. The Arabs are credited with the present way of writing down a fraction with a bar placed between the two integers. Sources from these two civilizations show that both of them knew how to divide a fraction by another by inverting the divisor. The techniques somehow mysteriously disappeared until the seventeenth century, but thereafter has come to stay as a useful tool in operations with fractions.

Figure 6.1

$\frac{1}{3} =$ ⊓⊓⊓ $\frac{1}{12} =$ ⊓⊓⊓ $\frac{1}{21} =$ ⊓⊓⊓

For More Information: Smith, D. E. (1958). *History of mathematics, Volume II.* New York: Dover Publications.

A fraction is a representation of a number of the form $\frac{a}{b}$ where a and b can be any numbers. The top number, a, is called the numerator and the bottom number, b, is the denominator. A fraction can have one of three meanings: (a) a part of a whole, (b) a ratio, or (c) the quotient in a division problem.

When a fraction represents **part of a whole**, the denominator represents the number of equal-sized pieces that the whole has been divided into whereas the numerator indicates how many of those pieces we are considering at that time. For example, the fraction $\frac{4}{5}$ suggests that some whole, lets say a rectangular region, has been divided into 5 equal-sized pieces. The numerator, 4, suggests that we are interested in only 4 of the 5 pieces. See Figures 6.2 and 6.3.

6.1.1
Fractions
Representing
Part of a Whole

Figure 6.2
A whole region divided into
five equal-sized pieces

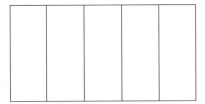

Figure 6.3
Illustrating $\frac{4}{5}$ of the whole by equal
shading in 4 of the 5 pieces

Figure 6.4
One whole region divided
into 3 equal-sized pieces

Figure 6.5
Two whole regions broken
into 3 equal-sized pieces
with 4 of those pieces
shaded to represent $\frac{4}{5}$

6.1.2
Fractions
Representing Ratios

A fraction also can represent a **ratio**. A ratio is a comparison of two or more quantities. In a typical fraction with a numerator over a denominator, the amount in the numerator is being compared to the amount in the denominator. For example, if there are 30 students in a class and 10 of those students are male and 20 are female, the ratio of males to females could be expressed as 10 to 20, 10:20 or $\frac{10}{20}$. Thus, the fraction $\frac{10}{20}$ does not represent part of the whole in this situation. Rather, the ratio of 10 to 20 indicates that there are twice as many women in the class as men.

6.1.3
Fractions as
Representing a
Division Problem

Fractions sometimes simply represent a **quotient**. For example, when computing the division problem 27 ÷ 4, the answer can be expressed as $\frac{27}{4}$ or $6\frac{3}{4}$. Because of this interpretation of fractions, students often learn to interpret the bar that separates the numerator from the denominator as a division sign.

RELATED TOPICS   Rational Numbers | The Set of Rational Numbers | Equivalent Fractions
Simplifying Fractions | Improper Fractions and Mixed Numbers
Adding Rational Numbers | Subtracting Rational Numbers
Multiplying Rational Numbers | Dividing Rational Numbers | Ratios

TOPIC 6.2 EQUIVALENT FRACTIONS

Fractions | Rational Numbers | Integer Multiplication | Integer Division
Least Common Multiple | Divisibility | Greatest Common Divisor
Prime Factorization

INTRODUCTION

Equivalent fractions are fractions that represent the same value. Equivalent fractions are extremely useful when adding and subtracting fractions because we often have to find a common denominator before we can perform the operation. An equivalent fraction, with the correct denominator, is a key to engaging in addition and subtraction. Equivalent fractions also help us solve proportion problems and help us find multiple representations of a particular fraction. In this topic set, we explore equivalent fractions and methods for determining equivalent fractions.

DID YOU KNOW?

The notion of equivalent fractions as we currently understand and express them took some time to develop. Although the Egyptians had developed a means of representing unit fractions, they had no means of representing other types of fractions, except the fraction $\frac{2}{3}$. Thus, they certainly had no means of expressing a fractional amount in more than one way.

In Renaissance times, Arabs developed a method of representing fractions that occasionally used Roman numerals like $\frac{IX}{XI}$ to represent $\frac{9}{11}$. Because the Roman Numeration system does allow for some multiple representation of whole numbers, it is conceivable that Arabian fractions expressed with Roman numerals may have resulted in multiple representations of fractions. For example, because the number 49 can be represented in Roman numerals as IL or XLIX, the fractional representation of $\frac{1}{49}$ could have been either $\frac{1}{IL}$ or $\frac{1}{XLIX}$. Although this multiple representation of a fraction differs greatly from our current notion of equivalent fractions, it does provide some sense of the evolution of the concept of equivalent fractions

For More Information: Smith, D. E. (1958). *History of mathematics, Volume II*. New York: Dover Publications.

6.2.1
Finding Equivalent Fractions

Given a fraction $\frac{a}{b}$, we can find fractions equivalent to $\frac{a}{b}$ by multiplying or dividing both the numerator and denominator by the same nonzero number; that is, fractions of the form $\frac{a \times k}{b \times k}$ or $\frac{a \div k}{b \div k}$, provided $k \neq 0$ are equivalent to $\frac{a}{b}$. To generate a list of fractions equivalent to $\frac{2}{3}$, we could easily multiply both numerator and denominator by the natural numbers, generating the following list of equivalent fractions:

$$\frac{2}{3}, \frac{2 \times 2}{2 \times 3} = \frac{4}{6}, \frac{3 \times 2}{3 \times 3} = \frac{6}{9}, \frac{4 \times 2}{4 \times 3} = \frac{8}{12}, \frac{5 \times 2}{5 \times 3} = \frac{10}{15}, \frac{6 \times 2}{6 \times 3} = \frac{12}{18}, \text{ and so on.}$$

6.2.2
Testing Whether Fractions are Equivalent

There are a variety of ways to determine whether two given fractions are equivalent. One way would be to **find a common denominator** between the two fractions, rewrite each fraction using the common denominator, and then compare numerators to see if they are also the same. For example, to check whether $\frac{3}{8}$ is equivalent to $\frac{5}{12}$, first rewrite each fraction using the common denominator of 24: $\frac{3}{8} = \frac{9}{24}$, and $\frac{5}{12} = \frac{10}{24}$. Clearly the numerators differ, thus the two fractions are not equivalent.

Another method of testing whether two fractions are equivalent is **cross-multiplication**; that is, $\frac{a}{b} = \frac{c}{d}$ if $ad = bc$. So, given the fractions, $\frac{4}{5}$ and $\frac{7}{8}$, we can verify that they are not equivalent because $4 \times 8 \neq 5 \times 7$. Using the cross-multiplication method is essentially a "short-cut" to the common denominator method described above. For example, if we were to find a common denominator for $\frac{4}{5}$ and $\frac{7}{8}$, we might choose 5×8 or 40 as the common denominator. To convert these fractions to forms with this common denominator, we would multiply numerator and denominator of $\frac{4}{5}$ by 8 and numerator and denominator of $\frac{7}{8}$ by 5: $\frac{8 \times 4}{8 \times 5} = \frac{32}{40}$ and $\frac{5 \times 7}{5 \times 8} = \frac{35}{40}$.

Notice that when we compare numerators, we are checking whether the products 4×8 and 5×7 are equal. These are the same products we checked when using the cross-multiplication method. Thus, cross-multiplication provides a quick way of checking whether or not fractions would have the same numerator if we were to convert them to fractions having a common denominator.

6.2.3
Ordering Fractions

When placing fractions in order from smallest to largest or largest to smallest, we can use the same methods we used to compare fractions to check for equivalence; that is, to order a set of fractions from smallest to largest, we could first **find a common denominator** that they all share and then compare numerators to place them in order. If there is a large set of fractions to order, this could be a time-consuming, although effective, approach.

Using a variation of the **cross-multiplication method** is a useful means of comparing and ordering fractions. Given two fractions $\frac{a}{b}$ and $\frac{c}{d}$, we say that $\frac{a}{b} < \frac{c}{d}$ if $ad < bc$. Similarly, $\frac{a}{b} > \frac{c}{d}$ if $ad > bc$. Thus, we can verify that $\frac{3}{2} > \frac{5}{4}$ because $3 \times 4 > 2 \times 5$.

RELATED TOPICS   The Set of Rational Numbers | Simplifying Fractions
Improper Fractions and Mixed Numbers | Adding Rational Numbers
Subtracting Rational Numbers | Multiplying Rational Numbers
Dividing Rational Numbers Ratios

TOPIC 6.3 SIMPLIFYING FRACTIONS

INTRODUCTION

Many people believe that simpler is better. Consequently, they often try to simplify their lives, frequently by making "big jobs" smaller. This idea of simplification transfers to working with fractions; that is, rather than manipulate fractions that involve large numbers, it is preferable for most people to simplify fractions to equivalent versions using smaller numbers. In the following sections, we examine the process of simplification of fractions.

DID YOU KNOW?

Until the early 1900's, the simplification (or reduction) of a fraction to lower or lowest terms was commonly known as *abbreviation*. The word *depression* was also used.

Today we use simplified fractions in our everyday conversations. For example, when you want to order a half of a pound of cheese at the deli, it is unconventional to say, "I'll have $\frac{6}{12}$ of a pound of cheese." Simplified fractions are easier for us to work with because we can more readily picture part of a whole if that whole is broken in a small number of equal-sized pieces.

**6.3.1
Relatively Prime**

A fraction is in **simplest form** when the numerator and denominator are **relatively prime**, that is, when the numerator and denominator have no factors in common other than 1. Thus, the fraction $\frac{5}{6}$ is in simplest form because 5 and 6 have no factors in common other than 1. On the other hand, the fraction $\frac{8}{12}$ is not in simplest form because 8 and 12 share a common factor of 4, which means this fraction can be simplified further.

**6.3.2
Simplifying Fractions
by Looking for
Common Factors**

One means of simplifying a fraction is to look for **factors that the numerator and denominator share**. We can simplify a fraction by dividing numerator and denominator by any factor that they have in common (other than 1). Often, students determine a factor the numerator and the denominator share either by recognizing something they have in common based on experience or by using divisibility tests to check what factors they might share. In the case of the fraction $\frac{12}{18}$, students might notice that 18 and 12 both share 2 as a factor, so they will divide both numerator and denominator by 2 and reduce the fraction to $\frac{6}{9}$. Students might then notice that 6 and 9 have a common factor of 3 and so divide numerator and denominator by 3, reducing the fraction further to $\frac{2}{3}$. Because 2 and 3 have no factors other than 1 in common, we can conclude that the fraction is now in simplest form.

Rather than reduce a fraction in multiple steps as in the above example, a more efficient method of reducing a fraction to simplest form is to determine the **greatest common factor** that the numerator and denominator share and to divide both by this factor to find simplest form in one step. Thus, for the fraction $\frac{12}{18}$, the greatest common factor of 12 and 18 is 6. Dividing numerator and denominator by 6 reduces the fraction to its simplest form of $\frac{2}{3}$ in one step.

**6.3.3
Simplifying
Fractions
Using Prime
Factorization**

Another method of reducing fractions to simplest form is to find the prime factorizations of the numerator and denominator and factor out all prime factors that the two numbers share. For example, the fraction $\frac{24}{36}$ can be written in prime factorization as $\frac{2 \times 2 \times 2 \times 3}{2 \times 2 \times 3 \times 3}$. Noticing that the numerator and the denominator share two 2s and one 3 as prime factors, one can divide by those factors, or cancel out pairs of those prime factors that appear in numerator and denominator, to yield a simplified form of $\frac{2}{3}$.

RELATED TOPICS   The Set of Rational Numbers | Equivalent Fractions
Improper Fractions and Mixed Numbers | Adding Rational Numbers
Subtracting Rational Numbers | Multiplying Rational Numbers
Dividing Rational Numbers Ratios

TOPIC 6.4 IMPROPER FRACTIONS AND MIXED NUMBERS

Fractions | Rational Numbers | Integer Multiplication | Integer Division
Least Common Multiple | Divisibility | Greatest Common Divisor
Prime Factorization

CORNERSTONE

INTRODUCTION

Too often people restrict their image of fractions to fractions between 0 and 1. There are an infinite number of fractions that can be represented as improper fractions or mixed numbers. Fractions that must be represented by mixed number or improper fractions are those that fall between any two integers other than between 0 and 1 or between 0 and −1. Between any two other integers, say between 3 and 4, the rational numbers on the number line will have a value of 3 plus some fractional part. For example, $3\frac{1}{3}$ or $3\frac{1}{2}$ would be between 3 and 4 on the number line. In the sections that follow, we examine mixed numbers and improper fractions and methods for converting fractions to such forms.

DID YOU KNOW?

Historically, the idea of mixed numbers took quite a while to develop. At first, cultures were only able to represent unit fractions, those of the form $\frac{1}{n}$, where n was some natural number. In the Middle Ages, these unit fractions were sometimes called "simple fractions" while the more general form were known as "composite fractions." The Babylonians were among the first to represent fractions other than unit fractions such as the fractions $\frac{2}{3}$, $\frac{2}{18}$, $\frac{4}{18}$, $\frac{5}{6}$ and other cases of a similar level of difficulty.

Fractions within the work of the Hindu mathematician, Brahmagupta, who lived around A.D. 598-c. 665, were among the first fractions to appear much like the fractions we write today. The Hindus wrote fractions by placing integers on top of each other, without a line between them. For example, the fraction $\frac{2}{3}$ would have been represented as $\frac{2}{3}$. The Hindus were also the first culture to represent mixed numbers. They represented mixed numbers using a type of compound fraction notation. For example, they would write the mixed number $1\frac{1}{3}$ as three integers being place one on top of the other: $\frac{1}{\frac{1}{3}}$

For More Information: Smith, D. E. (1958). *History of mathematics, Volume II.* New York: Dover Publications.

6.4.1 Improper Fractions and Mixed Numbers

Fractions with a numerator that is greater than the denominator are called **improper fractions**. Thus, improper fractions are positive fractions greater than 1 or negative fractions less than −1. Examples of improper fractions include $\frac{9}{7}$ and $-\frac{4}{3}$.

A **mixed number** is a number that has both a whole number and fractional component. Examples of mixed numbers include $3\frac{1}{2}$ and $-2\frac{2}{5}$. The word *and* is usually used in expressing the mixed number. For example, $3\frac{1}{2}$ would be expressed as "three and one-half," indicating that there are 3 wholes and $\frac{1}{2}$ of another whole.

It is sometimes useful to express an improper-fraction as a mixed-number or a mixed number as an improper fraction. Converting fractions back and forth from improper fraction to mixed number form is particularly helpful when preparing to perform operations with fractions and later simplifying results of operations with fractions.

6.4.2
Changing Mixed Numbers to Improper Fractions

To change a mixed number to an improper fraction, one should first rewrite the whole number part of the mixed number to an equivalent fraction form. The best choice of denominator would be the denominator of the fractional part of the mixed number. For example, with the mixed number $4\frac{2}{3}$, read as "four and two-thirds," one should first rewrite 4 as $\frac{12}{3}$. Then what we have instead of 4 and $\frac{2}{3}$ is $\frac{12}{3}$ and $\frac{2}{3}$ which can be computed as $\frac{12}{3} + \frac{2}{3} = \frac{14}{3}$.

In the case of a negative mixed number, such as $-2\frac{4}{5}$, one can express this number as negative "2 and $\frac{4}{5}$." Changing the whole number, 2, to $\frac{10}{5}$, we then have negative $\frac{10}{5}$ and $\frac{4}{5}$ or negative $\frac{10}{5} + \frac{4}{5}$ = negative $\frac{14}{5} = -\frac{14}{5}$.

In general, when you have a mixed number of the form $k\frac{a}{b}$, it can be expressed as an improper fraction using the following formula: $\frac{kb+a}{b}$. Revisiting the example of $4\frac{2}{3}$ used above, one can use the formula finding $4\frac{2}{3} = \frac{4\cdot3+2}{3} = \frac{14}{3}$. This formula essentially provides a shortcut to rewriting the whole number piece as a fraction using a common denominator with the fractional piece.

6.4.3
Changing Improper Fractions to Mixed Numbers

To change an improper fraction to a mixed number, one could view the fraction as a division problem. For instance, with the fraction $\frac{13}{4}$, we could divide 13 by 4 to determine how many times the number 4 goes into 13. Solving with long division, we find $13 \div 4 = 3$ with a remainder of 1. Viewing this remainder as a part of the number of times four goes into 13, we can express this remainder as the fractiond $\frac{1}{4}$. Thus, we can write the answer to the division problem $13 \div 4$ as $3\frac{1}{4}$. Thus, $\frac{13}{4} = 3\frac{1}{4}$.

In general, we can convert an improper fraction $\frac{k}{b} (k > b)$ to a mixed number using the long-division procedure. Thus, $k \div b = n\frac{a}{b}$, where n is some natural number, a is the remainder, and b is the divisor. For the improper fraction $\frac{16}{15}$, long division of $16 \div 5 = 1$ with a remainder of 1 suggests that s, $\frac{16}{15} = 1\frac{1}{15}$.

RELATED TOPICS   The Set of Rational Numbers | Equivalent Fractions | Simplifying Fractions
Adding Rational Numbers | Subtracting Rational Numbers
Multiplying Rational Numbers | Dividing Rational Numbers

IN THE CLASSROOM

The fourth of the five chapters whose focus is on the *Number and Operations Content Standard*, this chapter also emphasizes the *Representation Process Standard*. Given that "instructional programs from pre-kindergarten through grade 12 should enable all students to use representations to model and interpret physical, social, and mathematical phenomena" and that "representations should be treated as essential elements in supporting students' understanding of mathematical concepts and relationships" (NCTM, 2000, p. 67), we believe that you should develop a strong understanding of (a) the concept of fraction as dependent on knowing what constitutes the "one" (Activities 6.1-6.7), and (b) operations with fractions as extending prior concepts of arithmetic operations (Activities 6.8-6.16).

How Activities 6.1-6.16 help you develop an adult-level perspective on the above expectations.

- By examining fractional models and representations and relationships between them you develop an understanding of fraction as parts of the unit whole. You realize this understanding depends on understanding division as sharing equally.

- By working with different region models you develop the concepts of unit fractions and equivalent fractions and construct a deeper understanding of the relationship between the numerical representations of a fraction and the concept of the fraction.

- By using models appropriate to the context you associate meaning with each and become confident in making sense of problems which involve fractions. For example, you may use the set (discrete) model in the context of a number (discrete) of people, but the linear (continuous) model in the context of time (continuous) elapsed.

- By identifying the arithmetic operations involved and modeling them using different fractional models, you reinforce your understanding of the models of operations learned in Chapter 3. Misconceptions such as "multiplication always makes bigger" or "division always makes smaller" are thus challenged and replaced by models of operations that will encompass all real numbers.

Some expectations of your future students

Pre-K-2 (NCTM, 2000, p. 78)	connect number words and numerals to the quantities they represent using various physical models and representations
	understand and represent commonly used fractions such as $\frac{1}{4}$, $\frac{1}{3}$, and $\frac{1}{2}$
	understand situations that entail multiplication and division, such as equal groupings of objects and sharing equally
Grades 3-5 (NCTM, 2000, p. 148)	develop understanding of fractions as parts of unit wholes, as parts of a collection, as locations on number lines, and as divisions of whole numbers
	use models, benchmarks, and equivalent forms to judge the size of fractions
	use visual models, benchmarks, and equivalent forms to add and subtract commonly used fractions

BIBLIOGRAPHY

Behr, M. J., Post, T. R., & Wachsmuth, L. (1986). Estimation and children s concept of rational number size. In H. L. Schoen (Ed.), *Estimation and mental computation* (pp.103-111). Reston, VA: National Council of Teachers of Mathematics.

Bezuk, N. S. (1988). Fractions in the early childhood mathematics curriculum. *Arithmetic Teacher, 35,* 56-60.

Bezuk, N. S., & Bieck, M. (1993). Current research on rational numbers and common fractions: Summary and implications for teachers. In D. T. Owens (Ed*.), Research ideas for the classroom: Middle grades mathematics* (pp. 118-136). Old Tappan, NJ; Macmillan.

Bezuk, N. S., & Cramer, K. (1989). Teaching about fractions: What, when, and how? In P R. Trafton (Ed.), *New directions for elementary school mathematics* (pp. 156-161). Reston, VA: National Council of Teachers of Mathematics.

Cramer, K., & Bezuk, N. (1991). Multiplication of fractions: Teaching for understanding. *Arithmetic Teacher, 39,* 34-37.

Dorgan, K. (1994). What textbooks offer for instruction in fraction concepts. *Teaching Children Mathematics, 1,* 150-155.

Edge, D. (1987). Fractions and panes. *Arithmetic Teacher, 34,* 13-17.

Ettline, J. F. (1985). A uniform approach to fractions. *Arithmetic Teacher, 32,* 42-43.

Greenwood, J. (1989). Problem solving with fractions. *Mathematics Teacher, 82,* 44-50.

Hollis, L. Y. (1984). Teaching rational numbers—Primary grades. *Arithmetic Teacher, 31,* 36-39.

Howard, A. C. (1991). Addition of fractions: The unrecognized problem. *Mathematics Teacher, 84,* 710-713.

Kieren, T. E. (1984). Helping children understand rational numbers. *Arithmetic Teacher, 31,* 3.

Kieren, T., Davis, B., & Mason, R. (1996). Fraction flags: Learning from children to help children learn. *Mathematics Teaching in the Middle School, 2,* 14-19.

Lester, F. K. (1984). Preparing teachers to teach rational numbers. *Arithmetic Teacher 31,* 54-56.

Mack, N. K. (1993). Making connections to understand fractions. *Arithmetic Teacher, 40,* 362-364.

Moss, J., & Case, R. (1999). Developing children's understanding of the rational numbers: A new model and an experimental curriculum. *Journal for Research in Mathematics Education, 30,* 122-147.

Ockenga, E. (1984). Chalk up some calculator activities for rational numbers. *Arithmetic Teacher, 31, 51-53.*

Ott, J. M., Snook, D. L., & Gibson, D. L. (1991). Understanding partitive division of fractions. *Arithmetic Teacher, 39,* 7-11.

Post, T. R. & Cramer, K. (1987). Children's strategies in ordering rational numbers. *Arithmetic Teacher, 35,* 33-35.

Pothier, Y. & Sawada, D. (1990). Partitioning: An approach to fractions. *Arithmetic Teacher, 38,* 12- 16.

Sinicrope, R. & Mick, H. W. (1992). Multiplication of fractions through paper folding. *Arithmetic Teacher, 40,* 116- 121.

Skypek, D. H. B. (1984). Special characteristics of rational numbers. *Arithmetic Teacher, 31,* 10-12.

Steffe, L. P. & Olive, J. (1991). Research into practice: The problem of fractions in the elementary school. *Arithmetic Teacher, 38,* 22-24.

Trafton, P. R., & Zawojewski, J. S. (1984). Teaching rational number division: A special problem. *Arithmetic Teacher, 31*(6), 20-22.

Witherspoon, M. L. (1993). Fractions: In search of meaning. *Arithmetic Teacher, 10,* 482-485.

REAL NUMBERS: RATIONALS & IRRATIONALS

7

TOPIC

7.1	Ratio
7.2	Proportion
7.3	Introduction to Decimals
7.4	Decimals and Fractions
7.5	Terminating and Repeating Decimals
7.6	Decimal Addition and Subtraction
7.7	Decimal Multiplication
7.8	Decimal Division
7.9	Percent
7.10	Interest
7.11	Rational Numbers
7.12	Looking at Rational Numbers as the Set of Rational Numbers
7.13	Adding Rational Numbers
7.14	Subtracting Rational Numbers
7.15	Multiplying Rational Numbers
7.16	Dividing Rational Numbers
7.17	Irrational Numbers
7.18	Real Numbers
	In the Classroom
	Bibliography

CHAPTER OVERVIEW

As technology (especially calculators) becomes more and more prevalent for everyday use, as well as for scientific purposes, so does the use of decimals (and percent). At the same time, ratio and proportion are also quite useful to solve a variety of real-world problems. In this chapter you can learn some interesting facts about rational and irrational numbers, and examine some concepts and procedures involving real number ideas.

BIG MATHEMATICAL IDEAS

- Problem-solving Strategies
- Conjecturing
- Verifying
- Decomposing
- Generalizing
- Representation
- Using Language and Symbolism
- Limit
- Mathematical Structure

NCTM PRINCIPLES & STANDARDS LINKS

Number and Operation
Problem Solving
Reasoning
Communication
Connections
Representation

TOPIC 7.1 RATIO

CORNERSTONE	Fractions	Rational Numbers

INTRODUCTION

Whether you want to compute the speed we are driving or whether we need to figure out how much it would cost to purchase three sets of an item given that we know the cost of one set, we are working with ratios. In the following sections, you will learn the definition of a ratio and examine different types of ratios. You will also learn of some of the relationships between ratios and fractions.

DID YOU KNOW?

The **Golden Ratio** is a ratio that describes the relationship between the lengths of line segments formed when we divide a line segment *AB* into two segments at an interior point, P, between A and B so that the ratio of the length of *AB* to *AP* is equal to the ratio of the length of *AP* to *PB*. Dividing a line segment according to this ratio is said to create a division that the ancient Greeks thought was pleasing to the eye. Related to the Golden Ratio is the **Golden Rectangle**, which essentially is a rectangle divided into two sections, one a square and one a rectangle, so that the ratio of the sides of the rectangle is the Golden Ratio. Rectangular shapes that are Golden Rectangles are also said to be shapes that are pleasing to the eye. Many architectural designs are built according to the Golden Ratio. One such famous landmark of Greek architecture is the Parthenon.

For More Information: Bunt, L. N. H., Jones, P. S., & Bedient, J. D. (1988). *The historical roots of elementary mathematics*. New York: Dover Publications.

7.1.1
Definition of Ratio

A **ratio** is a comparison of two or more quantities. In most day-to-day situations, we generally compare two quantities. For example, in a classroom we might compare the number of boys in the classroom (which is 15) to the number of girls in a classroom (which is 10). We would say, the ratio of boys to girls is 15 to 10.

7.1.2
Ratio Notation

Ratios can be expressed several ways. One way to express the comparison of 15 boys in a classroom to 10 girls in a classroom is expressing the ratio using the word "to," saying the ratio is **15 to 10**. Instead of using the word *to* we often represent ratios using a colon symbol ":". Thus we can say the ratio is **15:10**. A final way to express a ratio is writing the ratio as a fraction where the numerator is one quantity be compared and the denominator is the other quantity. Thus, the ratio can be expressed $\frac{15}{10}$.

7.1.3
Types of Ratios

When comparing two quantities, we can create ratios of three different varieties. We can compare (1) part to a part, (2) part to a whole, or (3) whole to a part.

Comparing **a part to a part** takes place when we take a whole set and break it into two subsets to compare. For example, of the 500 employees at Mathematics Incorporated, 400 of the employees own foreign cars and 100 own domestic cars. Thus, we can talk about the ratio of foreign car owners to domestic car owners as 400:100.

Sometimes we compare a **part to a whole**. In the example of the employees at Mathematics Incorporated, we could say the ratio of foreign car owners to total employees is 400:500. We can also compare **a whole to a part.** For example, comparing the total number of employees to the number of domestic car owners is 500:100.

We often express ratios using the term *per* in the comparison. For example, when comparing how far we have traveled in a certain period of time, we often describe our speed in terms of miles per hour. Whenever we compare a given quantity to time, we are describing a **rate**. Some frequently used rates are comparisons of distance : time (speed), growth : time (growth rate), money earned : time (interest rate).

To compute a rate, such as speed, we can express the comparison of quantities as a ratio in fraction form, and perform the division suggested by the fraction representation to simplify the rate. For example, if I know I traveled 165 miles in 3 hours, I can compute my speed in terms of miles per hour (mph) as $\frac{165}{3} = 55$ mph.

Because one representation of a ratio is to express a ratio as a fraction, we should explore when we can manipulate ratios like fractions and when they should be treated differently. A key similarity between fractions and ratios is the notion of equivalence. Like finding equivalent fractions, we can find **equivalent ratios**, and we find them by multiplying or dividing numerator and denominator by the same non-zero amount; that is, given the ratio $\frac{a}{b}$, then for any real number, k, $k \neq 0$, $\frac{a}{b} = \frac{a \times k}{b \times k} = \frac{a \div k}{b \div k}$.

For example, if there are 200 men and 100 women at the movie theater, then the ratio of men to women at the movie theater is $\frac{200}{100}$. By dividing numerator and denominator by 100, we can simply say that the ratio of men to women at the movie theater is $\frac{2}{1}$, indicating that there are twice as many men as women.

A key difference between ratios and fractions is how we add them. For example, when adding fractions, we find a common denominator and then add numerators, placing the sum over the common denominator (see Adding Rational Numbers for more details and examples). For example, $\frac{2}{3} + \frac{1}{4} = \frac{8}{12} + \frac{3}{12} = \frac{11}{12}$.

On the other hand, in the **addition of ratios**, we sometimes add numerators and add denominators to create a new ratio. For example, suppose on a first quiz, a student earned 6 points out of 8 points possible. Thus, the ratio of points earned to total points possible is $\frac{6}{8}$. Then suppose on a second quiz this student earned 8 points out of 10 possible points. Thus the ratio of points earned to total possible points on the second quiz is $\frac{8}{10}$. Now if we want to compute the ratio of the total number of points earned on quizzes to total possible points, we can find the total number of points earned by adding the numerators of the ratios for each quiz, and then find the total number of points possible for the two quizzes by adding the denominators. We then find that the ratio of total points earned to total points possible on the two quizzes is: $\frac{6}{8} + \frac{8}{10} = \frac{14}{18}$.

Proportion | Percent

RELATED TOPICS

TOPIC 7.2 PROPORTION

INTRODUCTION

We encounter proportional relationships regularly. When we view models of the floor plans of a house or read maps, we have to understand the scale used to depict these models. The scale defines a proportional relationship between the model and the actual dimensions of the house or the actual distance between locations on a map. In the following sections, we learn what proportions are and how to solve proportions where some piece of information in a proportion is unknown.

DID YOU KNOW?

When solving a proportion, there are three knowns and one unknown. Historically, the three knowns were given many names. However, the process for using the three terms and arithmetically solving for the fourth term was known as the **Rule of Three**. This expression originated with the Hindus around the year A.D. 620. The Rule of Three was so important for solving mercantile problems that among merchants this rule of proportions became known as the **Golden Rule**.

For More Information: Smith, D. E. (1958). *History of mathematics, Volume II.* New York: Dover Publications.

**7.2.1
Definition of
Proportion**

A **proportion** is an equation where both expressions on either side of the equals sign are ratios; that is, if $\frac{a}{b}$ and $\frac{c}{d}$ are two ratios such that $\frac{a}{b} = \frac{c}{d}$, then this equality statement is called a proportion. Examples of proportions are: $\frac{1}{2} = \frac{3}{6}$, $\frac{2}{3} = \frac{10}{15}$, and $\frac{x}{x+1} = \frac{2x}{2x+2}$.

**7.2.2
Solving Proportions
Using Equivalent
Ratios**

Proportions are useful in solving problems involving ratios where we have one piece of missing information. For example, if eggs cost 90 cents per one dozen, how much will it cost to buy 4 dozen eggs? In this situation, we can set up a proportion comparing number of dozens to cost per dozen:

$$\frac{1}{90} = \frac{4}{x}$$

Given this situation, we need to solve for x. Because we know we are seeking an equivalent ratio, we can create a series of ratios equivalent to until we find the one we need:

$$\frac{1}{90} = \frac{2}{180} = \frac{3}{270} = \frac{4}{360} = \frac{5}{450} \ldots$$

From this list of equivalent ratios, we conclude that it will cost 360 cents or $3.60 for 4 dozen eggs.

In a second example, if we want to solve the proportion $\frac{3}{5} = \frac{x}{25}$, we can again generate a list of ratios equivalent to n $\frac{3}{5}$: $\frac{3}{5} = \frac{6}{10} = \frac{9}{15} = \frac{12}{20} = \frac{15}{25} = \frac{18}{30} = \frac{21}{35} \ldots$. We conclude, then that x must be 15.

**7.2.3
Solving Proportions
Using Cross
Multiplication**

Proportions are frequently solved using **cross multiplication**; that is, given a proportion $\frac{a}{b} = \frac{c}{d}$, then $ad = bc$. Knowing this fact of cross multiplication, we can solve any proportion involving an unknown by setting up the cross multiplication and solving for x.

For example, given the proportion: $\frac{4}{10} = \frac{9}{x}$, we know that

$$4x = 9 \times 10$$
$$4x = 90$$
$$x = \frac{90}{4} = \frac{45}{2} = 22\frac{1}{2}, \text{ or } 22.5.$$

In a second example, suppose the ratio of men to women at State University is 4 to 5. If there are 2,200 women at State University, how many men are there? We solve by setting up a proportion, cross multiplying, and solving for x:

$$\frac{4}{5} = \frac{x}{2200}$$

Then,

$$4 \times 2200 = 5x$$
$$8800 = 5x$$
$$1760 = x.$$

If two items x and y are proportional, that is if x is **proportional** to y, then there exists some **constant of proportionality**, k, such that $x = ky$ or $\frac{x}{y} = k$.

For example, if we want to show that 40 is proportional to 8, we try to find a value, k, such that $40 = 8k$. Solving for 5, we identify the constant of proportionality is 5. Therefore, 40 is proportional to 8.

Most of the time when the claim is made that two numbers are proportional, the intended meaning is that the two numbers are directly proportional. So, when we have the relationship where $x = ky$, we can say that x is **directly proportional** to y. On the other hand, when the relationship between x and y is such that $x = \frac{1}{k} \cdot y$ or $x = \frac{y}{k}$, we claim that x is **indirectly proportional** to y.

For example, we can show that 6 is indirectly proportional to 30. Setting up the equation, we have: $6 = \frac{1}{k} \cdot 30$; solving for k we find that $k = 5$. Thus, because we could find a value for k that satisfies the equation, we verified that 6 is indeed, indirectly proportional to 30.

**7.2.4
Directly and
Indirectly
Proportional**

Percent

RELATED TOPICS

TOPIC 7.3 INTRODUCTION TO DECIMALS

CORNERSTONE Base Ten | Place Value | Integers

INTRODUCTION

Decimals are a natural part of our base ten system. We usually think of fractional amounts when we hear the term "decimal" because we envision a decimal point separating a whole number part from a fractional part. In this section we explore the definition of a decimal, where a decimal point features in the determination of place value, and how to compare and order decimals.

DID YOU KNOW?

Several mathematicians are credited with having done work leading to the invention of decimal notation of fractions. One man, Jean de Meurs, who wrote in the early 14th century, brought intuition to the benefits of decimal notation in his work with the extraction of roots associated with $\sqrt[3]{a}$. Another influence leading to the invention of the decimal fraction was the rule for dividing by numbers of the form $a \times 10^n$. Work is this area is attributed to mathematicians Piero Borghi and Francesco Pellos in the mid-1400's. The first mathematician, however, to fully comprehend the significance of decimals is Christoff Rudolff whose work with decimals appeared in Augsburg in 1530. Notably, he used a decimal bar, "|" instead of a decimal point, but his concept of place values was as it is today.

For More Information: Smith, D. E. (1958). *History of mathematics, Volume II.* New York: Dover Publications.

7.3.1 Definition of Decimal

When most people use the term **decimal**, they refer to a number that has some **decimal fraction** component. A **decimal point**, represented by the symbol "." separates integer value parts of a decimal number (comprised of symbols to the left of the decimal point) from fractional value parts of a decimal number (comprised of symbols to the right of the decimal point.). Some examples of decimal numbers are: 10.34, −3.67421, and 0.9. When a number is expressed as a decimal fraction plus an integer, it is often referred to as a **mixed decimal**.

7.3.2 Decimals, Base Ten, & Place Value

The decimal point in a decimal number helps to indicate the place value of the digits in the number. The places to the left of the decimal point are the places we use to express whole number and integer amounts: ones place, tens place, hundreds place, and so on. The places to the right of the decimal point are used to express fractional amounts: tenths place, hundredths place, thousandths place, and so on. The place value chart in Figure 7.1 illustrates places to the right and the left of the decimal point in the decimal system. Notice that, consistent with a base ten system, each place value represents a power of ten. Places to the right of the decimal point can be expressed as 10 raised to a negative integer power.

Figure 7.1

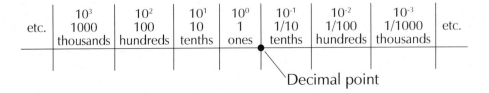

etc.	10^3 1000 thousands	10^2 100 hundreds	10^1 10 tenths	10^0 1 ones	10^{-1} 1/10 tenths	10^{-2} 1/100 hundreds	10^{-3} 1/1000 thousands	etc.

Decimal point

Using the chart in Figure 7.1, we can interpret decimal numbers and their values. For example, the number 34.8 can be interpreted as representing "thirty-four and eight tenths." Note that the decimal point is read as the word *and* indicating that the integer amount is combined with the fraction amount. The number 2.01 is read as "two and one hundredth."

When reading decimals that have more than one significant digit to the right of the decimal point, it is proper to express the string of digits to the right of the decimal point as a fraction where the numerator is the whole number represented by those digits and the denominator is the place where the right-most significant (nonzero) digit sits. For example, the decimal 12.345 would be read as "twelve and three hundred forty-five thousandths." Similarly, the decimal 0.99 would be read as "ninety-nine hundredths."

7.3.3
Expressing a Decimal Number

Decimal numbers can include zeros to hold place value. Thus, the decimal 1.504 represents 1 one, 5 tenths, and 4 thousandths. The number 1.504 would be read "one and five hundred four thousandths." Although we could add an infinite string of zeros to the right of the last nonzero digit in a decimal number and not affect the value of that decimal, it is a universally accepted practice to end a decimal number with a nonzero, right-most digit. Thus while 15.670 is technically equivalent in value to 15.67, it is best to write the decimal without additional zeros. Exceptions to this rule include situations where scientific or statistical measurements require answers expressed to certain degrees of accuracy. For example, it might be necessary to provide a scientific measurement rounded to the nearest thousandth. If the actual measurement is 0.1495773 centimeters (cm), the appropriate measurement rounded to the nearest thousandth would be 0.150 cm.

7.3.4
Zeros in Decimals

Base-ten blocks provide an excellent tool for modeling decimal fractions. Letting the flat block represent 1 whole, the long block then represents one tenth and the unit block represents one hundredth. With these values defined, we can represent the decimal number 3.25 using base ten blocks as illustrated in Figure 7.2.

Modeling decimals using base ten blocks can be extremely helpful when trying to visualize the addition and subtraction of decimal numbers.

7.3.5
Base-Ten Blocks as a Model for Decimals

Figure 7.2

7.3.6
Rounding of Decimals

In many practical problems involving decimals, it is necessary to round a decimal number to a particular decimal place. The place to which we round is determined by the degree of accuracy we want in our solution. The rules for rounding decimal fractions are similar to the rules for rounding whole number amounts.

To round a decimal number to a particular place, check the digit to the right of that place to determine whether you round up or down. If the digit to the right of the place to which you are rounding is 5 or more, then round up. If the digit is less than 5, round down. Unlike when rounding whole numbers where all digits to the right of the place to which you are rounding become zeros, when rounding to a fractional decimal place, we truncate, or cut off, the rounded number at the place to which we are rounding, showing no digits to the right of that place.

For example, to round 78.569 to the nearest hundredth, we check the digit in the thousandths place. Because that digit is a 9 we will round the 6 in the tenths place up to a 7 and then truncate the number at that point. Thus, 78.569 rounded to the hundredths place is 78.57. Rounding 0.78927 to the nearest thousandth, we get the number 0.789.

RELATED TOPICS Decimals and Fractions | Adding Decimals | Subtracting Decimals
Exponents

TOPIC 7.4 DECIMALS AND FRACTIONS

Decimals | Fractions | Rational Numbers

INTRODUCTION

When we think of fractions, we generally picture a numerator over a denominator. However, fractional amounts can also be expressed as decimals. There is a connection between decimal and common fractions. In the following sections we examine a method for converting certain fractions to terminating decimal form and a means of converting terminating decimals to common fraction form.

DID YOU KNOW?

Fractional amounts were originally expressed in the form of a numerator over a denominator. When computing business transactions, performing long-division problems, fractions began to take on very complicated forms. By the advent of printing capabilities in the mid-1400's, a need for a more varied method of expressing fractional amounts was clearly necessary. Decimal representation helped to alleviate the problem of expressing very complicated fractions.

For More Information: Smith, D. E. (1958). *History of mathematics, Volume II.* New York: Dover Publications.

Decimal fractions and **common fractions** (a fraction written as a numerator and a denominator) both represent part of a whole. All decimal fractions with a right-most significant (nonzero) digit can be expressed as a common fraction with a numerator and denominator. Similarly, common fractions can be written in one of several decimal forms.

7.4.1
Decimals and Common Fractions

Decimals that have a right-most significant (non-zero) digit are called terminating decimals. All terminating decimals can be expressed as common fraction form. For example, $0.25 = \frac{25}{100}$ and $0.374 = \frac{374}{1000}$. A procedure to follow to convert terminating decimals to common fraction form is as follows:

7.4.2
Converting Decimals to Common Fraction Form

1. Determine the place value of the right-most significant digit. This place will be the denominator of the common fraction form.

2. Write the digits of the decimal number in order without the decimal point. This number will be the numerator of the common fraction form.

For example, to convert the decimal 0.1254 to a fraction, we observe that the place value of the right-most digit is the ten thousandths place. Thus, the denominator will be 10,000. Next, writing the digits without the decimal point, we have the number 1254, which will be the numerator of the fraction. Thus, $0.1254 = \frac{1254}{10,000}$.

Mixed decimals are converted in the same manner. For example, the decimal 65.2 is converted to fraction form by determining the denominator to be ten because the right-most digit is in the tenths place, and writing the digits 652 in the numerator. Therefore, $65.2 = \frac{652}{10}$.

Common fractions that have a denominator that is a power of 10, such as 10, 100, 1,000, and so on, can easily be converted to decimal form. A set of procedures that guide the conversion is the following:

7.4.3
Converting Certain Common Fractions to Decimals

1. The denominator of the common fraction indicates the place value of the right-most digit in the decimal to which we are converting the fraction.

2. The numerator will be written as is and the decimal point will be placed so that the last digit ends in the place value indicated by the denominator.

For example, the fraction $\frac{87}{100}$ has a denominator of 100, so when converting to decimal form, the decimal's right-most digit will be in the hundredths place. The number 87 is written as is and a decimal point is inserted so that the digit 7 is in the hundredth's place. Consequently, $\frac{87}{100} = 0.87$.

Converting the number $\frac{2189}{100}$ to decimal form, note that we write the number 2189 and place the decimal point so that the digit 9 is in the hundredth's place. Thus, $\frac{2189}{100} = 21.89$.

In a situation where you want to write $\frac{85}{1000}$ as a decimal, we write the number 85 and next need to place the decimal point so that the digit 5 is in the thousandths place. In order to do so, we need to add a place holding zero in front of the 85. Thus, $\frac{85}{1000} = 0.085$.

7.4.4
Fractions That Do Not Have Power-of-10 Denominators

For common fractions that do not have a denominator that is a power of ten, many can still be converted to terminating decimal form. Those fractions that can be converted to terminating decimals have the following characteristic: *If the prime factorization of the denominator of a common fraction, when in simplest form, involves only powers of 2, powers of 5 or combinations of powers of 2 and 5, then the fraction can be re-written with a denominator that is a power of 10.* For example, given the fraction $\frac{3}{20}$, we observe that the prime factorization of the denominator, $20 = 2 \times 2 \times 5$, consists of only twos and fives. Therefore, we know that we can find a fraction equivalent to that has a denominator that is a power of ten. Multiplying numerator and denominator of $\frac{3}{20}$ by $\frac{5}{5}$ we find that $\frac{3}{20}$ can be written in the equivalent form $\frac{15}{100} = 0.15$.

7.4.5
Using a Calculator for Converting

Another method for converting common fractions to decimal form is to recall that fractions can represent division problems. Thus, dividing the numerator by the denominator by long division or by using a calculator will yield the decimal form of the fraction. Use caution when using the calculator when converting fractions to decimal form. Calculators will round or truncate decimals after they have exceeded their digit capacity. This is particularly true for fractions that cannot be re-written with a denominator that is a power of ten. These fractions will convert to non-terminating decimals (described in a section entitled Terminating and Repeating Decimals). Calculators will present non-terminating decimals as if they were terminating.

7.4.6
Comparing and Ordering Decimals Using Base-Ten Blocks

To determine which of the decimals 0.35 and 0.4 is larger, it is sometimes useful to model these decimals using base ten blocks and then compare. Figure 7.3 illustrates the base-ten block representations of 0.35 and 0.4.

Letting one flat base ten block represent one whole, the longs represent tenths and the units represent hundredths. Thus, the decimal 0.4 represents 4 tenths, or 4 longs, and the decimal 0.35 represents 35 hundredths, or 3 tenths and 5 hundredths. From this representation, it is clear that 0.4 > 0.35.

$$0.4 = \quad\quad\quad 0.35 = $$

Figure 7.3

To compare decimals, one method involves lining up decimal points and comparing place value by place value. For example, to order the decimals: 2.3333, 2.3434, 2.3, 2.4343, and 2.4435, begin by lining up the decimal points of each decimal number, adding zeros to the right of the right-most digits so that we have the same number of digits to compare in each number.

7.4.7
Ordering Decimals
By Lining Up
Decimal Points

(1) 2.3333
(2) 2.3434
(3) 2.3000
(4) 2.4343
(5) 2.4435

Let us order these decimals from smallest to largest. Start by comparing the left-most digit of all the numbers. Because all five numbers have a two in the ones place, we cannot distinguish between them, so we move to the right to the tenths place. In this place, the smallest-valued digit is a 3. Three appears in the first three numbers, so one of these three will be the smallest decimal. To further compare these three numbers, we move to the hundredth's place. The first has a 3 in the hundredth's place, the second has a 4 in the hundredth's place, and the third has a 0 in the hundredth's place. Thus, the third number is the smallest of the three, the second number is next smallest, and the first number is the largest of the three. Therefore the three smallest decimals in order are: 2.3, 2.3333, and 2.3434.

To determine which of the last two decimal numbers is the largest, compare the hundredth's places. The last decimal number has a 4 whereas the fourth decimal number has a 3 in the hundredths place. Therefore 2.4343 < 2.4435. So the order of the five decimal numbers from smallest to largest is: 2.3, 2.3333, 2.3434, 2.4343, 2.4435.

Decimals can be ordered on a number line. We can show tenths by breaking a unit length into ten equal-sized pieces, each worth one tenth. See Figure 7.4. To show 0.2, 0.3, 0.25, and 0.28 on a number line, we see, that 0.25 and 0.28 are between 0.2 and 0.3, with 0.25 < 0.28. Imagining breaking the length between 0.2 and 0.3 into ten equal-sized parts, we can estimate the placement of 0.25 and 0.28 on the number line.

7.4.8
Ordering Decimals
On a Number Line

From the number-line representation of these decimals, it is clear that 0.2 < 0.25 < 0.28 < 0.3.

Figure 7.4

Terminating and Repeating Decimals

RELATED TOPICS

TOPIC 7.5 TERMINATING AND REPEATING DECIMALS

CORNERSTONE | Decimals | Decimals and Fractions | Rational Numbers

INTRODUCTION

Rational numbers can be expressed in decimal form as either terminating decimals or repeating decimals. In the following sections, we examine these types of decimals through definitions and examples. We also provide a methods for converting fractions to repeating decimal form and for converting repeating decimals to common fraction form.

DID YOU KNOW?

Probably the most popular use for decimal fractions is representing dollars and cents. Decimals that represent dollar and cents amounts are terminating decimals. Often times, money amounts must be rounded to the nearest hundredth so that a comprehensible money amount can be established.

7.5.1 Terminating Decimals

Terminating decimals are decimal numbers that have a right-most significant (nonzero) digit. Examples of terminating decimals are: 10.234, −567.2, 0.336677.

7.5.2 Repeating Decimals

Some decimals do not terminate; rather, they continue on in an identifiable, repeating pattern. Thus, with these **repeating decimals**, there is no right-most digit. Examples of repeating decimals are: 0.33333… and 0.16666…. The ellipses—that is the symbols "…"—indicates that the digits continue in the same pattern. In the first example, the digit 3 keeps repeating over and over again. In the second example, the digit 6 repeats continuously.

Rather than writing repeating decimal with an ellipsis, you can use what is called a **repeating bar** to indicate the **repeatand**, or the string of digits that repeats. For example, we can write 0.33333… as $0.\overline{3}$. Similarly, the decimal 0.16666… can be written as $0.1\overline{6}$. Notice on this second example that only the digit 6 appears under the repeating bar, indicating that only the digit 6 repeats.

In another example, given the repeating decimal $0.\overline{257}$, we can write this in ellipsis form as .257257257…. Note that in this example, all three digits are under the repeating bar, thus all three digits repeat continuously in the same order.

7.5.3 Rational Numbers as Repeating Decimals

A rational number is any number that can be expressed as $\frac{a}{b}$ where a and b are both integers and $b \neq 0$. Any rational number can be converted to decimal form using long division. Terminating decimals ultimately get to a point where the remainder is zero in the long division. Repeating decimals, on the other hand, get to a point where a quotient begins to repeats. For example, to convert the rational number $\frac{4}{9}$ to decimal form, we divide 9 into 4:

$$
\begin{array}{r}
.44 \\
9\overline{)4.00} \\
-3\,6 \\
\hline
40 \\
-36 \\
\hline
4
\end{array}
$$

We observe that because the remainder continues to be 4, we are caught in a loop that will continue to repeat itself. Thus, we can conclude that the quotient in the repeating decimal .

As a second example, let us verify that $\frac{1}{7}$ can be written in decimal form as $0.\overline{142857}$.

$$
\begin{array}{r}
.142857\ldots \\
7\overline{)1.0000000} \\
-7 \\
\hline
30 \\
-28 \\
\hline
20 \\
-14 \\
\hline
60 \\
-56 \\
\hline
40 \\
-35 \\
\hline
50 \\
-49 \\
\hline
1
\end{array}
$$

Notice that once we reach a point where the remainder is 1, we are essentially in the same division situation we were in during the first step of our division process; that is, when we initially divided 7 into 1, the first step was to bring down a zero and note that 7 goes into 10 one time with a remainder of 3. If we were to continue with the long division problem, we would bring down a zero, divide 7 into 10 and note that it goes in one time with a remainder of 3. Thus, we would begin repeating what has been done before. So, we know to stop and to indicate that the string $0.\overline{142857}$ repeats infinitely.

Checking the results of our long division using a calculator, note that the calculator rounds the repeating decimal to the closest terminating decimal it can fit into its view screen. Thus, a reminder: Take caution when using a calculator.

7.5.4 Converting Repeating Decimals to Rational Number Form

All repeating decimals are rational numbers; that is, they can be written in the form $\frac{a}{b}$ where a and b are integers, with $b \neq 0$. Thus, there is an established procedure for converting repeating decimals to rational-number form.

The procedure is algebraic in nature. We will illustrate the procedure by converting the decimal $0.\overline{56}$ to rational-number form. First, be clear that $0.\overline{56} \neq 0.56$. Therefore, $0.\overline{56} \neq \frac{56}{100}$. Also, because $0.\overline{56} = 0.565656\ldots$ then $100 \times 0.\overline{56} = 56.565656\ldots = 56.\overline{56}$. Finally, note that the overall goal of the algorithm is to create two decimals with the same repeating part so that we can subtract away the repeating part.

The algorithm for converting repeating decimals to rational number form is as follows:

Example 1: Let $x = 0.\overline{56}$. Then $100x = 56.\overline{56}$. Because $x = 0.\overline{56}$, subtracting x from the left side of the equation $100x = 56.\overline{56}$ and subtracting $0.\overline{56}$ from the right-hand side of the equation should still maintain the equality of the equation. Thus, we find:

$$
\begin{array}{r}
x = 0.\overline{56} \\
100x = 56.\overline{56} \\
-x \quad -0.\overline{56} \\
\hline
99x = 56
\end{array}
$$

Solving for x by dividing both sides of the equation by 99 we find:
$$x = \frac{56}{99}.$$

Example 2: Suppose we want to convert the decimal $5.\overline{142}$. Letting $x = 5.\overline{142}$, we want to create a new decimal that is a multiple of $5.\overline{142}$ so that the repeating strand of the new decimal "lines up with" the repeating strand of $5.\overline{142}$. This time, because the repeating strand is three digits in length, we multiply $5.\overline{142} \times 1000 = 5142.\overline{142}$. Thus, performing the algorithm we find:

$$
\begin{array}{r}
x = 5.\overline{142} \\
1000x = 5142.\overline{142} \\
-x \quad -5.\overline{142} \\
\hline
999x = 5137
\end{array}
$$

Solving for x we find:
$$x = \frac{5137}{999}.$$

Example 3: To convert the decimal $0.1\overline{4}$, we can follow the same procedure, adding an extra step at the end.

$$
\begin{array}{r}
x = 0.1\overline{4} \\
10x = 1.4\overline{4} \\
-x \quad -0.1\overline{4} \\
\hline
9x = 1.3
\end{array}
$$

Note that at this point, we have eliminated the repeating part. Now, when solving for x we find:
$$x = \frac{1.3}{9}.$$

At this point, the solution is not in rational-number form because the numerator is not an integer. We can multiply numerator and denominator by 10 to find an equivalent fraction that is in rational-number form:
$$x = \frac{13}{90}.$$

RELATED TOPICS   Irrational Numbers

TOPIC 7.6 DECIMAL ADDITION AND SUBTRACTION

Decimals | Decimals and Fractions

The ability to add and subtract decimals is a valuable tool, particularly when it comes to working with money and balancing financial accounts. In the following sections, the rules for decimal addition and decimal subtraction are introduced and modeled using base-ten blocks.

INTRODUCTION

Simon Stevin (1548–1620) is considered to be among the most influential Dutch mathematicians. He is best noted for his contributions in numerical computation including rational and real numbers. In particular, his numerical computations extended the use of the Hindu-Arabic base-ten system, representing decimal amounts in his numeric computations.

DID YOU KNOW?

For More Information: Smith, D. E. (1958). *History of mathematics, Volume II.* New York: Dover Publications.

The rule for adding decimals says to (1) add decimals vertically, (2) line up decimal points in the addends, and (3) add digits in the same place-value positions together beginning from the right-most digits, carrying sets of 10 to the next column when necessary. Once the decimal addends are lined up, any place where there is a digit missing in one of the addends can be replaced with a zero so that both addends have the same number of digits to the right of the decimal point.

7.6.1
Adding Decimals

For example, to add 345.7256 + 16725.89, we first write the addends vertically, making sure to line up decimal points and to add two zeros on to the end of the second addend:

$$345.7256$$
$$+\ 16725.8900$$

Then, adding column by column, carrying when appropriate, we find the sum:

$$345.7256$$
$$+\ 16725.8900$$
$$17071.6156$$

Addition of decimals can be modeled using base-ten blocks. Exchanges made when carrying can be clearly visualized with this model. For example, modeling the addition problem 0.77 + 1.56, we first build each addend with base-ten blocks as shown in Figure 7.5.

7.6.2
Modeling the Addition of Decimals

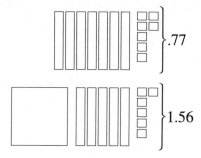

Figure 7.5

Next we combine units (hundredths) and exchange one set of ten units for a long (tenth) as seen in Figure 7.6.

Figure 7.6

Then, the longs are combined and ten of the longs (tenths) are exchanged for one flat (one whole) as shown in Figure 7.7.

Figure 7.7

Once this exchange is done, we combine flats (one wholes) and see that our sum consists of 2 flats, 3 longs, and 3 units, which represents a sum of 2.33 (see Figure 7.8).

Figure 7.8

7.6.3
Subtracting Decimals

The rules for subtracting decimals are similar to those for addition: (1) subtract the decimals vertically, (2) line up decimal points in the minuend and subtrahend, and (3) subtract digits in the same place value positions beginning from the right-most digits, exchanging one from a column to a set of ten for the next column when necessary. Once the decimals are lined up, any place where there is a digit missing in one of the minuend or subtrahend can be replaced with a zero so that both decimals have the same number of digits to the right of the decimal point.

For example, to subtract 235.98 from 300, we first write the minuend and subtrahend vertically, making sure to line up decimal points and to add two zeros on to the end of the minuend:

$$
\begin{array}{r}
300.00 \\
- \ 235.98 \\
\hline
\end{array}
$$

Now subtract column by column, exchanging when necessary to find the difference:

$$
\begin{array}{r}
300.00 \\
- \ 235.98 \\
\hline
64.02
\end{array}
$$

Subtraction of decimals can be modeled using base-ten blocks. Exchanges made when borrowing can be clearly visualized with this model. For example, modeling the subtraction problem 3.23 − 1.56, we first build the minuend, 3.23, with base-ten blocks as shown in Figure 7.9.

**7.6.4
Modeling the
Subtraction of
Decimals**

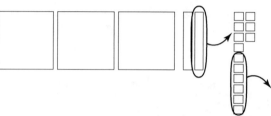

Figure 7.9

Starting with the units (one-hundredths), we need to subtract 6 units as indicated in the digit 6 in the decimal 1.56. To subtract 6 units, we exchange one long (one-tenth) for 10 units (hundredths) and then take away 6 units as seen in Figure 7.10.

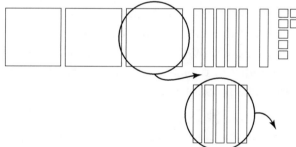

Figure 7.10

Then, we are left with 1 long, but need to subtract 5 longs, as indicated by the digit 5 in the subtrahend 1.56. To do so, we exchange one flat (one whole) for 10 longs (tenths). From the 11 longs (tenths), we can remove 5 longs (tenths). See Figure 7.11.

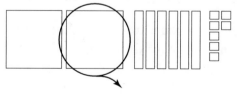

Figure 7.11

Finally, left with two flats (wholes), six longs (tenths), and 7 units (hundredths), we can subtract one whole (as seen in Figure 7.12) as indicated by the digit 1 in the subtrahend 1.56.

Figure 7.12

After all exchanges and subtractions, the base-ten blocks (See Figure 7.13) reveal that the difference found in the problem 3.23 − 1.56 is 1.67.

Figure 7.13

Decimal Multiplication

RELATED TOPICS

TOPIC 7.7 DECIMAL MULTIPLICATION

INTRODUCTION   *The multiplication of decimals involves a very interesting rule. In this section the rule is explained and examined as to why the rule makes sense. Examples of decimal multiplication are provided as well.*

DID YOU KNOW?   Mathematician Leonard of Pisa, better known as Fibonacci (1180–1250), was an Italian mathematician who helped to make the use of Hindu-Arabic numerals common throughout Europe. He is best known for the Fibonacci Sequence which is an infinite, iterative sequence of numbers where the next number in the sequence is found by determining the sum of the two prior numbers in the sequence. The basic Fibonacci Sequence is: 0, 1, 1, 2, 3, 5, 8, 13, 21, 34, 55, 89, 144,…Fibonacci sequences have been found to be related to decimal representations of certain rational numbers. For example, the rational number $\frac{1}{89}$ = .01123595506…. Notice, interestingly, that the first six digits to the right of the decimal point mirror the first six numbers in the Fibonacci Sequence. Also note that, $\frac{1}{89} = \frac{0}{10^1} + \frac{1}{10^2} + \frac{1}{10^3} + \frac{2}{10^4} + \frac{3}{10^5} + \frac{5}{10^6} + \frac{8}{10^7} + \frac{13}{10^8} +$…. Notice in this representation that the string of numerators exactly matches the Fibonacci Sequence.

For More Information: Reimer, L., & Reimer W. (1995). *Mathematicians are people, too: Stories from the lives of great mathematicians, Volume 2.* Palo Alto, CA: Dale Seymour Publications.

**7.7.1
Rule for Decimal Multiplication**

When multiplying decimals, the following steps apply: (1) multiply the decimals as if they were integers, (2) find the sum of the number of digits to the right of the decimal point of each factor, (3) place the decimal point in the product so that the number of decimal points to the right of the decimal point is equal to the sum of digits found in step (2).

Example 1: When multiplying the decimals 12.64 × 3.8, we first find the product as if the factors were integers: 1264 × 38 = 48032. Then, because the number of digits to the right of the decimal in 12.64 is two, and the number of digits to the right of the decimal point of 3.8 is one, we find the sum 2 + 1 = 3, and place a decimal point in the number 48032 so that there are 3 digits to the right of the decimal point. Thus, 12.64 × 3.8 = 48.032.

Example 2: To find the product 100.335 × 2.55, we find the product 100335 × 255 = 25585425, then place the decimal point so that there are five digits to the right of the decimal point. Thus, 100.335 × 2.55 = 255.85425.

**7.7.2
Connection Between Decimal and Fraction Multiplication**

To understand why the rule for multiplication of decimals makes sense, it helps to see the connection between decimal and fraction multiplication. When we change decimals to their equivalent common fraction forms, we can multiply the fractions and gain insight into why the rule for decimal multiplication works.

For example, multiplying 2.5 × 3.01 using the rules for decimal multiplication, we find a product of 7.525. Notice that the number of digits in the product is three, which is the sum of the number of digits to the right of the decimal points of the two factors. Now, writing these two factors as fractions, we have the multiplication problem $\frac{25}{10} \times \frac{301}{100}$. Using rules for multiplying fractions (see Rational Number Multiplication) by multiplying numerators and denominators, we find the product $\frac{25}{10} \times \frac{301}{100} = \frac{7525}{1000} = 7.525$.

Notice that the denominator in the first factor is 10 or 10^1 and the denominator in the second factor is 100 or 10^2. The denominator in the product is 1,000 or 10^3. Multiplying $10^1 \times 10^2 = 10^{1+2} = 10^3$ (see Exponents section). The exponent indicates the number of zeros in the power of ten. Note that the number of zeros in the denominator of the product is equal to the sum of the number of zeros in the denominators of the two factors. Thus, the rule for decimal multiplication where we add the number of digits in the decimal factors is akin to adding the number of zeros in the denominators of the fractional factors.

The area model is a visual means of representing multiplication of common fractions (see Rational-Number Multiplication). The area model can also illustrate multiplication of decimal fractions. To illustrate 0.4×0.6 with the area model, we break the region into ten rows, each row representing one tenth, and ten columns, each column representing one tenth (see Figure 7.14).

7.7.3
**Area Model
of Decimal
Multiplication**

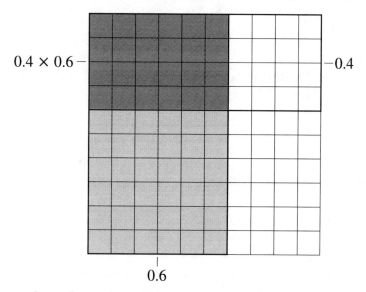

0.4×0.6 —

—0.4

0.6

Figure 7.14

The area where the region of 4 rows representing 0.4 overlaps the region of 6 columns representing 0.6 is a region representing the product 0.4×0.6. This product region covers 24 small units, each worth one hundredth. Thus, the product is 24 hundredths, or 0.24.

TOPIC 7.8 DECIMAL DIVISION

CORNERSTONE | Decimals | Decimals and Fractions | Integer Division

INTRODUCTION

Decimal division may seem a complicated process to many. However, described in the following sections is a set of procedures to follow for successful decimal division. Further, a means of explaining why decimal division works the way it does is included.

DID YOU KNOW?

Archimedes (287–212 B.C.) was the greatest mathematician of ancient times. Archimedes loved challenges. Once, he set out to determine how much sand it would take to fill the universe. To begin, he counted the number of grains of sand that made up a cluster the size of a poppy seed. Then, he counted the number of poppy seeds that would fit on a man's finger. Then he counted the number of fingers it would take to fill a stadium. He kept going until he came up with 10^{63} grains. Thus, he was the first to develop a system of writing large numbers with exponents. In another challenge to himself, Archimedes was determined to find the exact ratio between the circumference of a circle and its diameter. After much experimentation, he concluded that the ratio was somewhere between $3\frac{1}{7}$ and $3\frac{10}{71}$. This ratio, called pi (π), has now been calculated to many decimal places, but is most often approximated as 3.14.

For More Information: Reimer, L., & Reimer W. (1990). *Mathematicians are people, too: Stories from the lives of great mathematicians, Volume 1.* Palo Alto, CA: Dale Seymour Publications.

7.8.1
Rule for
Decimal Division

When the divisor in a division problem is a decimal fraction, the steps for long division are to (1) move the decimal point in the divisor the number of places to the right until the decimal point is to the right of the last digit, (2) simultaneously move the decimal point in the dividend the same number of places that we moved the decimal point in the divisor, (3) place a decimal point above the dividend where the quotient will be written so that the decimal point in the quotient lines up with where the decimal point in the dividend is, and finally, (4) divide the numbers as if they were integers, paying attention to keep the decimal point in the final quotient where indicated in step (3).

Example 1: To divide $507.45 \div 0.15$, we first write the problem in long division form:

$$.15\overline{)507.45}$$

Then, noting that we must move the decimal point in the divisor two places to the right, we simultaneously move the decimal point in the dividend two places to the right. Thus the division problem becomes:

$$15.\overline{)50745.0}$$

Note that the decimal point in the quotient corresponds to the placement of the decimal point in the dividend. Now, completing the long division, we find the quotient to be 3383:

$$15.\overline{)50745.0}^{\,3383.0}$$

Example 2: To solve the problem $10.68 \div 3.2$, we set up the long division problem

$$3.2\overline{)10.68}$$

and then move the decimal points in both the dividend and divisor one place to the right:

$$32\overline{)10\overset{.}{6}.8}$$

Performing the long division of 106.8 32, we find the quotient to be 3.3375:

$$\begin{array}{r} 3.3375 \\ 32\overline{)106.8000} \end{array}$$

In any division problem, if we multiply both dividend and divisor by the same non-zero amount, the quotient is unaffected. For example, $10 \div 5 = 2$. Similarly, $(3 \times 10) \div (3 \times 5) = 30 \div 15 = 2$. Essentially, the factor introduced in the dividend is divided by itself in the divisor, thus essentially forming a name for 1. Therefore, a quotient is unaffected when both dividend and divisor are multiplied by the same nonzero amount.

From another perspective, viewing the division problem $10 \div 5$ written in fraction form, $\frac{10}{5}$, we can think of multiplying numerator and denominator by the same number (a name for one) to form an equivalent fraction. That is, $\frac{10}{5} = \frac{3 \times 10}{3 \times 5} = \frac{30}{15} = 30 \div 15 = 2$. Again, the value of the quotient in the division problem is unaffected.

To understand why the rule for decimal division works, we can look to the connection between decimal and fraction division. For example, consider the problem $30.45 \div 0.6$:

$$0.6\overline{)30.45} \longrightarrow 6\overline{)304.50}^{\,50.75}$$

To verify that these two division problems are equivalent, rewrite the division problem $30.45 \div 0.6$ in fraction form as $\frac{3045}{1000} \div \frac{6}{10}$. Multiplying both quotient and divisor by the 10, we produce a new division problem that will have the same quotient as the original, as explained in the previous section. Therefore,

$$30.45 \div 0.6 = \frac{3045}{100} \div \frac{6}{10} = \frac{30450}{100} \div \frac{60}{10} = 304.5 \div 6.$$

Thus, the rule for decimal division essentially leads the problem solver to multiply both dividend and divisor by the appropriate power of ten that creates a whole-number divisor. No matter what power of 10 both dividend and divisor are multiplied by, the quotient is unaffected while the division problem is made easier.

7.8.2
A Key Fact
About Division

7.8.3
Connection
Between Decimal
and Fraction
Division

Decimal Multiplication

RELATED TOPICS

TOPIC 7.9 PERCENT

INTRODUCTION

Whether we are computing a tip or determining what our salary will be after a certain cost of living increase, percents are a part of the calculations. Percents also provide a means of describing how likely it is to rain on a given day or how much of a chance we have at winning the lottery. In the following sections, we define percent and illustrate a process of solving simple percent problems.

DID YOU KNOW?   The word *percent* comes from the Latin phrase *per centum*, meaning "per hundred."

7.9.1
Definition of Percent

A **percent** is a ratio where one of the items being compared is the amount 100. In general, given any nonnegative real number, r, we say r percent, denoted $r\%$, is the ratio $\frac{r}{100}$. For example, we say $45\% = \frac{45}{100}$. Likewise, $250\% = \frac{250}{100}$.

7.9.2
Percents and Decimals

Because percents can be written as fractions with a denominator of 100, they can also easily be written as decimal numbers. To translate a percent to its decimal equivalent, first write the percent in fraction form. Then, convert the fraction to decimal form (see Decimals and Fractions for more details of converting fractions to decimals). Some examples of equivalent percent, fraction, and decimal representations are provided in Table 7.1.

Table 7.1

Percent	Fraction Form	Decimal Equivalent
20%	$\frac{20}{100}$	.20
35%	$\frac{35}{100}$	.35
150%	$\frac{150}{100}$	1.50
1%	$\frac{1}{100}$	0.01
0.5%	$\frac{.5}{100}$	0.005
3.5%	$\frac{3.5}{100}$	0.035

7.9.3
Solving Basic Percent Problems

To solve basic percent problems, we can set up a proportion where one of the ratios is a fractional representation of a percent. Thus, to solve a percent problem, we can set up a ratio: $\frac{A}{B} = \frac{C}{100}$, where A, B and C are real numbers, $B \neq 0$. Most percent problems involve knowing two of the three unknowns A, B and C, and having to solve for the third, most likely using the cross multiplication method of solving proportions.

Example 1: What is 30% of 65? In this situation, we know the value for $C = 30$. We also know the value for $B = 65$. What we do not know is the value of A. Thus, we set up the proportion: $\frac{A}{65} = \frac{30}{100}$. Solving, using cross multiplication, we find:

$$100 \times A = 30 \times 65$$
$$100 \times A = 1950$$
$$A = \frac{1950}{100} = 19.5$$

Thus, we conclude that 19.5 is 30% of 65.

Example 2: Fifty is 40% of what number? In this case, we know the value for C = 40. We also know the value for A. We need to find the value for B. We set up the proportion: $\frac{50}{B} = \frac{40}{100}$. Solving with cross-multiplication, we determine:

$$50 \times 100 = 40 \times B$$
$$5000 = 40 \times B$$
$$200 = B.$$

Therefore, 50 is 40% of 200.

Example 3: What percent of 80 is 20? In this example, we know $A = 20$ and B = 80, but we do not know the value for C. The proportion we need to solve is: $\frac{20}{80} = \frac{C}{100}$. Solving we find:

$$20 \times 100 = 80 \times C$$
$$2000 = 80 \times C$$
$$25 = C.$$

So, 25% of 80 is 20.

7.9.4
Percent Change

Sometimes we want to determine the percent by which an amount increased or decreased. In these cases, we need to compute a percent change. To compute a **percent change,** we set up and solve the proportion: $\frac{\text{Actual Change}}{\text{Original Amount}} = \frac{x}{100}$.

Example 1: If your salary increased from $20,000 to $24,000, by what percent did your salary increase? First we compute the actual change in salary to be $4,000: 24,000 − 20,000 = 4,000. Noting that the original salary is $20,000, we set up the proportion: $\frac{4,000}{20,000} = \frac{x}{100}$. Solving, we find that the percent increase was 20%.

Example 2: Suppose enrollment at the local college dropped from 8,000 students to 7,500 students. What was the percent decrease? Using the actual change in student population of 500 and the original student enrollment of 8,000, we compute the percent decrease with the proportion: $\frac{500}{8,500} = \frac{x}{100}$. Solving for x, we find the percent decrease was 6.25%.

Example 3: If at the beginning of the day the temperature was 30°, and during the day the temperature rose 10%, what was the high temperature of the day? In this case, we know the original temperature and we know the percent change, but we do not know the actual change. We can set up the proportion: $\frac{x}{30} = \frac{10}{100}$. Solving for x we find the actual change in temperature was 3°. Therefore, the high temperature for the day must have been 3° + 30° = 33°.

Interest | Probability   **RELATED TOPICS**

TOPIC 7.10 INTEREST

INTRODUCTION

Interest is a concept that is involved in such financial transactions as computing a mortgage on a house, determining the monthly cost of a car loan, or predicting how money in a savings account will grow over time. In the following sections, we define terms associated with financial transactions entailing interest and learn how to compute the value of transactions involving simple interest and compound interest.

DID YOU KNOW?

To solve most problems involving interest, we rely on computers or calculators because we need to compute exponential values, often with very large exponents. Calculator keys that allow us to input a base amount and raise that amount to a given exponent are usually labeled with symbols such as: x^y or $x \wedge y$ or simply the symbol, $\wedge$.

7.10.1
Basic Terms in an Interest Problem

When we make a financial investment, the initial amount we invest is called the **principal**. When we invest the principal at a certain interest rate, we earn additional money called **interest**. **Interest rates** are generally expressed as percents, such as $r\%$. Most interest rates in investments are **annual percentage rates** (APR), implying that at the end of a year, the principal amount you invested will earn the interest computed by the APR.

For example, if you invest $1,000 for one year at an annual percentage rate of 6%, then at the end of the year, you have earned an amount of interest that is 6% of $1,000, which is $60. Thus, the total value of your investment at the end of the year is equal to your initial principal investment plus your interest earned, which equals $1,000 + $60 = $1,060.

7.10.2
Computing Simple Interest

If you invest your money and you earn interest **once** at the end of each year, then this is a **simple interest** situation. If you invest a principal amount, P, and earn $r\%$ interest at the end of one year, then the value of your investment at the end of one year, denoted A, is $A = P + \frac{r}{100}P$. By factoring out P, A can be expressed as $A = P(1 + \frac{r}{100})$.

Now, suppose you keep your money invested for another year. The amount invested at the beginning of the second year includes the original principal plus the interest earned from the first year. So, at the end of the second year, you have earned interest on the entire amount $P(1 + \frac{r}{100})$. Thus, at the end of the second year, your investment is worth: $A = P(1 + \frac{r}{100})[1 + \frac{r}{100}]$ or $A = P(1 + \frac{r}{100})^2$.

Continuing in this manner, we can find that at the end of the third year of investing this same principal amount that the value at the end of the third year is

$$A = P\left(1 + \frac{r}{100}\right)\left[1 + \frac{r}{100}\right]\left[1 + \frac{r}{100}\right] \text{ or } A = P\left(1 + \frac{r}{100}\right)^3.$$

In general, when computing the value of an investment involving simple interest, that is interest that is computed once at the end of a year, the value of a principal investment, *P*, at the of *t* years, at an APR of *r* is $A = P(1 + \frac{r}{100})^t$.

For example, if you invest $600 for 8 years at an annual interest rate of 5%, the value of your investment at the end of the 8 years is:

$$A = 600\left(1 + \frac{6}{100}\right)^8 = 600(1 + .06)^8 = 600(1.06)^8 = 1110.56 \text{ or } \$1,110.56.$$

When interest is computed for an investment more than once during a year, we say that **interest is compounded** during the year. Given an annual interest rate of $r\%$, we can have interest compounded n times during a year, each time the currently value of the account, including any previously-earned interest, is increased by $r\%$. To compute the value of an account where interest is compounded n times during a year at an annual interest rate of $r\%$, we use the formula:

$$A = P\left(1 + \frac{r/100}{n}\right)^{nt}.$$

Example 1: Suppose you invest \$400 for 5 years at an annual percentage rate of 7% compounded quarterly (that is 4 times during the year). The value of your investment at the end of the 5 years is:

$$A = 400\left(1 + \frac{7/100}{4}\right)^{4(5)} = 400(1.0175)^{20} = 565.91 \text{ or } \$565.91.$$

Example 2: Suppose you borrow \$100,000 for 20 years and your debt grows at an annual interest rate of 4% compounded monthly (that is, 12 times during the year). How much will you have to pay back to the lender at the end of the 20 years? To solve, compute:

$$A = 100,000\left(1 + \frac{4/100}{12}\right)^{20(12)} = 100,000\,(1.0033)^{240} = 220,493.07 \text{ or } \$220,493.07.$$

Ratio | Proportion | Percent | Exponents   **RELATED TOPICS**

TOPIC 7.11 RATIONAL NUMBERS

CORNERSTONE	Natural Numbers | Whole Numbers | Integers | Whole-Number Division Integer Division | Fractions

INTRODUCTION	*The word **rational** stems from **ration** which refers to an allotment or a portioning out of a fixed amount. Thus, the action of division is linked to rationing. The term **rational number** usually causes people to think of a fraction of some sort. However, as you will see in the sections that follow, a rational number is a special kind of fraction and can be represented by three distinct models.*

DID YOU KNOW?	One model for representing the whole in the part-whole definition of rational numbers is a linear model. Rational numbers are often understood as points on a number line. For example, a twelve-inch ruler provides an image of a total length being divided into equal-sized sections representing 1 inch, $\frac{1}{2}$ inch, $\frac{1}{4}$ inch, $\frac{1}{8}$ inch, and $\frac{1}{16}$ inch,

7.11.1
Definition of a Rational Number

A **rational number** is a number that can be expressed as a fraction of the form $\frac{a}{b}$ where both a and b are integers (provided that b $\neq$ 0). The number $\frac{6}{7}$, for example, is a rational number because both 6 and 7 are integers. It can also be said that the number 0.4 is a rational number because it can be expressed in an equivalent form of $\frac{4}{10}$, which is a fraction with an integer numerator, 4, and integer denominator, 10.

7.11.2
Rational Numbers Versus Fractions

The terms *fractions* and *rational numbers* are often used interchangeably. However, we should be clear about the relationship between the two expressions. In comparing the definitions of the two terms, we see that the set of rational numbers can almost be viewed as a subset of the set of fractions.

Fractions are any number expressions written as a numerator over a denominator. Rational numbers, on the other hand, are those numbers that can be written as fractions whose numerators and denominators are both integers. Thus, although $\frac{\pi}{2}$ is a fraction, it is not a rational number because the number π is not an integer.

It is tempting to conclude that the set of rational numbers, is necessarily a subset of the set of fractions; however, we have to acknowledge that rational numbers can be expressed in forms other than fraction form. For example, the rational number $\frac{1}{2}$ can be expressed as 0.5. Thus it seems inappropriate to state that the Set of Rational Numbers, which includes numbers that may be written in decimal form, is a subset of the Set of Fractions.

7.11.3
Three Models of Rational Numbers

There are three models that are used to illustrate rational numbers. These models are (a) the region (or area) model, (b) the linear (or number line) model, and the (c) set (or discrete) model. Each of these models are most easily demonstrated using the part of a whole interpretation of a rational number fraction.

The Region Model. The model selected to represent a rational number is generally determined by the whole being described in a given context. In the **region model**, for example, the whole represents some enclosed two-dimensional area that is being divided into equal-sized parts. Suppose that when you left a cake to cool on the counter, your dog ate $\frac{3}{4}$ of the cake. The pictorial image that comes to mind for representing a cake is a rectangular region. Thus, $\frac{3}{4}$ of the cake can be represented as in Figure 7.15:

Figure 7.15

The Linear Model. A second model of rational numbers is a **linear model**. Linear representations make sense when the whole being divided into equal-sized parts is some one-dimensional measure, such as distance (e.g., length, width), time, temperature, or money. Thus, if one were to illustrate that Grandpa had walked $\frac{2}{5}$ of the way home before stopping to rest, $\frac{2}{5}$ could be represented as in Figure 7.16. As in the region model, the whole, in this case a line segment, was broken into 5 equal-sized pieces as indicated by the denominator, and 2 of those 5 pieces, as suggested by the numerator, were highlighted to represent the rational number $\frac{2}{5}$ in this context.

Figure 7.16

The Set Model. The third model of rational numbers is the **set model**. A set model is called for when the whole being described is a collection of discrete objects. For example, if one were to make the statement that $\frac{3}{8}$ of the class was wearing blue jeans on a given day, the whole is the class, which is made up of a group of individual people. Often, in a set model, we can refer to the whole, such as the class, without knowing how many objects are actually in the set. In these cases, drawing an accurate image of $\frac{3}{8}$ of the class using the set model might be difficult.

A context in which the set model is the best means of representing a rational number and can easily be done is in the situation where a student claims that in her bag of 15 gum drops, $\frac{3}{5}$ of them are licorice. The image that comes to mind is see in Figure 7.17:

Figure 7.17

In the above set model, the 15 gum drops are represented by 15 individual circles. The collection of circles is divided into 5 same-sized groups (3 in each group). Then, as the numerator suggests, 3 of those 5 groups (or nine circles altogether) are shaded in to represent $\frac{3}{5}$ of the set.

The Set of Rational Numbers | Equivalent Fractions | Simplifying Fractions   **RELATED TOPICS**
Improper Fractions and Mixed Numbers | Adding Rational Numbers
Subtracting Rational Numbers | Multiplying Rational Numbers
Dividing Rational Numbers | Ratios

TOPIC 7.12 LOOKING AT RATIONAL NUMBERS AS THE SET OF RATIONAL NUMBERS

CORNERSTONE | Sets | The Set of Natural Numbers | The Set of Whole Numbers | The Set of Integers | Fractions | Rational Numbers | Whole-Number Division | Integer Division

INTRODUCTION

The set of rational numbers is related to other sets of numbers such as the set of integers, the set of whole Numbers, and the set of natural numbers. These sets of numbers share some common properties. However, the set of rational numbers introduces new properties unique to this set.

Try to visualize the set of points on a number line corresponding to all the rational numbers. If we concentrate only on those rational numbers between 0 and 1, this task might seem a bit more manageable. Note that on a number line, it is easy to determine that the next whole number after 0 is 1. (See Figure 7.18.) However, can we say what the next rational number after 0 is in the same sense? Pursuing an answer to this simple questions may lead one to the very interesting discovery of the density property of rational numbers that is discussed in detail, along with the definition of and properties of rational numbers, in the sections that follow.

Figure 7.18

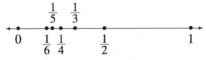

DID YOU KNOW?

The set of natural numbers seem to have served the purposes of most civilized societies until about the sixteenth century. Up to then, people broke items into pieces and spoke of the parts, but even after weights of measure came into use, it was not the custom to speak of such a fraction as, for example, $\frac{3}{4}$ of a pound. The world avoided fractions by creating smaller units. For example, the Romans used the following. A pound of copper was referred to as a *denarius*. To talk about less than one denarius, they created the term *as* to refer to $\frac{1}{16}$ of a denarius or an ounce. So, to talk about an amount equivalent to what we would express as $\frac{1}{8}$ of a pound, the Romans would call it *2 asses* instead.

As the need for representing rational number amounts emerged more distinctly, cultures began to slowly represent unit fractions (those with a one in the numerator). As late as the 17th century, Russian manuscripts on surveying spoke of a "half-half-half-half-half-third" of a certain measure instead of $\frac{1}{96}$ of the measure. Even today the unit fraction is used to some extent in the diamond trade in speaking of parts of a carat. Over time, however, most enduring cultures developed a means of expressing not only the set of unit fractions, but also the larger set of the rational numbers written in fraction form.

For More Information: Smith, D. E. (1958). *History of mathematics, Volume II.* New York: Dover Publications.

**7.12.1
Comparing Sets
of Numbers**

The **Set of Rational Numbers** refers to the entire collection of numbers that can be expressed in the form $\frac{a}{b}$ where both *a* and *b* are integers (provided that b ≠ 0). Consequently, the set of rational numbers (denoted *Q*) includes all natural numbers (denoted *N*), whole numbers (denoted *W*), and integers (denoted I), as well as non-integer fractions of the form $\frac{a}{b}$ where both a and b are integers. Thus, the set of rational numbers can be viewed as a set containing very important subsets as suggested by the following:

$$N \subset W \subset I \subset Q$$

This chain of subsets indicates that any natural number is also a rational number. Thus, any natural number can be expressed in fraction form where numerator and denominator are both integers. For example, the number 3 can be expressed as $\frac{3}{1}$, which meets the criteria of a rational number because 3 and 1 are both integers. The same can be said of any whole number or integer in that any whole number or integer can be expressed as itself in the numerator over a denominator of 1.

7.12.2
Infinite Sets

A **finite set** is a set whose cardinal number is a whole number. An **infinite set** is one that is not finite. Each of the sets of numbers N, W, I, and Q are infinite sets. If each set is infinite, it might seem difficult to compare the sizes of the sets. For example, the set of whole numbers can be defined as the set of natural numbers plus the number zero. With this definition of the set of whole numbers, it is tempting to say that the set of whole numbers is "bigger" than the set of natural numbers because we know it contains one more element, zero. However, because both sets are infinite, and because we can show a one-to-one correspondence between the two sets, that is, match each element in the set of natural numbers to exactly one element in the set of whole numbers as seen in Figure 7.19, we say that sets N and W are the same size.

Natural Numbers: 1 2 3 4 5 6 7 . . . n . . .

Whole Numbers: 0 1 2 3 4 5 6 . . . .n−1. . .

Figure 7.19

7.12.3
**The Density of the
Set of Rational
Numbers**

The set of rational numbers is an infinite set, and because a one-to-one correspondence can be shown to exist between the set of whole numbers and the set of rational numbers, one can conclude that the sets Q and W are the same size. However, although the set of rational numbers is technically the same size as the other infinite sets mentioned above, it has a property that distinguishes it from the other sets. This property is called the Density Property of rational numbers.

The Density Property of Rational Numbers says that between any two rational numbers there is an infinite number of rational numbers. This property suggests that a number line would be "dense" with rational numbers. Thus, given any two rational numbers, say $\frac{7}{9}$ and $\frac{8}{9}$, we should be able to find an infinite number of rational numbers between them.

One way to find at least one rational number between $\frac{7}{9}$ and $\frac{8}{9}$ and is to write equivalent forms of each fraction and search to find an "obvious" rational number between them. For example, rewrite $\frac{7}{9}$ and $\frac{8}{9}$ as $\frac{14}{18}$ and $\frac{16}{18}$, respectively, and note that $\frac{15}{18}$ clearly falls between them. This process can be carried further to find other rational numbers between $\frac{7}{9}$ and $\frac{8}{9}$.

Another strategy for finding at least one number between and would be to find the midpoint between them by averaging them, that is, add the two rational numbers together and divide by 2: $(\frac{7}{9} + \frac{8}{9}) \div 2 = \frac{15}{9} \div 2 = \frac{15}{9} \times \frac{1}{2} = \frac{15}{18}$. Because of the Density Property, this strategy can be repeated endlessly, finding other numbers between $\frac{7}{9}$ and $\frac{8}{9}$ by next finding the midpoint between $\frac{7}{9}$ and $\frac{15}{18}$ and the midpoint betweenn $\frac{8}{9}$ and $\frac{15}{18}$, and so on.

7.12.4
Other Properties of Rational Numbers

The set of rational numbers has properties, other than the Density Property, that describe how numbers within the set relate to one another. For example, like the sets of natural numbers, whole numbers, and integers, the set of rational umbers is closed under addition and closed under multiplication.

Closure Properties for Addition and Multiplication of Rational Numbers. Given any two rational numbers a and b, the sum $a + b$ is a rational number. Therefore, the **set of rational numbers is closed under addition.** For example, choose $a = \frac{1}{3}$ and $b = \frac{2}{5}$. Then $a + b = \frac{1}{3} + \frac{2}{5} = \frac{11}{15}$, and $\frac{11}{15}$ is a rational number.

Similarly, given any two rational numbers a and b, the product $a \cdot b$ is a rational number. Therefore, the **Set of Rational Numbers is closed under multiplication.** For example, choose $a = \frac{1}{4}$ and $b = \frac{3}{7}$. Then $a \times b = \frac{1}{4} \times \frac{3}{7} = \frac{3}{28}$, and $\frac{3}{28}$ is a rational number.

Commutative Properties of the Addition and Multiplication of Rational Numbers. For any two rational numbers a and b, $a + b = b + a$. Thus, the **set of rational numbers is commutative under addition.** Similarly for any two rational numbers a and b, $a \times b = b \times a$, illustrating that the **set of rational numbers is commutative under multiplication.** Therefore, with either operation, the order of addends or factors does not affect the sum or product, respectively, of the rational numbers. For example, $\frac{1}{5} + \frac{3}{4} = \frac{19}{20}$ and $\frac{3}{4} + \frac{1}{5} = \frac{19}{20}$. Likewise, $\frac{3}{8} \times \frac{2}{7} = \frac{6}{56}$ and $\frac{2}{7} \times \frac{3}{8} = \frac{6}{56}$.

The Associative Properties for the Addition and Multiplication of Rational Numbers. Given any three rational numbers a, b, and c, the sum of the three numbers, even when added using different groupings, does not change; that is, $(a + b) + c = a + (b + c)$, meaning that the **set of rational numbers is associative under addition.** For example, when adding $\frac{1}{2}$, $\frac{1}{3}$, and $\frac{1}{4}$, we find:

$$\left(\frac{1}{2} + \frac{1}{3}\right) + \frac{1}{4} = \frac{5}{6} + \frac{1}{4} = \frac{13}{12}$$

$$\frac{1}{2} + \left(\frac{1}{3} + \frac{1}{4}\right) = \frac{1}{2} + \frac{7}{12} = \frac{13}{12}.$$

Further, given any three rational numbers a, b, and c, the product of the three numbers, even when regrouped, is not affected; that is, $(a \times b) \times c = a \times (b \times c)$, meaning that the **set of rational numbers is associative under multiplication.** For example, when multiplying $\frac{1}{2}$, $\frac{1}{3}$, and $\frac{1}{4}$, we find:

$$\left(\frac{1}{2} \times \frac{1}{3}\right) \times \frac{1}{4} = \frac{1}{6} \times \frac{1}{4} = \frac{1}{24}$$

$$\frac{1}{2} \times \left(\frac{1}{3} \times \frac{1}{4}\right) = \frac{1}{2} \times \frac{1}{12} = \frac{1}{24}.$$

Identity Properties for the Addition and Multiplication of Rational Numbers. Like for the addition and multiplication of integers, the set of rational numbers has additive and multiplicative identities. **The additive identity for the set of rational numbers is 0** because for any rational number, a, $a + 0 = 0 + a = a$. For example $\frac{1}{6} + 0 = 0 + \frac{1}{6} = \frac{1}{6}$. Further, **the multiplicative identity for the set of rational numbers is 1** because for any rational number, a, $a \times 1 = 1 \times a = a$. For example, $\frac{1}{6} \times 1 = 1 \times \frac{1}{6} = \frac{1}{6}$.

Multiplication by Zero for the Set of Rational Numbers. As with the set of integers, the set of rational numbers has a special property associated with **multiplication by zero**; that is, for any rational number, a, $a \times 0 = 0 \times a = 0$. Thus, any rational number times zero is zero.

The Distributive Property of Multiplication over Addition for the Set of Rational Numbers. For any three rational numbers a, b, and c, the **Distributive Property of multiplication over addition** holds in that $a \times (b + c) = (a \times b) + (a \times c)$. For example, choosing three rational numbers $\frac{2}{3}$, $\frac{4}{5}$, and $\frac{5}{2}$:

$$\frac{2}{3} \times \left(\frac{4}{5} + \frac{5}{2}\right) = \frac{2}{3} \times \frac{33}{10} = \frac{66}{30} = \frac{11}{5}$$
$$\left(\frac{2}{3} \times \frac{4}{5}\right) + \left(\frac{2}{3} \times \frac{5}{2}\right) = \frac{8}{15} + \frac{10}{6} = \frac{66}{30} = \frac{11}{5}.$$

The Additive Inverse Property for the Set of Rational Numbers. Like the set of integers, the set of rational numbers has an **Additive Inverse Property** that states for any rational number, a, there exists some other rational number, b, such that $a + b = 0 = b + a$. The additive inverse of a usually takes the form $-a$. Thus, the Additive Inverse Property can be stated as, for any rational number, a, there exists some other rational number, $-a$, such that
$$a + -a = 0 = -a + a.$$
For example, given the rational number $\frac{5}{6}$, there exists the rational number $-\frac{5}{6}$, so that $\frac{5}{6} + -\frac{5}{6} = 0$ and $-\frac{5}{6} + \frac{5}{6} = 0$.

The Multiplicative Inverse Property for the Set of Rational Numbers. A new property that holds for the set of rational numbers that does not hold for the set of integers is the **Multiplicative Inverse Property**. According to this property, given any rational number, a, there exists some other rational number, b, such that $a \times b = 1$ and $b \times a = 1$. We say that b is the multiplicative inverse of a. Generally, b takes the form of $\frac{1}{a}$. Thus, the multiplicative inverse property can be stated as, for every rational number, a, there exists some other rational number, $\frac{1}{a}$, such that $a \times \frac{1}{a} = 1$ and $\frac{1}{a} \times a = 1$. This multiplicative inverse is also referred to as the reciprocal.

For example, for the rational number $\frac{4}{3}$ there exists the rational number $\frac{1}{\frac{4}{3}}$ or $\frac{3}{4}$, such that $\frac{4}{3} \times \frac{3}{4} = \frac{3}{4} \times \frac{4}{3} = 1$.

Equivalent Fractions | Simplifying Fractions
Improper Fractions and Mixed Numbers | Adding Rational Numbers
Subtracting Rational Numbers | Multiplying Rational Numbers
Dividing Rational Numbers Properties of Integers | Ratios

RELATED TOPICS

TOPIC 7.13 ADDING RATIONAL NUMBERS

CORNERSTONE	Fractions | Rational Numbers | Equivalent Fractions | Simplifying Fractions Improper Fractions and Mixed Numbers | Integer Addition Integer Multiplication | Integer Division | Least Common Multiple

INTRODUCTION

Addition of rational numbers is a key concept in the school mathematics curriculum. From young students to adults of all ages, people use the addition of rational numbers to solve real-life problems. There are many situations where you have two fractional amounts and want to find out how much you have altogether. In many cases, adding two or more rational numbers involves finding a common denominator before the addition can take place. Within this topic, we will demonstrate methods for adding rational numbers.

DID YOU KNOW?

Early mathematicians dealt with the addition of fractions. The Egyptians, for example, preferred to express ordinary proper fractions as the sum of two or more "subfractions." To indicate that a particular fraction was a "subfraction" the Egyptians used an accent symbol to indicate that the fraction is a subfraction. So using the accented symbol for one-half, $\angle'$, followed by the accented symbol for one-fourth, δ', the Egyptian system represents $\angle'\delta' = \frac{1}{2}\ \frac{1}{4}$ or $\frac{1}{2} + \frac{1}{4} = \frac{3}{4}$.

Later mathematicians, using fraction representation that we use today, added fractions much as we do currently. They usually chose a common denominator by finding the product of the denominators of the two addends.

For More Information: Smith, D. E. (1958). *History of mathematics, Volume II.* New York: Dover Publications.

7.13.1
Addition of Rational Numbers with Common Denominators

When adding two rational numbers that have a common denominator, we simply add the numerators and put the sum over the common denominator. For example, $\frac{3}{8} + \frac{4}{8} = \frac{7}{8}$. The number line model clearly illustrates the addition. Breaking one whole unit into 8 equal-sized pieces, each piece representing $\frac{1}{8}$, we can see the addition of $\frac{3}{8} + \frac{4}{8}$. See Figure 7.20:

Figure 7.20

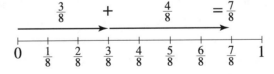

7.13.2
Formal Definition of the Addition of Rational Numbers

In most cases, when adding two rational numbers, the rational numbers do not have a common denominator. So, the first step is to find a common denominator. A simple choice for the common denominator is the product of the two denominators. In the case of $\frac{1}{4} + \frac{2}{3}$, one could choose 12 as the common denominator, re-writing the problem as $\frac{3}{12} + \frac{8}{12}$, then adding $\frac{3+8}{12} = \frac{11}{12}$.

The process of finding the common denominator before adding fractions can be nicely illustrated on the number line model. For example, when adding $\frac{1}{4} + \frac{2}{3}$, we can break one whole unit on the number line into 4 equal-sized pieces as suggested by the 4 in $\frac{1}{4}$ (see Figure 7.21) and then break each of those four pieces into 3 equal-sized pieces as suggested by the 3 in $\frac{2}{3}$. The result in Figure

7.22 is a whole unit broken into 12 equal-sized pieces, each representing $\frac{1}{12}$. Thus, the number line in Figure 7.22 could be used to illustrate the addition of $\frac{1}{4} + \frac{2}{3}$ as $\frac{3}{12} + \frac{8}{12}$ rather easily. Notice that $\frac{1}{4} + \frac{2}{3} = \frac{1 \times 3 + 4 \times 2}{4 \times 3} = \frac{3+8}{12} = \frac{11}{12}$.

The addition of two rational numbers can be expressed formally in this way: $\frac{a}{b} + \frac{c}{d} = \frac{ad + bc}{bd}$, which combines the processes of finding a common denominator, adding numerators, and placing the sum of the numerators over the common denominator. Thus $\frac{2}{5} + \frac{4}{9}$, can be found by $\frac{2 \times 9 + 4 \times 5}{5 \times 9} = \frac{18 + 20}{45} = \frac{38}{45}$.

Figure 7.21

Number line divided into fourths

Figure 7.22

Number line divided into twelfths

When adding two rational numbers where one or more of the addends is a mixed number, you can use two strategies.

7.13.3
Addition of Mixed Numbers

Method 1. Add the whole number parts and the fractional parts separately, and then find the total sum by combining the two parts together. For example, adding $1\frac{1}{3} + 4\frac{2}{5}$, you can rewrite the problem and solve as follows:

$$1\frac{1}{3} + 4\frac{2}{5} = 1 + \frac{1}{3} + 4 + \frac{2}{5} = (1+4) + \left(\frac{1}{3} + \frac{2}{5}\right) = 5 + \left(\frac{5}{15} + \frac{6}{15}\right) = 5 + \frac{11}{15} = 5\frac{11}{15}.$$

Using this method, you may encounter problems where the sum of the fractional parts is greater than one. For example, in the problem $2\frac{2}{3} + 4\frac{3}{4}$, the above method yields the following sum:

$$2\frac{2}{3} + 4\frac{3}{4} = 2 + \frac{2}{3} + 4 + \frac{3}{4} = (2+4) + \left(\frac{2}{3} + \frac{3}{4}\right) = 6 + \left(\frac{8}{12} + \frac{9}{12}\right) = 6 + \frac{17}{12} = 6\frac{17}{12}.$$

Because $\frac{17}{12}$ is an improper fraction, we need to change this to a mixed number so that the total sum can be expressed simply as a mixed number. The $\frac{17}{12}$ can be expressed as $1\frac{5}{12}$. Therefore, the sum is $6 + 1\frac{5}{12} = 7\frac{5}{12}$.

Method 2. A second method for adding rational numbers where one or more of the addends is a mixed number is to first change the mixed numbers to improper fraction form. Then add the fractions, finding a common denominator. Finally, convert your answer back to mixed number form.

For example, $3\frac{3}{7} + 10\frac{7}{12}$, can be rewritten as $\frac{24}{7} + \frac{127}{12}$. Finding a common denominator of 84, the problem can again be rewritten as $\frac{288}{84} + \frac{889}{84} = \frac{288 + 889}{84} = \frac{1177}{84} = 14\frac{1}{84}$.

The Set of Rational Numbers | Subtracting Rational Numbers
Multiplying Rational Numbers | Dividing Rational Numbers

RELATED TOPICS

TOPIC 7.14 SUBTRACTING RATIONAL NUMBERS

CORNERSTONE Fractions | Rational Numbers | Equivalent Fractions | Simplifying Fractions
Improper Fractions and Mixed Numbers | Integer Addition
Integer Subtraction | Integer Multiplication | Integer Division
Least Common Multiple | Adding Rational Numbers

INTRODUCTION *Subtraction of rational numbers is much like the addition of rational numbers. As with addition of rational numbers, there are many real-life problems that can be solved by subtracting two rational numbers. There are many situations where subtraction makes sense. Whether you have a situation where subtraction stems from a take-away context, a missing addend context, or a comparison context, rational numbers are often involved in the problem. In many cases, subtracting one rational number from another involves finding a common denominator before the subtraction can take place.*

DID YOU KNOW? Early mathematicians, using fraction representation that we use today, subtracted fractions much like our current practices. They found common denominator, using the product of the denominators of the two fractions involved in the subtraction problem.

For More Information: Bunt, L.N., Jones, P. S., & Bedient, J.D. (1998). *The Historical Roots of Elementary Mathematics.* New York: Dover Publications

7.14.1
The Subtraction of Rational Numbers with Common Denominators

Much like the addition of rational numbers, subtraction of two rational numbers that share a common denominator can be expressed as finding the difference between the numerators and placing that difference over the common denominator. For example, $\frac{5}{6} - \frac{3}{6} = \frac{5-3}{6} = \frac{2}{6}$.

On a number line, the subtraction of rational numbers can be seen when one whole unit is broken into 6 equal-sized parts, each representing $\frac{1}{6}$. See Figure 7.23.

Figure 7.23

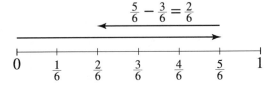

$$\frac{5}{6} - \frac{3}{6} = \frac{2}{6}$$

$$0 \quad \frac{1}{6} \quad \frac{2}{6} \quad \frac{3}{6} \quad \frac{4}{6} \quad \frac{5}{6} \quad 1$$

7.14.2
Formal Definition of the Subtraction of Rational Numbers

When subtracting two rational numbers that do not have a common denominator, we can find a common denominator by multiplying the two denominators together. In the example $\frac{6}{7} - \frac{3}{5}$, the common denominator of 35 ($7 \cdot 5 = 35$) yields the equivalent problem $\frac{30}{35} - \frac{21}{35} = \frac{9}{35}$.

In general, the definition for the subtraction of any two rational numbers can be expressed as follows: $\frac{a}{b} - \frac{c}{d} = \frac{ad - bc}{bd}$. Using this definition, we can determine a common denominator and find the difference between the numerators, placing the difference over the common denominator. For example, $\frac{6}{9} - \frac{3}{5} = \frac{6 \times 5 - 3 \times 9}{9 \times 5} = \frac{30 - 27}{45} = \frac{3}{45}$.

In addition to the number-line model, the region model can illustrate the addition and subtraction of rational numbers. For the subtraction problem $\frac{3}{4} - \frac{2}{6}$

we can begin by breaking the region into four equal-sized rows (suggested by the 4 in the denominator in $\frac{3}{4}$), each row representing $\frac{1}{4}$ (see Figure 7.24), and six equal-sized columns (suggested by the 6 in the denominator in $\frac{2}{6}$), each column representing $\frac{1}{6}$ (See Figure 7.25). Therefore, the region is broken into 24 equal-sized rectangles, each $\frac{1}{24}$ in size, illustrating one such common denominator, 24. See Figure 7.26.

Figure 7.24   **Figure 7.25**   **Figure 7.26**

$\frac{1}{24}$

The subtraction of $\frac{3}{4} - \frac{2}{6}$ can be explained using this region model. First, illustrate that $\frac{3}{4}$ can be represented by shading in three rows or a total of 18 rectangles. See Figure 7.27. Because each column, or 4 rectangles, is $\frac{1}{6}$ of the whole, then $\frac{2}{6}$ is represented by 8 rectangles. So, when subtracting $\frac{2}{6}$ from $\frac{3}{4}$, this can be illustrated by removing 8 rectangles from the shaded 18 rectangles. (See Figure 7.28.) The difference is 10 rectangles or $\frac{10}{24}$.

Figure 7.27   **Figure 7.28**

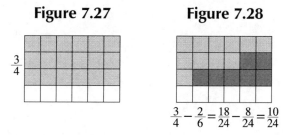

$\frac{3}{4}$

$$\frac{3}{4} - \frac{2}{6} = \frac{18}{24} - \frac{8}{24} = \frac{10}{24}$$

The subtraction of rational numbers, when one or more of the elements of the subtraction problem is a mixed number, can be done using two different methods.

7.14.3
Subtraction of
Mixed Numbers

Method 1. Keep the rational numbers written as mixed numbers. Subtract the whole number part from the whole number part and the fractional part from the fractional part. For example, in the problem $5\frac{4}{5} - 2\frac{1}{2}$, you can think of the problem as follows:

$$5\frac{4}{5} - 2\frac{1}{2} = (5 - 2) + \left(\frac{4}{5} - \frac{1}{2}\right) = 3 + \left(\frac{8}{10} - \frac{5}{10}\right) = 3 + \frac{3}{10} = 3\frac{3}{10}.$$

This method works easily unless the fractional part of the number being subtracted is greater than the fractional part of the minuend. For example, the problem $6\frac{1}{3} - 1\frac{3}{4}$ can be rewritten as $(6 - 1) + (\frac{1}{3} - \frac{3}{4})$. However, we now have a problem with subtracting $\frac{1}{3} - \frac{3}{4}$. What we must do is rethink the problem in a way so that we "borrow" one from the whole part of the minuend and rewrite the fractional part as an improper fraction. For example, rewrite $6\frac{1}{3} - 1\frac{3}{4}$ as $5\frac{4}{3} - 1\frac{3}{4}$. Then, we can break the subtraction of the mixed number into the whole and fractional pieces:

$$5\frac{4}{3} - 1\frac{3}{4} = (5 - 1) + \left(\frac{4}{3} - \frac{3}{4}\right) = 4 + \left(\frac{16}{12} - \frac{9}{12}\right) = 4 + \frac{7}{12} = 4\frac{7}{12}.$$

Method 2. A second method for subtracting rational numbers when mixed number are involved is to first convert mixed numbers to improper fractions and then subtract using common denominators. For example, we can rewrite the problem $10\frac{1}{6} - 3\frac{2}{3}$ as $\frac{61}{6} - \frac{11}{3}$. Then, finding common denominators, the problem is solved by $\frac{61}{6} - \frac{11}{3} = \frac{61}{6} - \frac{22}{6} = \frac{61-22}{6} = \frac{39}{6} = 6\frac{3}{6} = 6\frac{1}{2}$, converting the final answer to a mixed number.

RELATED TOPICS   The Set of Rational Numbers | Multiplying Rational Numbers
Dividing Rational Numbers

TOPIC 7.15 MULTIPLYING RATIONAL NUMBERS

Fractions | Rational Numbers | Equivalent Fractions | Simplifying Fractions
Improper Fractions and Mixed Numbers | Integer Addition
Integer Subtraction | Integer Multiplication | Integer Division
Least Common Multiple | Adding Rational Numbers | Subtracting Rational Numbers

CORNERSTONE

Multiplication of rational numbers is helpful in solving problems that involve finding "part of a part;" that is, if you want to know what one-half of one-third is, the operation to choose to solve this problem is multiplication. We could solve by finding $\frac{1}{2} \times \frac{1}{3} = \frac{1}{6}$. In the sections that follow, we examine the algorithm for multiplying rational numbers, illustrating the multiplication using various models.

INTRODUCTION

Early mathematicians in the Egyptian and Greek cultures encountered difficulties with the multiplication of fractions because of the nature of the symbols used to represent fractions. Other early mathematicians struggled with the concept that the product of two proper fractions, that is, two fractions between 0 and 1, would be less than the factors themselves.

In general, the process of multiplication of simple fractions has not changed dramatically during the last few centuries. One notable difference, however, is that early mathematicians did not cancel common factors between the numerators and denominators of the factors prior to the multiplication of numerator times numerator and denominator times denominator. Today, we readily recognize the advantages canceling common factors before multiplying.

For More Information: Bunt, L. N. H., Jones, P. S., & Bedient, J. D. (1988). *The Historical Roots of Elementary Mathematics.* New York: Dover Publications.

DID YOU KNOW?

To understand what happens when multiplying two rational numbers, it is easiest to start with the multiplication of two rational numbers between zero and one. When multiplying $\frac{1}{3}$ and $\frac{1}{2}$, you could ask the question, "what is $\frac{1}{3}$ of $\frac{1}{2}$?" Asking the multiplication problem this way, we could imagine having a picture of $\frac{1}{2}$ and then determining what $\frac{1}{3}$ of this amount is. Using a number line, as in Figure 7.29, we can show $\frac{1}{2}$ of a whole length and then break this have into three equal-sized pieces in order to examine $\frac{1}{3}$ of this half.

7.15.1
Understanding Multiplication of Two Rational Numbers

| **Figure 7.29** | **Figure 7.30** |

$\frac{1}{3}$ of $\frac{1}{2}$, which equals $\frac{1}{6}$ of the whole

We can further illustrate this idea of taking "part of a part" using the region model. To show $\frac{2}{3} \times \frac{3}{4}$, using the region model, we can break the region into 3 equal-sized rows and 4 equal-sized columns, breaking the region into 12 equal-sized rectangles. See Figure 7.30.

In Figure 7.31, we see that to find $\frac{2}{3}$ of $\frac{3}{4}$, we first illustrate $\frac{3}{4}$ by shading in 3 columns, and then viewing the $\frac{3}{4}$ as divided into 3 equal-sized groups, we can show $\frac{2}{3}$ of $\frac{3}{4}$ by shading 6 of the 9 rectangles. Thus, the solution is $\frac{6}{12}$ or $\frac{1}{2}$.

Figure 7.31

7.15.2
Definition of Multiplication of Rational Numbers

The product of two rational numbers can be found by multiplying numerators and multiplying denominators to find the numerator and denominator, respectively, of the product of the two rational numbers. Formally, we say, $\frac{a}{b} \times \frac{c}{d}$ $= \frac{a \times c}{b \times d}$. For example, $\frac{2}{7} \times \frac{3}{4} = \frac{2 \times 3}{7 \times 4} = \frac{6}{28}$.

7.15.3
Multiplication of Mixed Numbers

When multiplying rational numbers where one or more of the factors are mixed numbers, there are two approaches.

Method 1. One way of multiplying mixed numbers is to first convert the mixed numbers to improper fraction form. Once in improper fraction form, the formal definition can be used to find the product. The product can then be converted back to mixed number form. For example,

$$2\frac{2}{5} \times 5\frac{2}{3} = \frac{12}{5} \times \frac{17}{3} = \frac{12 \times 17}{5 \times 3} = \frac{204}{15} = 13\frac{9}{15} = 13\frac{3}{5}.$$

Method 2. Mixed numbers can be multiplied in mixed number form. However, it requires using the distributive property of multiplication over addition. For example, in the problem above $2\frac{2}{5} \times 5\frac{2}{3}$, we can rewrite the problem as $(2 + \frac{2}{5}) \times (5 + \frac{2}{3})$, and then use the Distributive Property of multiplication over addition in two stages as seen below:

$$\left(2+\frac{2}{5}\right)\times\left(5+\frac{2}{3}\right)=2\times\left(5+\frac{2}{3}\right)+\frac{2}{5}\times\left(5+\frac{2}{3}\right)=(2 \times 5)+\left(2\times\frac{2}{3}\right)+\left(\frac{2}{5}\times 5\right)+\left(\frac{2}{5}\times\frac{2}{3}\right).$$

Multiplying to find these products we finish the problem, finding the same solution in Method 1:

$$=10+\frac{4}{3}+2+\frac{4}{15}=12+\left(\frac{20}{15}+\frac{4}{15}\right)=12+\frac{24}{15}=12+1\frac{9}{15}=13\frac{3}{5}.$$

RELATED TOPICS The Set of Rational Numbers | Dividing Rational Numbers

TOPIC 7.16 DIVIDING RATIONAL NUMBERS

CORNERSTONE

Fractions | Rational Numbers | Equivalent Fractions | Simplifying Fractions
Improper Fractions and Mixed Numbers | Integer Addition
Integer Subtraction | Integer Multiplication | Integer Division
Least Common Multiple | Adding Rational Numbers
Subtracting Rational Numbers | Multiplying Rational Numbers

INTRODUCTION

The operation of division, whether dividing whole numbers, integers, or rational numbers, involves answering the question, "How many of one set fits inside another set?" For example, when dividing $20 \div 4$, one might ask the question, "How many fours are in twenty?" Likewise, when dividing $\frac{3}{5} \div \frac{1}{2}$, one might translate the problem into answering the question, "How many one-halves are there in three-fifths?" Within this topic, we illustrate the process of rational number division using several models and discuss the relationship between rational number multiplication and division.

DID YOU KNOW?

Historically, the division of rational numbers was the most difficult operation to develop. Even though we regularly accept division by a rational number as equivalent to multiplication by the reciprocal of the rational number, this process only came into general use in the early 1900's. Nevertheless, early versions of this process were used in the Middle Ages by both the Hindus and the Arabs. The roots of the process stemmed from the fact that it seemed natural to substitute division by an integer with multiplication by its reciprocal. For example, $\frac{2}{3} \div 4 = \frac{2}{3} \times \frac{1}{4}$. The idea that dividing by 4 is akin to finding one-fourth of a number, that is, multiplying by one-fourth, led to further explorations into division of rational numbers.

Early methods to expand the notion of division by rational numbers included finding a common denominator for the two fractions in the division problem; that is, for the problem $\frac{2}{3} \div \frac{3}{4}$, mathematicians would rewrite the problem with common denominators as $\frac{8}{12} \div \frac{9}{12}$. Then, they would find their solution by taking the quotient of the numerators: $\frac{8}{12} \div \frac{9}{12} = \frac{8 \div 9}{12 \div 12} = \frac{8/9}{1} = \frac{8}{9}$.

Today, division by a rational number helps to solve problems that involves finding how many times a part of something fits into another part. As with the other operations, division of rational numbers can be situated within the context of a linear model, a region model, or a set model. However, division in the context of a set model is difficult to illustrate because with division of rational numbers, the quotient is often much larger than the fractions representing the dividend or the divisor in the problem.

For More Information: Smith, D. E. (1958). *History of mathematics, Volume II*. New York: Dover Publications.

7.16.1
Understanding Division of Rational Numbers

It is essential to understand what question is really being asked when we divide a number by a rational number. In the problem $\frac{1}{3} \div \frac{1}{6}$, the question being asked is, "How many $\frac{1}{6}$s are there in $\frac{1}{3}$? Illustrating this question on a number line helps provide some understanding.

In Figure 7.32, we have broken one whole unit into 3 equal-sized parts to get a picture of $\frac{1}{3}$. Then, knowing that we want to know how many $\frac{1}{6}$s are in $\frac{1}{3}$, we illustrate $\frac{1}{6}$ of the whole, noting that two $\frac{1}{6}$s fit into $\frac{1}{3}$.

Figure 7.32

7.16.2
Definition of Reciprocal

When working with rational numbers of the form $\frac{a}{b}$, where a and b are integers, we say that the **reciprocal** of $\frac{a}{b}$ is the fraction $\frac{b}{a}$. This reciprocal is the multiplicative inverse of the number; that is, $\frac{a}{b} \times \frac{b}{a} = 1$.

7.16.3
Definition of Dividing Rational Numbers

When dividing one rational number by another, we use the definition $\frac{a}{b} \div \frac{c}{d} = \frac{a}{b} \times \frac{d}{c} = \frac{a \times d}{b \times c}$. Many learn this definition by saying, "When dividing by a rational number $\frac{a}{b}$, simply multiply by the reciprocal $\frac{b}{a}$ instead." For example, in the problem $\frac{1}{3} \div \frac{1}{6}$, we can use the definition to find that $\frac{1}{3} \div \frac{1}{6} = \frac{1}{3} \times \frac{6}{1} = \frac{6}{3} = 2$.

7.16.4
Why Can We Multiply by the Reciprocal?

There are several ways to explain why multiplying by the reciprocal yields the same answer as dividing by a rational number. Consider the problem $\frac{1}{2} \div \frac{1}{4}$. The definition for division by rational numbers says that the answer to this problem is the same as the answer to the problem $\frac{1}{2} \times \frac{4}{1}$. Let us illustrate the two problems using a region model for fractions.

Figure 7.33 illustrates the problem $\frac{1}{2} \div \frac{1}{4}$, asking the question, "How many $\frac{1}{4}$s are in $\frac{1}{2}$?" The answer is that there are 2 one-fourths in one-half. Thus, the numeric answer is 2.

Figure 7.33

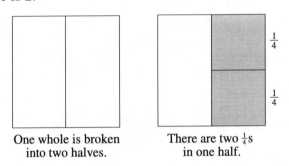

One whole is broken into two halves.

There are two $\frac{1}{4}$s in one half.

When we illustrate the problem $\frac{1}{2} \times \frac{4}{1}$ in Figure 7.34, we see that when we have one-half times 4 or 4 $\frac{1}{2}$s. When we put the four $\frac{1}{2}$s together, they make 2 wholes. Thus, the numeric answer is, again, 2.

Figure 7.34

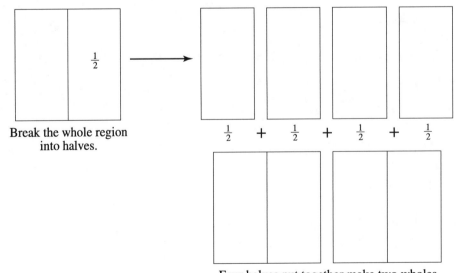

Break the whole region into halves.

$\frac{1}{2}$ + $\frac{1}{2}$ + $\frac{1}{2}$ + $\frac{1}{2}$

Four halves put together make two wholes.

**7.16.5
Dividing Mixed
Numbers**

When dividing rational number that are mixed numbers, the best method is to convert mixed numbers to improper fraction form first. Then, we can easily use the definition of division to find the quotient. For example, in the problem $2\frac{1}{2} \div 3\frac{3}{4}$, we can rewrite these mixed numbers as improper fractions and solve using the definition: $\frac{5}{2} \div \frac{15}{4} = \frac{5}{2} \times \frac{4}{15} = \frac{20}{30} = \frac{2}{3}$.

The Set of Rational Numbrs | Decimal Fractions

RELATED TOPICS

TOPIC 7.17 IRRATIONAL NUMBERS

CORNERSTONE   Terminating and Repeating Decimals

INTRODUCTION   *Irrational numbers are most easily described through examples. Herein, we will define irrational numbers and discuss the decimal representation of irrational numbers. We also highlight the concept of "roots" and other notable examples of irrational numbers.*

DID YOU KNOW?   The discovery of irrational numbers was marked by a great deal of secrecy. The Pythagoreans, who first discovered such numbers, were unable to accept their existence. The Pythagoreans were a society of Greek scholars that was started by Pythagoras (c. 540 B.C.). The society became so secretive about its work it is believed that Hippasus, one of its members, was drowned after he shared the secret of irrational numbers with an outsider! By 300 B.C., many irrational numbers were known.

Examples of such numbers include $\sqrt{2}$, $\sqrt{3}$, and $\sqrt{6}$. By the first century A.D., the Hindus were performing operations on irrational numbers. Among the most interesting irrational numbers is the number denoted, π, and defined as the ratio of the circumference of a circle to its diameter. The value of pi is most often represented by the truncated decimal 3.14, even though its true value is an infinite string of decimals with no identifiable pattern.

For More Information: Reimer, L., & Reimer W. (1990). *Mathematicians are people, too: Stories from the lives of great mathematicians, Volume 1.* Palo Alto, CA: Dale Seymour Publications.

7.17.1
Nonterminating, Nonrepeating Decimals

Some decimals are **nonterminating, nonrepeating decimals**. These types of decimals have an infinite string of digits to the right of the decimal point and the string of digits has no repeating pattern. Examples of nonterminating, nonrepeating decimals are: 0.12112111211112..., - 23.034213531..., 3.141592654..., and 1.414213562....

7.17.2
Definition of Irrational Numbers

Numbers that have a decimal representation as nonterminating, nonrepeating decimals are **irrational numbers**. These are numbers that cannot be represented in the form $\frac{a}{b}$, where a and b are integers, $b \neq 0$; that is, irrational numbers are numbers that are not rational numbers. Many irrational numbers can be expressed in forms other than nonterminating, nonrepeating decimals. Two examples of irrational numbers expressed in a form other than decimal form are π (pronounced "pi") and $\sqrt{2}$ (the square root of two). Note, $\pi = 3.141592654...$ and $\sqrt{2} = 1.414213562...$ in decimal form.

7.17.3
Square Roots

The **square root** of a number is a number, when multiplied by itself, produces the given number. A positive (real) number has two square roots (a positive and a negative real number). A negative (real) number does not have any real number square roots. The notation for square root is the symbol $\sqrt{}$. Thus, $\sqrt{x}$ is read as "the square root of x." Positive numbers that are perfect squares have whole number square roots. For example, $\sqrt{16} = 4$ and $\sqrt{16} = -4$ because $4 \times 4 = 16$ and $(-4) \times (-4) = 16$. To indicate that the square root includes both the positive and negative root value, we often use the symbol $\pm$. Thus, we can write, $\sqrt{16} = \pm 4$.

Positive numbers that are not perfect squares still have square roots. However, the square roots will not be whole numbers. In fact, in many cases the square roots will be irrational numbers. There are methods for approximating square roots of numbers, however the calculator is an available and sufficient tool for completing this task. Just note that calculators often do not indicate both the positive and negative square root values. Rather, they simply display the positive square root. Also, because many square roots are irrational numbers, calculators will not fully represent the nonterminating, nonrepeating nature of the decimal. Therefore, take caution when using calculators for finding square roots.

7.17.4
Roots

Just as we can raise numbers to exponential powers other than 2, we can take roots of numbers other than square roots. For example, we can find the cube root of a number. A cube root of a number is a number, when multiplied by itself twice, produces the given number. The notation for a cube root is the symbol $\sqrt[3]{}$. For example, $\sqrt[3]{8} = 2$ because $2^3 = 2 \times 2 \times 2 = 8$.

We can find any numbered root of a number; that is, we can find the "fourth root," written, $\sqrt[4]{}$, the "sixth root," written, $\sqrt[6]{}$, and so on. In general, *the "nth root," written, $\sqrt[n]{}$, is a number, when multiplied by itself n − 1 times, produces the number itself.*

7.17.5
Rational Exponents

Roots of numbers can be expressed using **rational exponents**, that is, exponents that are rational numbers. Symbolically, we have $\sqrt[n]{x} = x^{1/n}$. For example, $100^{1/2} = \sqrt{100} = 10$. Likewise, $\sqrt[4]{81} = 81^{1/4} = 3$.

Real Numbers

RELATED TOPICS

TOPIC 7.18 REAL NUMBERS

CORNERSTONE | Whole Numbers | Integers | Rational Numbers | Irrational Numbers

INTRODUCTION

The set of real numbers includes whole numbers, negative numbers, fractional numbers, and beyond. In the following sections, we will examine the definition of a real number and how the set of real numbers relates to other numbers systems.

DID YOU KNOW?

An important and dramatic area of mathematics is the theory of infinity. The pioneer in this area was German mathematician named Georg Cantor (1845–1918). Cantor was able to prove that there are an overwhelming number of irrational numbers among the real numbers. Relatedly, he also proved that two line segments, regardless of their lengths, have the same number of points.

For More Information: Bunt, L. N. H., Jones, P. S., & Bedient, J. D. (1988). *The Historical Roots of Elementary Mathematics.* New York: Dover Publications.

7.18.1
The Set of Real Numbers

A **real number** is any rational or irrational number. The **set of real numbers** is the collection of all rational and irrational numbers. The set of real numbers can also be described as the infinite set of all points on a number line. See Figure 7.35.

Figure 7.35

7.18.2
Relationship Between the Reals and Other Number Syustems

The set of real numbers (the reals) is the largest set of numbers that most people have the opportunity to explore. The teals contains many other sets of numbers. The relationship between the teals and other number systems is expressed using subset notation in Figure 7.36.

Figure 7.36

$$\textit{Natural Numbers} \subset \textit{Whole Numbers} \subset \textit{Integers} \subset \textit{Rational Numbers} \subset \textit{Real Numbers}$$

$$\underbrace{\hphantom{aaaaaaaaaaaaaaaaaa}}_{\text{Rational + Irrationals}}$$

The notation indicates that the set of real numbers contains the rational numbers which in turn contain all the Integers, which contain the whole numbers, which contain the natural numbers.

7.18.3
Properties of the Real Numbers

Because the real numbers contains all rational numbers, the reals have the same properties that the rational numbers have. The addition of the irrational numbers into the set of reals does not add any new properties. The properties for rational numbers are described in detail in the section entitled, "Properties of Rational Numbers." A list and an abbreviated description of the properties of real numbers is provided below:

1. The set of real numbers is closed under addition, subtraction, multiplication, and division; that is, the sum, difference, product, or quotient of any two real numbers is also a real number.

2. The set of real numbers is Commutative under addition and multiplication. This says that the order of addends or the order of factors does not affect the sum or product, respectively.

3. The set of real numbers is Associative under addition and multiplication. This property says that when adding or multiplying three real numbers together, the way we choose to group the addends or factors together when adding or multiplying two at a time will not affect the sum or product.

4. The set of real numbers has an Additive Identity of zero. When you add any real number, a, to zero, the sum is always a.

5. The set of real numbers has a Multiplicative Identity of 1. When you multiply any real number, a, by one, the product is always a.

6. The set of real numbers has Additive Inverses. For any real number a, there exists another real number, $-a$, so that $a + -a = 0$.

7. The set of real numbers has Multiplicative Inverses. For any real number a, there exists another Real Number, $\frac{1}{a}$, so that $a \times \frac{1}{a} = 1$.

8. The set of real numbers has the Distributive Property of multiplication over addition; that is, for any real numbers a, b, and c, $a \times (b + c) = a \times b + a \times c$.

| Properties of Rational Numbers | RELATED TOPICS |

IN THE CLASSROOM

Some expectations of your future students

Pre-K-2 (NCTM, 2000, p. 78)

use multiple models to develop initial understandings of place values and the base-ten number system

develop a sense of whole numbers and represent and use them in flexible ways, including relating, composing, and decomposing numbers

Grades 3-5 (NCTM, 2000, p. 148)

understand the place-value structure of the base-ten number system and be able to represent and compare whole numbers and decimals

recognize and generate equivalent forms of commonly used fractions, decimals, and percents

develop and use strategies to estimate computations involving fractions and decimals in situations relevant to students' experience

The last chapter to focus on the *Number and Operations Content Standard*, this chapter also emphasizes the *Connections Process Standard*: "Throughout the pre-K-12 span, students should routinely ask themselves, 'How is this problem or mathematical topic like things I have studied before'" (NCTM, 2000, p. 65). Given that these students should be enabled to "recognize and use connections among mathematical ideas" and "understand and apply mathematics in contexts outside of mathematics" (NCTM, 2000, p. 64), we believe it essential for you to have an understanding of (a) the concepts of ratio and proportion in relationship to fraction concepts, and a meaningful interpretation of different graphs used to represent these ideas (Activities 7.1-7.3), (b) the concepts of decimal and percent in relationship to fraction concepts and a meaningful extension of the base-ten numeration system for decimal representation (Activities 7.4-7.11), and (c) how decimal representations of real numbers indicate the existence of numbers that are not rational and how the latter can be conceptualized geometrically (Activities 7.12-7.14).

How Activities 7.1-7.14 help you develop an adult-level perspective on the above expectations.

- By exploring the concept of ratios in relation to that of fractions, you study the concept of proportion and construct a deeper understanding of equivalent fractions.

- By using proportional thinking, you apply the concepts of ratios and equivalent fractions in solving real life problems that model linear relationships or mathematical similarity.

- By building on your understanding of fractions and of how base-ten blocks represent our numeration system, you extend the latter to construct a model of the decimal system. You then extend prior models of operations to explain why algorithms using decimals work.

- By understanding percent representation in terms of decimals and fractions you develop multiple strategies for solving common problems involving percentages.

- By analyzing patterns in the decimal representations of real numbers, you realize the existence of numbers that are not rational. You learn to construct models of some rational numbers by using concepts studied in geometry and measurement. You thus learn to represent and use the real numbers in flexible ways, including relating, composing, and decomposing them.

BIBLIOGRAPHY

Ben-Chaim, D., Fey, J. T., Fitzgerald, W. M., Benedetto, C., & Miller, J. L. (1998). Proportional reasoning among 7th grade students with different curricular experiences. *Educational Studies in Mathematics, 36,* 247-273.

Bennett, A. B., & Nelson, L. T. (1994). A conceptual model for solving percent problems. *Mathematics Teaching in the Middle School, 1,* 20-25.

Bezuk, N. S., & Armstrong, B. E. (1992). Activities: Understanding fraction multiplication. *Mathematics Teacher, 85,* 729-733, 739-744.

Bezuk, N. S., & Armstrong, B. E. (1993). Activities: Understanding division of fractions. *Mathematics Teacher, 86,* 43-46, 56-60.

Boling, B. A. (1985). A different method for solving percentage problems. Mathematics *Teacher, 78,* 523-524.

Chappell, M. F., & Thompson, D. R. (1999). Modifying our questions to assess students' thinking. *Mathematics Teaching in the Middle School, 4,* 470-474.

Coburn, T. G. (1986). Percentage and the hand calculator. *Mathematics Teacher, 79,* 361-367.

Cramer, K., & Bezuk. N. (1991). Multiplication of fractions: Teaching for understanding. *Arithmetic Teacher, 39* (3), 34-37.6

Cramer, K. A., Post, T. R., & Behr, M. J. (1989). Interpreting proportional relationships. *Mathematics Teacher 82,* 445-452.

Cramer, K., & Karnowski, L (1995) The importance of informal language in representing mathematical ideas. *Teaching Children Mathematics,1,* 332-335.

Cramer, K., & Post,T. R. (1993). Making connections: A case for proportionality. *Arithmetic Teacher 40,* 342-346.

Cramer, K., Post, T. R., & Currier, S. (1993). Learning and teaching ratio and proportion: Research implications. In D. T. Owens (Ed.), *Research ideas for the classroom: Middle grades mathematics* (pp. 159-178). Old Tappan, NJ: Macmillan.

Dewar, J. M. (1984). Another look at the teaching of percent. *Arithmetic Teacher, 31,* 48-49.

Edwards, F. M. (1987). Geometric figures make the LCM obvious. *Arithmetic Teacher, 34 ,* 17-18.

Erickson, D. K. (1990). Activities: Percentages and Cuisenaire rods. *Mathematics Teacher, 83,* 648-654.

Glatzer, D. J. (1984). Teaching percentage: Ideas and suggestions. *Arithmetic Teacher, 31,* 24-26.

Grossman, A. S. (1983). Decimal notation: An important research finding. *Arithmetic Teacher, 30,* 32-33.

Haubner, M. A. (1992). Percents: Developing meaning through models. *Arithmetic Teacher, 40,* 232-234.

Hiebert, J. (1987). Research report: Decimal fractions. *Arithmetic Teacher, 34,* 22-23.

Huinker, D. (1992). Decimals and calculators make sense. In J. T. Fey (Ed.), *Calculators in mathematics education* (pp 56-04). Reston, VA: National Council of Teachers of Mathematics.

Hurd, S. P. (1991). Egyptian fractions: Ahmes to Fibonacci to today. *Mathematics Teacher, 84,* 561-568.

Langford, K., & Sarullo, A. (1993). Introductory common and decimal fraction concepts. In R. J. Jensen (Ed.), *Research ideas for the classroom: Early childhood mathematics* (pp. 223-247). Old Tappan. NJ: Macmillan.

Mack, N. K. (1998). Building a foundation for understanding the multiplication of fractions. *Teaching Children Mathematics, 5,* 34-38.

Meeks, K. I. (1992). Decimals, rounding, and apportionment. *Mathematics Teacher, 85,* 523-525.

Nowlin, D. (1996). Division with fractions. *Mathematics Teaching in the Middle School, 2,* 116- 119.

Oppenheimer, L., & Hunting, R. P. (1999). Relating fractions and decimals: Listening to students talk. *Mathematics Teaching in the Middle School, 4,* 318-321.

Ott, J. M. (1990). A unified approach to multiplying fractions. *Arithmetic Teacher, 37*(7), 47-49.

Owens, D. T. & Super, D. B. (1993). Teaching and reaming decimal fractions. In D T. Owens (Ed.), *Research ideas for the classroom: Middle grades mathematics* (pp. 137-158). Old Tappan, NJ: Macmillan.

Payne, J. N., &Towsley, A. E. (1990). Implementing the *Standards:* Implications of NCTM's *Standards* for teaching fractions and decimals. *Arithmetic Teacher, 37,* 23-26.

Payne, J. N., Towsley, A. E., & Huinker. D. M. (1990). Fractions and decimals. In J. N. Payne (Ed), *Mathematics for the young child (pp.* 175-200). Reston, VA: National Council of Teachers of Mathematics.

Prevost, F. J. (1984). Teaching rational numbers: Junior high school. *Arithmetic Teacher, 31*(6), 43-46.

Quintero, A. H. (1987). Helping children understand ratios. *Arithmetic Teacher, 34,* 17-21.

Rees, J. M. (1987). Two-sided pies: Help for improper fractions and mixed numbers. *Arithmetic Teacher, 35,* 28-32.

Sarver, V. T., Jr. (1986). Why does a negative times a negative produce a positive? *Mathematics Teacher, 79,* 178- 180.

Steiner, E. E. (1987). Division of fractions: Developing conceptual sense with dollars and cents. *Arithmetic Teacher, 34,* 36-42.

Thompson, C. S., & Walker, V. (1996). Connecting decimals and other mathematical content *Teaching Children Mathematics, 2,* 496-502.

Vance, J.M. (1986). Ordering decimals and fractions: A diagnostic study. *Focus on Laming Problems in Mathematics, 8*(2), 51-59.

Vance, J. M. (1986). Estimating decimal products: An instructional sequence. In H. L. Schoen (Ed.), *Estimation and mental computation* (pp. 127-134). Reston, VA: National Council of Teachers of Mathematics.

Warrington, M. A., & Kamii, C. K. (1998). Multiplication with fractions: A Piagetian, constructivist approach. *Mathematics Teaching in the Middle School, 3,* 339-343.

Wiebe, J. H. (1986). Manipulating percentages. *Arithmetic Teacher, 33* (5), 23-26.

Williams, S. E., & Copley, J. V. (1994). Promoting classroom dialogue: Using calculators to discover patterns in dividing decimals. *Mathematics Teaching in the Middle School, 1,* 72-75.

Williams, S. E., & Copley, J. V. (1994). Promoting classroom dialogue: Using calculators to discover patterns in dividing decimals. *Mathematics Teaching in the Middle School, 1,* 72-75.

Zawojewski, J. (1983). Initial decimal concepts: Are they really so easy? *Arithmetic Teacher, 30* (7), 52-56.

8 PATTERNS & FUNCTIONS

CHAPTER OVERVIEW

The concept of function is a central theme, a big idea, running through many areas of mathematics. In this chapter you can learn some interesting facts about functions, and examine some concepts and procedures involving function ideas.

BIG MATHEMATICAL IDEAS

- Problem-solving Strategies
- Functions and Relations
- Representation
- Conjecturing
- Verifying
- Mathematical Structure

NCTM PRINCIPLES & STANDARDS LINKS

Geometry and Spatial Sense
Problem Solving
Reasoning
Communication
Connections
Representation

TOPIC

8.1	Functions
8.2	Equations and Inequalities
8.3	Cartesian Coordinate System
8.4	Graphs and Equations of Lines
8.5	Systems of Linear Equations
8.6	Solving Systems of Linear Equations Symbolically
8.7	Exponents
8.8	Scientific Notation
	In the Classroom
	Bibliography

226

TOPIC 8.1 FUNCTIONS

Set Operations

Functions describe relationships. We often hear expressions such as "worker productivity is a function of employee satisfaction" and "wisdom is a function of time and experience." The message in these expressions is that functions provide a means of showing how one item affects or is related to another. In this section, we examine terminology and notation associated with functions as well as a variety of ways of representing functions.

INTRODUCTION

Russian mathematician, Sonya Kovalevsky (1850 - 1891) was inspired to study mathematics by an unusual source. Her father, General Krukovsky had retired from the military and moved his family into an ancient castle near the Lithuanian border. When her parents ordered wallpaper for all the rooms, they made a measuring error and did not order enough. When papering Sonya's room, instead of using wallpaper, her father covered her walls with a set of lithographed lectures on differential and integral calculus. These were topics he intended to study himself. Sonya became extremely interested in the writings on her walls and worked to decipher the formulas. From this experience, Sonya developed the basis of her mathematical understanding. When she grew up, she went on to win a renowned competition through the Paris Academy of Sciences for original work in mathematics and contributed greatly to the field of mathematics.

DID YOU KNOW?

For More Information: Reimer, L., & Reimer W. (1995). *Mathematicians are people, too: Stories from the lives of great mathematicians, Volume 2.* Palo Alto, CA: Dale Seymour Publications.

A **function** is a mapping, or association, of elements of one set to elements of another set. The mapping is such that each element of the first set is associated with **exactly one** element in the second set. For example, consider the function that maps the set of integers to the set of integers by the mapping $y = x + 1$. For any integer, x, in the first set, we associate it with the integer y in the second set, which can be determined by the mapping of adding 1 to x. Thus, with the function $y = x + 1$, we associate the x-value, 1, with the y-value of $1+1$ or 2. Likewise, the x-value -2 is associated with the y-value $-2 + 1$ or -1. Figure 8.1 illustrates this mapping.

8.1.1
Definition of Functions and Function Notation

We often write functions in terms of x and y, in that we describe how a value for y can be generated given a value for x. We say that y is a function of x, denoted $y = f(x)$. Thus, we can express the function $y = x + 1$ as $f(x) = x + 1$. Thus, to determine the y-value or function value associated with the x-value $x = 5$, we find $f(5) = 5 + 1 = 6$. We have associated $x = 5$ with the y-value, or $f(x)$ value, 6.

Figure 8.1

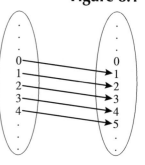

Not all mappings are functions. For example, the mapping $y = \sqrt{x}$ is not a function. A function associates exactly one y-value with each x-value. If we try to evaluate $y = \sqrt{x}$ at the x-value $x = 16$, we find that $\sqrt{16}$ has two values, 4 and -4. Therefore, $y = \sqrt{x}$ is not a function.

The **domain** of a function is the set of all x values in a set that can be mapped to another set according to the association described by the function. The **range** is the set of all y values that can be generated from mapping x-values in the domain according to the association described by the function.

8.1.2
Domain and Range

For example, given the function $y = \frac{x}{x+1}$, we describe the domain by all the x-values that can be mapped through this function to produce a corresponding y-value. Note, though, that fractions cannot have a zero in the denominator. Therefore, if we try to insert the x-value $x = -1$ into the function, we are in the situation of having the fraction $\frac{-1}{0}$. Because this fraction makes no sense, and is not defined, we cannot include the value $x = -1$ in the domain. Therefore, we can say that the domain of the function $y = \frac{x}{x+1}$ is the set of real numbers, except where $x = -1$.

To determine the range of this function, we can try to solve the function for x algebraically to see if there are any restrictions on what values y can take on. Rewriting $y = \frac{x}{x+1}$ so we express x as a function of y, we find:

$$y = \frac{y}{x+1}$$
$$y(x+1) = x$$
$$yx + y = x$$
$$y = x - yx$$
$$y = x(1-y)$$
$$\frac{y}{1-y} = x$$

When we examine the equation $y = \frac{y}{1-y}$, we find that y cannot take on the value $y = 1$ because this value would create a nonsensical fraction with zero in the denominator. Thus, we conclude that $y = 1$ will not be an element in the range. Therefore, the range of the function $y = \frac{y}{1-y}$ is the set of all real numbers except for $y = 1$.

8.1.3
Ways to Describe Functions

There are a variety of ways to describe and represent functions. These ways include: equations, graphs, function machines, tables, mappings, and sets of ordered pairs.

A common means of representing functions is through **equations**. Functions such as $y = 2x + 3$ show an algebraic relationship between two variables x and y. Given various values of x, we can use the equations to find corresponding values for y (or vice versa).

Graphs can also represent functions. From graphs, such as the one shown in Figure 8.2, we can infer a relationship between corresponding x and y values. From the graph in Figure 8.2 we can tell that there is a relationship between corresponding x and y values; that is, as x-values grow larger, y-values grow larger at a faster rate.

Figure 8.2

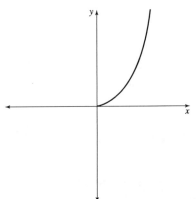

Functions can also be described through function machines. A **function machine** is like a "mystery box" that applies some rule to the x-value that is put into the function machine to produce a corresponding y-value that exits the function machine. Figure 8.3 illustrates a function machine.

With a function machine, we can "guess" the function or rule that is applied to input values to produce output values. In the example of Figure 8.3, we can verify that the function machine takes an input value and subtracts 2 from it to produce the corresponding output values.

Tables provide a means of describing a function. Consider the table of x- and y-values shown in Table 8.1.

We can understand the relationship between the x- and y-values shown to be that the y-value is 10 times the x-value. This relationship could be represented in equation form as $y = 10x$ or $f(x) = 10x$.

Sometimes a **mapping** is an effective way to illustrate a function. Figure 8.4 shows a mapping of the function that can be written in equation form as $f(x) = 3x + 2$.

A second example, seen in Figure 8.5, depicts a function that maps the value 1 in the domain to the value 4 in the range, maps the value 3 in the domain to the value 6 in the range, and so on.

Note that both the values 7 and 11 in the domain are mapped to the value 10 in the range. It is acceptable for a function to have two different x-values associated with the same y value. However it would not be a function if there was a single x-value mapped to two different y-values.

Another way of representing a function is through **ordered pairs**. An ordered pair is a pairing of and x-value and a y-value written parenthetically as (x, y). Given a collection of related ordered pairs, we can understand the function that relates each x-value to its partnered y-value.

For example, as we examine the ordered pairs $(1, 3)$, $(2, 6)$, $(3, 9)$, $(4, 12)$, $(10, 30)$, we can uncover the relationship between x and y as the function the y-coordinate in the ordered pair is three times the x-coordinate in the ordered pair.

Figure 8.3

Inputs

2 3 5 10

Function Machine

0 1 3 8

Outputs

Table 8.1

x	y
−2	−20
−1	−10
0	0
1	10
2	20
3	30
4	40
5	50

Figure 8.4

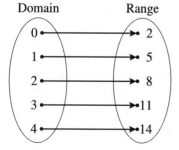

Domain   Range

0 → 2
1 → 5
2 → 8
3 → 11
4 → 14

Figure 8.5

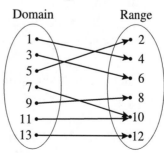

Domain   Range

1
3
5
7
9
11
13

2
4
6
8
10
12

8.1.4
Vertical-Line Test

One way to determine if a mapping is a function is to use the **vertical-line test**. To use this test we do the following:

1. Draw a graph of the mapping.

2. Conceptualize drawing all possible vertical lines (i.e., lines parallel to the vertical axis) through the graph.

3. Determine if any of the vertical lines intersect the graph at more than one point.

4. If no line touches the graph at more than 1 point, the mapping is a function.

5. If one or more lines touches the graph at more than 1 point, the mapping is not a function.

For example, consider the graphs in Figure 8.6. The first graph passes the vertical-line test, that is, represents a function, because any vertical line we can draw through the graph will only touch the graph at exactly one point. On the other hand, the second graph is not a function because we can find at least one vertical line that passes through two points of the graph.

The vertical-line test makes sense because what the test detects are points where there are two y-values associated with a single x-value. Thus, failing the vertical line tests means that the graph does not match the fundamental definition of a function.

Figure 8.6

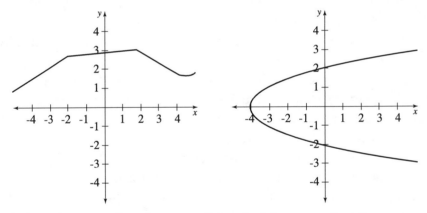

8.1.5
Composition of
Functions

When we have two functions, say $f(x)$ and $g(x)$, we can find the **composition** of $f(x)$ with $g(x)$, denoted $(f \circ g)(x)$ or $f(g(x))$, by evaluating the function $f(x)$ using the entire function $g(x)$ as the independent variable.

For example, given the functions $f(x) = 2x + 5$ and $g(x) = 10x - 1$, we can find $f(g(x))$ by substituting the function $10x - 1$ into the x-value in the function $f(x)$. That is, $f(g(x)) = 2(10x - 1) + 5 = 20x - 2 + 5 = 20x + 3$. We can evaluate the new function formed from the composition of f and g. For example, with the function $f(g(x)) = 20x + 3$, we can find $f(g(4)) = 20(4) + 3 = 27$.

As a second example, suppose we have the functions $f(x) = x^2 + 3x - 9$ and $g(x) = x + 2$, we find $f(g(x)) = (x + 2)^2 + 3(x + 2) - 9 = x^2 + 4x + 4 + 3x + 6 - 9 = x^2 + 7x + 1$. Evaluating $f(g(-1)) = (-1)^2 + 7(-1) + 1 = 1 - 7 + 1 = -5$. The function machine shown in Figure 8.7 shows the composition of these functions.

The composition of functions might be further clarified by picturing $f(g(x))$ as a mapping as depicted in Figure 8.8.

Figure 8.7

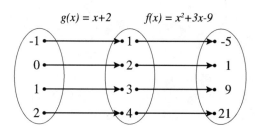

Figure 8.8

Patterns | Cartesian Coordinate System   **RELATED TOPICS**
Measurement and Coordinate Geometry

TOPIC 8.2 EQUATIONS AND INEQUALITIES

CORNERSTONE | Multiplying Rational Numbers | Dividing Rational Numbers
Adding Rational Numbers | Subtracting Rational Numbers

INTRODUCTION | *We make comparisons in almost everything we do. When those comparisons seek to find whether two things are numerically equal or if one is greater than the other, we must engage in solving an equation or an inequality. In the following sections, we examine the definitions of equations and inequalities and the properties associated with them.*

DID YOU KNOW? | Historically, equations were not classified clearly by type. Today, we have a system of describing polynomial equations by the highest degree, that is the largest exponent, that appears in the polynomial expression. For example, when the highest exponential power in an equation is one, the equation is called a linear equation. However, when the highest exponential power in an equation is two, the equation is classified as a quadratic equation.

8.2.1
Definition of Equation

An **equation** is a statement of equality between two expressions. The equality between the expressions is denoted by an **equals sign**, "=." Equations can relate any variety of expressions. Examples of equations include $4 = 2 + 2$, $7 = x + 3$, $y = 8x - 5$.

8.2.2
Properties of Equations

The beauty of equations, and the key behind solving algebraic equations, is that they have a number of properties that allow us to maintain the equality as we alter the expressions simultaneously:

Given any real number, a, and expressions x and y:

Addition Property of Equations. If $x = y$, then $x + a = y + a$; that is, adding the same amount to the expressions on both sides of an equation creates two new expressions that are also equal. For example, given that $4 = 2 + 2$, then $4 + 8 = 2 + 2 + 8$ ($12 = 12$).

Subtraction Property of Equations. If $x = y$, then $x - a = y - a$; that is, subtracting the same amount from the expressions on both sides of an equation creates two new expressions that are also equal. For example, given that $10 = 10$, then $10 - 3 = 10 - 3$ (that is, $7 = 7$).

Multiplication Property of Equations. If $x = y$, *then* $a \times x = a \times y$; that is, multiplying the same amount times the expressions on both sides of an equation creates two new expressions that are also equal. For example, given that $y = 5$, then $2 \times y = 2 \times 5$ (that is, $2y = 10$).

Division Property of Equations. If $x = y$, then $x \div a = y \div a (a \neq 0)$; that is, dividing the expressions on both sides of an equation by the same amount creates two new expressions that are also equal. For example, given that $x = 6$, then $x \div 2 = 6 \div 2$ ($\frac{x}{2} = 3$).

An **inequality** is a statement that one quantity is less than (or greater than) another. For real numbers a and b, if a is less than b, their relationship is denoted, $a < b$. Likewise, if a is greater than b, their relationship is denoted $a > b$. In some cases, we have the situation where a is either less than b or equal to b. In this case we say a is less than or equal to b, and denote the relationship by $a \leq b$. Similarly, when a is greater than or equal to b, we denote this with the symbols, $a \geq b$. Examples of inequality statements include: $5 < 13$, $7 > 2 + 3$, $x + 8 \leq 8$, and $3 \geq x$.

There are properties associated with inequalities that allow us to alter both sides of the inequalities simultaneously and still maintain the less than (or greater-than) relationship. The following properties are stated with regard to the less-than relationship, but also hold true for greater-than situations, less-than or equal-to situations, and greater-than or equal-to situations.

Given any real number , a, and quantities x and y:

Addition Property of Inequalities. If $x < y$, then $x + a < y + a$; that is, adding the same number to both sides of an inequality maintains the inequality. For example, given $2 < 7$, then $2 + 5 < 7 + 5$ (that is, $7 < 12$).

Subtraction Property of Inequalities. If $x < y$, then $x - a < y - a$; that is, subtracting the same number from both sides of an inequality maintains the inequality. For example, given $8 < 10$, $8 - 1 < 10 - 1$ (that is, $7 < 9$).

Multiplication Property of Inequalities. If $x < y$, then (a) $a \times x < a \times y$, when $a > 0$ and (b) $a \times x > a \times y$, when $a < 0$; that is, multiplying both sides of an inequality by the same amount affects an inequality differently, depending on whether the factor is positive or negative.

When multiplying by a positive factor, the inequality stays the same. For example, given $6 < 9$, then $10 \times 6 < 10 \times 9$, (that is, $60 < 90$). However, when multiplying by a negative factor, the inequality changes directions (that is, a less than becomes greater than and vice versa). For example, given $2 < 5$, then $-8 \times 2 > -8 \times 5$ (that is, $-16 > -40$).

Division Property of Inequalities. If $x < y$, then $x \div a < y \div a$, when $a > 0$ and $x \div a > y \div a$, when $a < 0$; that is, dividing both sides of an inequality by the same amount affects an inequality differently, depending on whether the divisor is positive or negative. (Note that division by 0 is undefined.)

When dividing by a positive factor, the inequality stays the same. For example, given $2 < 9$, then $2 \div 5 < 9 \div 5$, (that is, $\frac{2}{5} < \frac{9}{5}$). However, when dividing by a negative divisor, the inequality changes directions (that is, a less than becomes a greater than and vice versa). For example, given $6 < 20$, $6 \div (-2) > 20 (-2)$, (that is, $-3 > -10$).

Properties of Rational-Number Addition
Properties of Rational-Number Multiplication

RELATED TOPICS

TOPIC 8.3 CARTESIAN COORDINATE SYSTEM

INTRODUCTION

We often have to give directions to a particular location to others. Those directions often involve pinpointing a position on a map according to certain distances from one point to another. Understanding the location of points on a map is similar to understanding the Cartesian Coordinate System. In this section, we will examine key concepts related to the Cartesian Coordinate System and how to identify the location of points within the system.

DID YOU KNOW?

Rene Descartes (1596–1650) was a French mathematician who is credited with being the first to combine the study of algebra and geometry, creating coordinate geometry. In fact, the Cartesian coordinate system is named in his honor. It is said that Descartes slept a lot and that his insight into the field of coordinate geometry came to him in a dream.

For More Information: Reimer, L., & Reimer W. (1995). *Mathematicians are people, too: Stories from the lives of great mathematicians, Volume 2.* Palo Alto, CA: Dale Seymour Publications.

8.3.1
Definition of the Cartesian Coordinate System and Related Terms

The **Cartesian Coordinate System** is the set of all points in a plane that are identified by a pair of x- and y- coordinates. **Coordinates**, denoted together as the **ordered pair** *(x, y)*, are numbers that designate the position of a point in the plane where the first number indicates the position along the x-axis and the second number indicates the position along the y-axis. The coordinate plane is determined by two intersecting, perpendicular lines called the **x-axis and y-axis**. Note that the x- and y-axes each contain an infinite set of points equivalent to the real number line. The point where these axes intersect is called the **origin** and is denoted $(0, 0)$, indicating that the location of the point along the x-axes is at zero, and the location of the point along the y-axes is zero (see Figure 8.9).

The coordinate plane is broken into four sections, called **quadrants**, by the x- and y-axes. (See Figure 8.9). The first quadrant, denoted Q1, is the section where both the x- and y-coordinates are positive. Note that the point $(3, 1)$ in Figure 8.9 lies in the first quadrant. The second quadrant, Q2, is the section where the x-coordinate is negative and the y-coordinate is positive. The third quadrant, Q3, is the section where both the x- and y-coordinates are negative. The point $(-1, -3)$ as seen in Figure 8.9 is in Q3. Finally, the fourth quadrant, Q4, is the section where the x-coordinate is positive and the y-coordinate is negative.

Figure 8.9

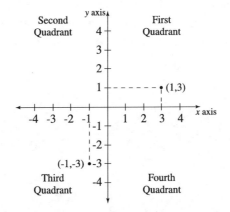

8.3.2
Equations of
Horizontal and
Vertical Lines

In the coordinate plane, we can represent any collection of points. It is often valuable to indicate a set of points that all lie on the same line. When those lines are vertical or horizontal lines, they can be identified by *x*- and *y*- coordinates, respectively. Examine the vertical line, *m*, in Figure 8.10. Notice that for each point that can be identified along line *m*, the *x*-coordinate is always 2. So, for any choice of *y*-coordinate, the *x*-coordinate is fixed at 2. Therefore, we can refer to vertical line *m* as the line $x = 2$. In general, a vertical line where the *x*-coordinate is always the same number, *a*, can be referred to as the line $x = a$.

Now, in examining the horizontal line, *n*, in Figure 8.10, we make a different observation. In this case, the points that are identified as being on line *n* all have the same *y*-coordinate of 3. Thus, given any *x*-coordinate, the *y*-coordinate is always the same number, 3. Therefore, we can refer to line *n* as the line $y = 3$. In general, horizontal lines where the *y*-coordinate is always the same number, *b*, can be referred to as $y = b$.

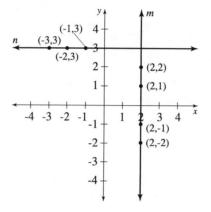

Figure 8.10

RELATED TOPICS

TOPIC 8.4 GRAPHS AND EQUATIONS OF LINES

INTRODUCTION

Many situations in life involve relationships that are considered linear. Some might say that there is a linear relationship between the amount of time spent studying and the grade you earn on an exam. In this section, we examine lines and related concepts such as slopes and points on a line, particularly points that intersect the x- and y-axes which are called intercepts.

DID YOU KNOW?

Maria Agnesi (1718–1799), the daughter of an Italian mathematics professor, was said to be a child prodigy. She is one of the most celebrated Italian woman of the scientific revolution. Her most noted work, the book entitled, *Foundations of Analysis*, includes a systematic presentation of algebra, analytic geometry, calculus, and differential equations. She made great strides in work related to the graphing of equations, particularly the "bell-shaped curve" often used to graphically describe a normal distribution of data.

For More Information: Reimer, L., & Reimer W. (1995). *Mathematicians are people, too: Stories from the lives of great mathematicians, Volume 2*. Palo Alto, CA: Dale Seymour Publications.

8.4.1
Slopes of Lines

Slope refers to the inclination of a line. A line that rises vertically as we trace along the line from left to right is said to have a **positive slope**. For example, in Figure 8.11, lines *a, b,* and *c* have positive slopes. The slope of line *b*, which runs exactly between the *x*-axis and the *y*-axis, is a slope of 1. The slope of line *c*, which is less steep than line *b* will be a positive fraction that is less than 1—approximately $\frac{1}{2}$. The slope of line *a*, which is steeper than line *b*, is a positive number greater than 1—approximately a slope of 3 as pictured in Figure 8.11.

A line that lowers vertically as we trace along the line from left to right is said to have a **negative slope**. For example, lines *d, e,* and *f* in Figure 8.12 have negative slopes. Line *e* has a slope of approximately −1. Line *d* is steeper than line *e* and has a slope of approximately −2. Finally, line *f* is less steep than line *e* and has a slope of approximately −$\frac{1}{2}$.

We should note that all lines are characterized by slope, even horizontal and vertical lines. Horizontal lines have a slope of zero; however, the slope of vertical lines are undefined. Vertical lines are said to have no slope.

Figure 8.11

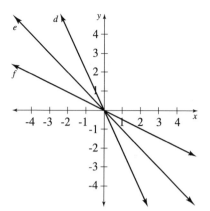

Figure 8.12

To determine the slope of a line, you need to know two points on the line. Given two points on a line, (x_1, y_1) and (x_2, y_2), we can determine the slope, denoted m, of the line between the points by computing $m = \frac{y_2 - y_1}{x_2 - x_1}$. For example, given points $(4, 3)$ and $(-1, 6)$, we compute the slope of the line between the points $m = \frac{6 - 3}{-1 - 4} = \frac{3}{-5} = -\frac{3}{5}$. Plotting the points and drawing the line that connects them, we verify that the slope of the line is, in fact, negative and that the line appears to have a slope of $-\frac{3}{5}$ (see Figure 8.13).

8.4.2
Computing the Slope of a Line

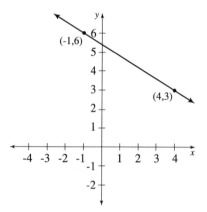

Figure 8.13

Lines in the plane that pass through the origin can be written in equation form by $y = mx$. The slope of the line through the origin is designated by m. For example, the line $y = 3x$ is a line that passes through the origin and has a slope of 3. We can approximate what the line looks like or we can use the slope, 3, and the fact that the line goes through the point $(0, 0)$, and determine a second point on the line.

8.4.3
Lines of the Form $y = mx$

Slope is determined by computing the change in y-values divided by the change in x-values, that is $y_2 - y_1$ divided by $x_2 - x_1$. Many describe slope as "rise over run" because the numerator describes how far (up or down) we rise from one point and how far we run (right or left) to locate another point on a line.

For example, we can view the slope of 3 as $\frac{3}{1}$ where the numerator, 3, denotes the change in y-values and the denominator, 1, denotes the change in x-values. Thus, starting at the origin $(0, 0)$, we can determine another point on the line by moving 3 units upward from $(0, 0)$ for the change in y direction, and moving 1 unit to the right for the change in the x direction (See Figure 8.14).

Figure 8.14

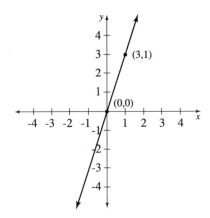

Moving up 3 units and to the right 1 unit, we identify another point on the line $y = 3x$ as the point $(1, 3)$. Connecting the two points with a line, we observe that the slope appears to be a slope of 3 as planned.

In a second example, given the line $y = -\frac{1}{2}x$, we can determine another point , other than the origin, on the line. Starting at the origin, we move down 1 unit (down because it is a negative number) and to the right 2 units (to the right because the 2 is positive). Thus, we identify that the point $(2, -1)$ is a point on the line $y = -\frac{1}{2}x$ and can now graph the line by joining the two points $(0, 0)$ and $(2, -1)$. See Figure 8.15.

Figure 8.15

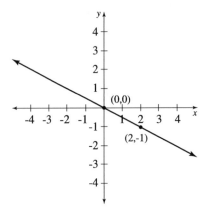

8.4.4
X- and Y-Intercepts

An intercept is a point that intersects one of the axes. An ***x*-intercept** is a point where a line intersects the *x*-axis. Because the *x*-intercept is a point on the *x*-axis, the corresponding *y*-value for any *x*-intercept is $y = 0$. Thus, given an equation of a line, for example, $y = 5x + 3$, we can determine any *x*-intercepts by setting $y = 0$ and solving for *x*:

$$y = 5x + 3$$

Setting y = 0 we find:

$$0 = 5x + 3$$
$$-3 = 5x$$
$$-\frac{3}{5} = x.$$

Thus, the *x*-intercept for the line $y = 5x + 3$ is the point $(-\frac{3}{5}, 0)$.

A **y-intercept** is a point that intersects the *y*-axis. For any point that intersects the *y*-axis, the *x*-value is zero. Thus, to find a *y*-intercept, we can set $x = 0$

and solve for *y*. For example, with the equation $y = 5x + 3$, we can determine
any *y*-intercepts by setting $x = 0$:

$$y = 5x + 3.$$

setting $x = 0$ we find:

$$y = 5 \times 0 + 3$$
$$y = 3.$$

Thus, the *y*-intercept for the line $y = 5x + 3$ is the point (0, 3). Plotting the *x*-
and *y*-intercepts for the line $y = 5x + 3$, we can then graph the line by connecting the intercepts. See Figure 8.16.

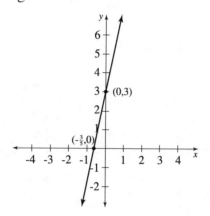

Figure 8.16

We call the equation of a line in the form $y = mx + b$ the **slope-intercept
form**. In this form, *m* is the slope, and *b* is the *y*-intercept. Thus, in the example
$y = 2x + 6$, the slope of the line is 2 and the *y*-intercept is the point (0, 6). In the
example $y = 4x - 5$, the slope is 4 and the *y*-intercept is the point (0, −5).

8.4.5
**Slope-Intercept
Form of a Line**
$y = mx + b$

Given the slope, *m*, of a line and a point (x_1, y_1) on the line, we can determine
the equation of the line using the Point-Slope Formula. The point-slope formula
is: $y - y_1 = m(x - x_1)$. For example, given the point $(x_1, y_1) = (2, 5)$ on a line
with slope $m = -2$, we can determine the equation of the line by $y - 5 = -2(x
- 2)$. Distributing the −2 across the parenthetical expression and adding 5 to
both sides of the equation, we simplify the equation to slope-intercept form:

$$y - 5 = -2(x - 2)$$
$$y - 5 = -2x + 4$$
$$y = -2x + 9.$$

8.4.6
**Point-Slope
Formula for the
Equation of a Line**

Systems of Linear Equations | Solving Systems of Linear Equations

RELATED TOPICS

TOPIC 8.5 SYSTEMS OF LINEAR EQUATIONS

CORNERSTONE The Cartesian Coordinate System | Solving Systems of Linear Equations

INTRODUCTION *When we try to determine a relationship between two variables, such as a relationship between smoking and lung cancer, we often have to work within certain constraints. The relationship, as well as these constraints, can be expressed as equations. To thoroughly understand the relationship between the variables at hand, we have to consider all equations simultaneously. In this section, we describe a process of considering linear equations simultaneously and a method of solving those equations.*

DID YOU KNOW? Professor George Dantzig from Stanford University is known for creating a technique for solving linear programming problems called the simplex method. The need for such a method of solving simultaneous linear equations was motivated by the problem of moving men and materials more efficiently during World War II. Dantzig's work provided the solution to this very immediate problem and aided the efforts of the allies in the war.

For More Information: Smith, D. E. (1958). *History of mathematics, Volume II.* New York: Dover Publications.

8.5.1 Simultaneous Equations

A **system of equations** is a collection of equations for which there is some relationship or for which together they set conditions on a mathematical situation. Two or more equations can have different sets of solutions. However, *sometimes we wish to consider the equations simultaneously* and determine what solutions solve all of the equations at the same time. For example, consider the equations $x + y = 2$ and $3x + y = 5$. Considered individually, the equations have many solutions. For example, the equation $x + y = 2$ has such solutions as $x = 3$ and $y = -1$, $x = 0$ and $y = 2$, $x = -4$ and $y = 6$, and so on. The equation $3x + y = 5$ has such solutions as $x = 0$ and $y = 5$, $x = 2$ and $y = -1$, $x = -3$ and $y = 4$, and so on. However, if we consider the two equations simultaneously, and try to determine values for x and y that solve both equations at the same time, we would find that only the solution $x = 1$ and $y = 1$ solves the equations simultaneously.

8.5.2 Geometrical Relationships of the Graphs of Two Lines

When we examine the relationship between two linear equations, we find that one of three relationship exists: (1) the lines intersect at some singular point, (2) the lines are parallel to each other and never intersect, or (3) the lines are coincidental, that is, they lie one on top of the other. Let us explore each of these relationships and their geometrical representations (see Figure 8.17).

In any situation where we have two linear equations with different slopes, the two lines will intersect at one singular point. For example, the lines $y = 2x + 6$ and $y = 5x - 2$ have slopes 2 and 5, respectively. Therefore, the two lines will, at some point, intersect. See Figure 8.18.

When two lines have the same slope, they will be parallel or coincidental. If two lines are coincidental, they are essentially the same line, but might be written in alternative forms. For example, the lines $y = x - 5$ and $2y = 2x - 10$ are essentially the same lines. If we divide both sides of the linear equation $2y = 2x - 10$, we have the equation $y = x - 5$. Therefore, the graphs of the to lines basically have the same slope and same y-intercept. Thus, the lines lie one on top of each other (see Figure 8.19).

Figure 8.17

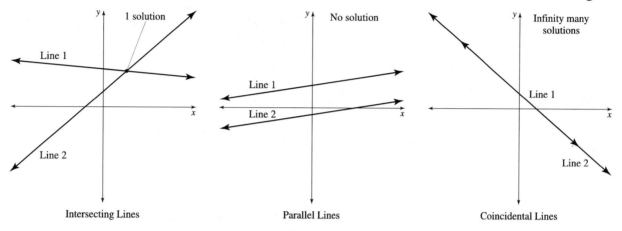

Intersecting Lines   Parallel Lines   Coincidental Lines

Figure 8.18

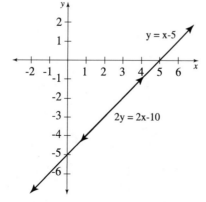

Figure 8.19

If two lines are parallel, they have the same slope, but different y-intercepts. For example, the lines $y = 3x + 1$, $y = 3x - 1$, $y = 3x$, and $y = 3x + 3$ are parallel because they all have a slope of 3 and different y-intercepts. See Figure 8.20 for a graphical representation of these lines.

When solving simultaneous linear equations, we will find that those lines that intersect at a single point will have a single simultaneous solution. On the other hand, two lines that are parallel will represent linear equations that have no simultaneous solutions. Finally, when two lines are coincidental, they represent linear equations that have an infinite number of simultaneous solutions.

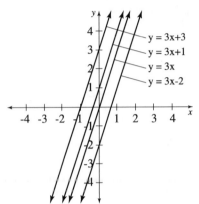

Figure 8.20

8.5.3
Solving
Simultaneous
Linear Equations

Given two linear equations, we can find simultaneous solutions by finding the point (or points) where they intersect. Consider, for example, the equations $y = 4x + 2$ and $y = -x + 3$. Graphically, we can see that the two lines intersect at one point (see Figure 8.21).

To determine the precise point of intersection, we use an algebraic process. Because we want to find when the equations take on the same value, let us set the two equations equal to each other and solve for x. So, given $y = 4x + 2$ and $y = -x + 3$, we form the equation:

$$4x + 2 = -x + 3.$$

Now, solving for x:

$$4x + 2 = -x + 3$$
$$5x = 1$$
$$x = \frac{1}{5}.$$

Then, because the two equations are equal at the point where $x = \frac{1}{5}$, we can find the corresponding y-value at the point by evaluating either of the equations at the x-value $x = \frac{1}{5}$. Solving we find that $y = \frac{14}{5}$. Referring back to the graph of the two equations in Figure 8.21, we can see that the point of intersection appears to have the coordinates $(\frac{1}{5}, \frac{14}{5})$.

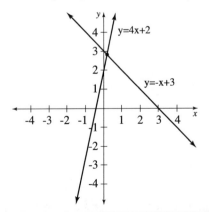

Figure 8.21

RELATED TOPICS   Solving Systems of Linear Equations Symbolically

TOPIC 8.6 SOLVING SYSTEMS OF LINEAR EQUATIONS SYMBOLICALLY

| Cartesian Coordinate System │ Graphs of Linear Equations Systems of Linear Equations | **CORNERSTONE** |

Solving systems of linear equations can be done in a variety of ways. In addition to solving systems of linear equations by looking for points of intersection, we can also use methods of substitution and elimination. In this section, we examine these methods and also develop a process for determining the equation of the line between two points.

INTRODUCTION

Narendra Karmarkar, a linear programmer with AT&T Bell Laboratories in 1984, invented a method for solving linear programming problems quickly. In fact, his method is so fast, it can be used to provide immediate answers to problems that arise requiring an efficient and accurate response.

DID YOU KNOW?

For More Information: Smith, D. E. (1958). *History of mathematics, Volume II.* New York: Dover Publications.

Given a set of linear equations, we can sometimes solve them through basic **substitution**. For example, given the equations: $y = x + 3$ and $y - 5 = 4x - 4$, we can substitute the expression $x + 3$ for y in the equation $y - 5 = 4x - 4$, getting: $(x + 3) - 5 = 4x - 4$. Solving for x algebraically we find: $x = \frac{2}{3}$.

8.6.1
Solving Systems of Equations by Substitution

In some cases, solving systems of equations involves **eliminating** one of the variables so that we can solve for the other. For example, given the equations: $y = -3x + 7$ and $2y = 2x + 1$, we can set the equations up vertically, lining up like variables and constants:

$$y = -3x + 7$$
$$2y = 2x + 1$$

8.6.2
Solving Systems of Equations by Elimination

First, to create a situation where we have the same number of x or y in each equation, we can multiply both sides of one equation by the appropriate number to create an equivalent equation. In this case, if we multiply both sides of the top equation by a factor of 2, we have the equations:

$$2y = -6x + 14$$
$$2y = 2x + 1$$

Next, we can view the top equation as the minuend in a subtraction problem and the bottom number as the subtrahend. Subtracting like terms from like terms, we find the difference between the two equations:

$$2y = -6x + 14$$
$$\underline{2y = 2x + 1}$$
$$0 = -8x + 13$$

Finally, because we have successfully eliminated the variable y from the equations, we can solve for x. We find that $x = \frac{13}{8}$. With this value of x, we can determine the corresponding value of y by evaluating one of the original equations at $x = \frac{13}{8}$, finding that $x = \frac{17}{8}$.

8.6.3
Determining the Equation of a Line Through Two Points

Given a point and the slope of a line, we can use the point-slope formula to determine the equation of a line. However, if all we know are two points on a line, we can still determine the equation of the line through those points. Using the two points, we can find the slope between the two points using the slope formula. Then, using this slope, and one of the points, we can then use the point-slope formula to determine the equation of the line.

For example, let us determine the equation of the line that passes through the points $(2, 3)$ and $(4, -3)$. First, we find the slope, $m = \frac{y_2 - y_1}{x_2 - x_1} = \frac{-3 - 3}{4 - 2} = \frac{-6}{2} = -3$. Then, choosing one of the points, say $(2, 3)$, we use the point-slope formula to find the equation of the line:

$$y - y_1 = m(x - x_1)$$
$$y - 3 = -3(x - 2)$$
$$y = -3x + 6 + 3$$
$$y = -3x + 9.$$

TOPIC 8.7 EXPONENTS

Base Ten | Order of Operations **CORNERSTONE**

Exponents provide a means of expressing many large amounts concisely. In this section we define exponents and related terms and introduce exponential notation. We also highlight well-known exponential numbers including square and cubic numbers.

INTRODUCTION

The concept of an exponent was known in theory well before practical uses for the exponent were developed. However, it was mathematician, John Wallis (c. 1650), who showed that x^0 should represent 1. Wallis was also the person who established notation for fractional and negative exponents.

DID YOU KNOW?

For More Information: Smith, D. E. (1958). *History of mathematics, Volume II*. New York: Dover Publications.

An **exponent** is a symbol placed above and after a number or expression, referred to as the **base**, that raises the base to the **power** designated by the symbol. In the example x^n, the expression x is the base and the exponent is n.

The operation that an exponential symbol represents is the multiplication of the designated base times itself the number of times indicated by the exponent. Thus, in the exponential expression, 10^3, we interpret the symbols to mean 10^3 = $10 \times 10 \times 10$ = 1,000. Because 1,000 can be expressed as 10^3, we can refer to 1,000 as *a power of ten*, indicating that the value 1,000 can be generated by multiplying 10 times itself a given number of times.

People often confuse the phrases *a power of* and *a multiple of*. To clarify, consider the expression *a power of 10*, for example. This refers to numbers generated by raising 10 to an exponential power such as $10^1 = 10$, $10^2 = 100$, $10^3 = 1,000$, $10^4 = 10,000$, $10^5 = 100,000$, and so on. On the other hand, *multiples of 10* refer to the set of numbers generated by multiplying 10 times an integer value, such as $1 \times 10 = 10$, $2 \times 10 = 20$, $3 \times 10 = 30$, $4 \times 10 = 40$, $5 \times 10 = 50$, and so on. Note that a number that is a power of 10, or of any base, is also a multiple of 10, or that base, but the reverse does not hold true.

8.7.1
Definition of Terms Associated with Exponents

We refer to the exponential expression of a base raised to the power of 2 as the **square** of that number. Similarly, we refer to the exponential expression of a base raised to the power of 3 as the **cube** of that number. For example, 4^2 is read, "four squared" and the number 16 is referred to as "the square of 4." Likewise, 5^3 is read as "five cubed" and the number 125 is referred to as "the cube of 5."

For powers other than 2 or 3, we generally refer to the exponential expression by the ordinal number represented by the exponent; that is, 2^4 is read, "two to the fourth power" and the number 16 is referred to as "the fourth power of two."

8.7.2
Squares and Cubes

When an exponent is zero, we say the value of that exponential expression is 1; that is, given any base, x, we say $x^0 = 1$. Thus, $10^0 = 1$, $2^0 = 1$, $(a + b)^0 = 1$, and so on.

8.7.3
Zero as an Exponent

8.7.4
Negative Exponents

Exponents can be negative. Given any base, x, and positive number, n, the value of $x^{-n} = \frac{1}{x^n}$; that is, the value of an exponential expression with a negative exponent is equal to the reciprocal of the exponential expression raised, instead, to the positive value (or absolute value) of the negative exponent. For example, $10^{-2} = \frac{1}{10^2} = \frac{1}{100}$, $3^{-2} = \frac{1}{3^2} = \frac{1}{9}$, $2^{-3} = \frac{1}{2^3} = \frac{1}{8}$ and so on.

8.7.5
Properties of Exponents

There are several properties of exponents that allow us to combine and simplify exponential expressions. Given rational numbers a, b, and c:

1. The product of two exponential expressions with the same base is equal to that base raised to the sum of the exponents in each factor; that is, $a^b \times a^c = a^{b+c}$. For example, $10^2 \times 10^3 = 10^{2+3} = 10^5$. This makes sense because in writing 10^2 as 10×10, and 10^3 as $10 \times 10 \times 10$, we verify that $10^2 \times 10^3 = 10 \times 10 \times 10 \times 10 \times 10 = 10^5$.

2. The quotient of two exponential expressions with the same base if equal to that based raised to the difference of the exponent in the dividend minus the exponent in the divisor; that is, $a^b \div a^c = a^{b-c}$ or, written in fraction form: $\frac{a^b}{a^c} = a^{b-c}$. For example, $10^5 \div 10^3 = 10^{5-3} = 10^2$. Writing the division problem in fraction form we can verify that the property makes sense:

$$\frac{10^5}{10^3} = \frac{10 \times 10 \times 10 \times 10 \times 10}{10 \times 10 \times 10} = \frac{10 \times 10}{1} = 10^2.$$

3. The value found when an entire exponential expression with base a and exponential power b is further raised to another power, c, is equal to the base, a, raised to the product of the exponents $b \times c$; that is $(a^b)^c = a^{b \times c}$.

   For example, $(2^2)^3 = 2^{2 \times 3} = 2^6 = 64$. Verifying, we notice that $(2^2)^3$ means, $(2^2) \times (2^2) \times (2^2) = (2 \times 2) \times (2 \times 2) \times (2 \times 2) = 2^6$.

RELATED TOPICS   Scientific Notation

TOPIC 8.8 SCIENTIFIC NOTATION

Decimals | Exponents

Scientific notation is a precise means of representing decimal numbers. In this section we discuss the definition of scientific notation. We also explore a means of interpreting decimal numbers written in scientific notation as well as a means of converting decimal expression to scientific notation.

If a calculation on a calculator produces a very large number with many digits, the answer in the display window of the calculator is often given in scientific notation. The presentation may take different forms, but generally, large amounts are presented as: 7.132507 representing the scientific notation: 7.1325×10^7. Notice that the calculator leaves a space between the factor, 7.1325, and the power of 10, 07. Some calculators use "E" instead of a space, as in 7.1325 E 07.

8.8.1
**Definition of
Scientific Notation**

Numbers can be written in what is called scientific notation. **Scientific notation** is the expression of a number as the product of (1) a number, x, such that $1 \le |x| < 10$, and (2) a power of ten that would position the decimal point to correctly represent the number at hand. The digits we write to express the factor, x, in the scientific notation are called **significant digits**.

Examples of numbers written in scientific notation are the following:

Example 1: 5.782×10^4
Example 2: 1.24409×10^{-3}
Example 3: -4.77×10^2

Example 1 above is a number written in scientific notation to 4 significant digits because there are 4 digits in the factor being multiplied by a power of 10. Likewise, in Example 2, the number is written to 6 significant digits and in Example 3 the number is written to 3 significant digits.

8.8.2
**Writing Numbers
Expressed in
Scientific Notation
as Decimals**

Each number written in scientific notation can be expressed more simply as a decimal. To do so, we use the fact that when we multiply a number by 10, the resulting product is the same digits in the original number with the decimal point moved one position to the right. Similarly, multiplying a number by 10^2 yields a product involving the same digits, but with the decimal point moved two positions to the right.

In general, when multiplying a number by a positive power of 10—that is by 10^n where $n > 0$—the resulting product is the same set of digits in the original number with the decimal point moved n positions to the right.

Example 1: The product of $4.98 \times 10^2 = 498$ because the decimal point in 4.98 was moved two positions to the right.

Example 2: The product of $1.398 \times 10^6 = 1,398,000$ because the decimal point in 1.398 is moved six positions to the right. Notice that zeros needed to be added to indicate that the decimal point was moving beyond the significant digits in 1.398.

When we multiply a number by 10^{-1}, it is akin to multiplying by $\frac{1}{10}$, which is the same as dividing the number by 10. Therefore, the result of multiplying a number by 10^{-1} is moving the decimal point in the original number one position to the left. Similarly, multiplying a number by 10^{-2} results in a product that has the digits in the original number with the decimal point moved two positions to the left.

Thus, in general, when multiplying a number by a negative power of 10—that is by 10^{-n}, where $n > 0$, the resulting product is the same set of digits in the original number with the decimal point moved n positions to the left.

Example 1: The product of $7.8855 \times 10^{-2} = 0.078855$ because the decimal point was moved two positions to the left. Notice that a zero needed to be added to indicate that the decimal point had moved beyond the significant digits in 7.8855.

Example 2: The product of $4.12 \times 10^{-8} = 0.0000000412$ because the decimal point was moved 8 positions to the left.

8.8.3
Writing Decimal Numbers in Scientific Notation

Given a decimal number, we can write that decimal number in scientific notation. To do so, we need to develop two factors: one that is a number greater than or equal to 1 and less than 10, and one that is the appropriate power of ten. The first factor is created by repositioning the decimal point in the given decimal number so that there is one nonzero digit to the left of the decimal point. The second factor is a power of 10 so that the exponent indicates the number of positions, to the left if negative and to the right if position, that the decimal point in the first factor needs to be moved to produce the original decimal number.

Example 1: To write the number 745,300 in scientific notation, we create the first factor by moving the decimal point in 745,300 so that only the digit 7 is to the left of the decimal point. Thus, the first factor is 7.453. Then the second factor is determined by finding how many positions the decimal point in 7.453 needs to be moved (and in which direction) in order to get back to the decimal number 745,300. Clearly, the decimal point needs to be 5 positions to the right, so the second factor must be 10^5. Therefore, $745,300 = 7.453 \times 10^5$ in scientific notation.

Other examples of decimal numbers written in scientific notation are:

Example 2: $0.00234 = 2.34 \times 10^{-3}$.

Example 3: $79512.14 = 7.951214 \times 10^4$.

Example 4: $-0.00000589 = -5.89 \times 10^{-6}$.

RELATED TOPICS   Irrational Numbers

IN THE CLASSROOM

This chapter focuses on the *Algebra Content Standard* with emphasis on the *Representation Process Standard*: "By viewing algebra as a strand in the curriculum from prekindergarten on, teachers can help students build a solid foundation of understanding and experience as a preparation for more sophisticated work in algebra in the middle grades and high school" (NCTM, 2000, p. 37); all students should be able to "select, apply, and translate among mathematical representations to solve problems" (NCTM, 2000, p. 67). Given that algebra has often been associated with symbolic manipulation, we believe you should develop a solid conceptual understanding of (a) variables and their multiple representations (Activities 8.1-8.4), and (b) patterns, functions, and equations (Activities 8.5-8.14).

How Activities 9.1-9.17 help you develop an adult-level perspective on the above expectations.

- By exploring the idea of variable in familiar contexts you develop an understanding of their representation in symbolic, tabular and graphical forms and the relationship between these representations.

- By investigating and describing numerical patterns you learn to represent them in tabular, graphical, and symbolic form and begin to understand the limitations of each representation or how they are to be interpreted in a given context.

- By analyzing the relationships underlying familiar situations that are described verbally, modeled geometrically, or demonstrated physically, you investigate how a change in one variable relates to a change in a second and discuss the concept of a function.

- By working with different functions, you discuss the concept of and develop multiple ways of understanding the rate of change of a function. These include functions that are represented graphically and those that you have to model kinesthetically as well as those represented in tabular form.

Some expectations of your future students

Pre-K-2 (NCTM, 2000, p. 90)

recognize, describe, and extend patterns such as sequences of sounds and shapes or simple numeric patterns and translate from one representation to another

analyze how both repeating and growing patterns are generated

describe quantitative change, such as a student growing two inches in one year

Grades 3-5 (NCTM, 2000, p. 148)

represent the idea of a variable as an unknown quantity using a letter or a symbol

model problem situations with objects and use representations such as graphs, tables, and equations to draw conclusions

investigate how a change in one variable relates to a change in a second variable

identify and describe situations with constant or varying rates of change and compare them

BIBLIOGRAPHY

Ajose, S. (1991). Activities: Patterns in the hundred chart. *Mathematics Teacher, 84,* 43-48, 118-124.

Bidwell, J. K. (1987). Using reflections to find symmetric and asymmetric patterns. *Arithmetic Teacher, 34*(7), 10-15.

Coburn, T. G. (1993). Patterns: *Addenda series, grades K-4.* Reston, VA: National Council of Teachers of Mathematics.

Coxford, A. F. (Ed.). (1988). *The ideas of algebra.* Reston, VA: National Council of Teachers of Mathematics.

Day, R. P. (1995). Using functions to make mathematical connections. In P. A. House (Ed.), *Connecting mathematics across the curriculum* (pp. 54-64). Reston, VA: National Council of Teachers of Mathematics.

Driscoll, M. J. (1999). *Fostering algebraic thinking: A guide for teachers, grades 6-10.* Portsmouth, NH: Heinemann.

Edwards, E. L. (Ed.). (1990). *Algebra for everyone.* Reston, VA: National Council of Teachers of Mathematics.

English, L. D., & Warren, E. A. (1998). Introducing the variable through pattern exploration. *Mathematics Teacher, 91,* 166-172.

Emie, K. T. (1995). Mathematics and quilting. In P. A. House (Ed), *Connecting mathematics across the curriculum (pp.* 170-176) Reston, VA: National Council of Teachers of Mathematics.

Falkner, K. P., Levi, L., & Carpenter, T. P. (1999). Children's understanding of equality: A foundation for algebra. *Teaching Children Mathematics, 6,* 232-236.

Fey, J. T., & Heid, M. K. (1995). *Concepts in algebra: A technological approach.* Dedham, MA: Janson.

Geer, C. P. (1992). Exploring patterns, relations, and functions. *Arithmetic Teacher, 39*(9), 19-21.

Giambrone, T. M. (1983). Challenges for enriching the curriculum: Algebra. *Mathematics Teacher, 76,* 262-263.

Greenes, C., & Findell, C. (1999). Developing students' algebraic reasoning abilities. In L. V. Stiff (Ed.), *Developing mathematical reasoning in grades K-12* (pp. 127-137). Reston, VA: National Council of Teachers of Mathematics.

Greenes, C., & Findell, C. (1999). *Groundworks: Algebraic thinking* (3 vols.: grades 1, 2, and 3). Chicago, IL: Creative Publications.

Greenes, C., & Findell, C. (1999). *Groundworks: Algebra puzzles and problems* (4 vols.: grades 4, 5, 6, and 7). Chicago, IL: Creative Publications.

Hastings, E. H., & Yates, D. S. (1983). Microcomputer unit: Graphing straight lines. *Mathematics Teacher , 76,* I81-186.

Kieran. C. (1991). Research into practice: Helping to make the transition to algebra. *Arithmetic Teacher, 38,* 49-51.

Litwiller, B. H., & Duncan, D. R. (1985). Pentagonal patterns in the addition table. *Arithmetic Teacher, 32,* 36-38.

Loewen, A. C. (1991). Lima beans, paper cups, and algebra. *Arithmetic Teacher, 38,* 34-37.

MacGregor, M., & Stacey, K. (1999). A flying start to algebra. *Teaching Children Mathematics, 6,* 78-85.

Morelli, L. (1992). A visual approach to algebra concepts. *Mathematics Teacher, 85,* 434-437.

National Council of Teachers of Mathematics & Mathematical Sciences Education Board (1998). *The nature and role of algebra in the K-14 curriculum: Proceedings of a national symposium, May 27 and 28, 1997.* Washington, DC: National Academy Press.

Nibbelink, W. H. (1990). Teaching equations. *Arithmetic Teacher, 38, 48-51.*

Onslow, B. (1990). Pentominoes revisited. *Arithmetic Teacher, 37,* 5-9.

Osbome, A., & Wilson, P. S. (1988). Moving to algebraic thought. In T. R. Post (Ed.), *Teaching mathematics in grades K-8: Research-based methods* (pp. 421-442). Needham Heights, MA: Allyn & Bacon.

Patterson, A. C. (1999). Grasping graphing. *Mathematics Teacher, 92,* 758-762.

Peitgen, H., Jürgens, H., & Saupe, D. (1992). *Fractals for the classroom part one: Introduction to fractals and chaos.* New York: Springer-Verlag.

Peitgen, H., Jürgens, H., Saupe, D., Maletsky, E., Perciante, T., & Yunker, L. (1991). *Fractals for the classroom: Strategic activities (Vol. 1).* New York: Springer-Verlag.

Phillips, E. (1991). *Patterns and functions: Addenda series, grades 5 - 8.* Reston, VA: National Council of Teachers of Mathematics.

Quinn, A. L., Koca, R. M., Jr., & Weening, F. (1999). Developing mathematical reasoning using attribute games. *Mathematics Teacher, 92,* 768-775.

Schifter, D. (1999). Reasoning about operations: Early algebraic thinking in grades K-6. In L. V. Stiff (Ed.), *Developing mathematical reasoning in grades K-12* (pp. 62-81). Reston, VA: National Council of Teachers of Mathematics.

Schoenfeld, A. H., & Arcavi, A. (1988). On the meaning of variable. *Mathematics Teacher, 81,* 424-427.

Schultz, J. E. (1991). Implementing the *Standards:* Teaching informal algebra. *Arithmetic Teacher, 38,* 34-37.

Specht, J. (2000). *More than graphs: Mathematics explorations for TI-73, TI-82, TI-83, and TI-83 Plus graphing calculators.* Emeryville, CA: Key Curriculum Press.

Thompson, A. G. (1985). On patterns, conjectures, and proof: Developing students' mathematical thinking. *Arithmetic Teacher, 33*(1), 20-23.

Van de Walle, J. A. & Holbrook, H. (1987). Patterns, thinking, and problem solving. *Arithmetic Teacher, 31*(8), 9-12.

Van Dyke, F. (1998). Visualizing cost, revenue, and profit. *Mathematics Teacher, 91,* 488-493, 500-503.

Vance, J. H. (1998). Number operations from an algebraic perspective. *Teaching Children Mathematics, 4,* 282-285.

Wagner, S. (1983). What are these things called variables? *Mathematics Teacher, 76,* 474-479.

Wagner, S., & Parker, S. (1993). Advancing algebra. In S. Wagner (Ed.), *Research ideas for the classroom: High school mathematics* (pp. 119-139). Old Tappan, NJ: Macmillan.

Wilson, M. R., & Shealy, B. E. (1995). Experiencing function relationships with a viewing tube. In P. A. House (Ed.), *Connecting mathematics across the curriculum* (pp. 219-224) Reston, VA: National Council of Teachers of Mathematics.

GEOMETRY 9

TOPIC

9.1 Two-dimensional Geometry Basics

9.2 Planes

9.3 Line Relationships

9.4 Line Segments

9.5 Rays and Angles

9.6 Angle Relationships

9.7 Polygons

9.8 Regular Polygons

9.9 Triangles

9.10 Quadrilaterals

9.11 Circles

9.12 Congruence

9.13 Symmetry

9.14 Line and Angles Constructions

9.15 Angle Bisector Constructions

9.16 Perpendicular Line Through a Point Constructions

9.17 Parallel Line Construction

9.18 Circumscribed Circle Constructions

9.19 Inscribed Circle Constructions

9.20 Triangle Congruence

9.21 Triangle Congruence Properties

9.22 Quadrilateral Properties

9.23 Similarity

9.24 Triangle Proportion Properties

9.25 Fractals and Rep-tiles

9.26 Three-dimensional Geometry Basics

9.27 Polyhedra, Prisms, and Pyramids

9.28 Regular Polyhedra

9.29 Cylinders, Cones, and Spheres

9.30 van Hiele Levels

In the Classroom

Bibliography

CHAPTER OVERVIEW

Geometry is among the richest and oldest branches of mathematics. We think of geometry as the study of space experiences. This study focuses mainly on shapes as abstractions from the environment, which can be informally investigated and analyzed. In this chapter you can learn some interesting facts about geometry, and examine some concepts and procedures involving geometry ideas.

BIG MATHEMATICAL IDEAS

- Problem-solving Strategies
- Shape and Space
- Congruence
- Similarity
- Verifying
- Conjecturing
- Generalizing
- Decomposing

NCTM PRINCIPLES & STANDARDS LINKS

Geometry and Spatial Sense
Problem Solving
Reasoning
Communication
Connections
Representation

TOPIC 9.1 TWO-DIMENSIONAL GEOMETRY BASICS

CORNERSTONE Cartesian Coordinate System

INTRODUCTION *Most ideas, whether in mathematics or not, have foundational ideas upon which other ideas are built. In geometry, three foundational ideas are point, line, and plane. These ideas are taken as **undefined**, meaning that no formal definition is given for them. But as foundational ideas in geometry, they are used to define and describe many other ideas in geometry and, thus, if they **were** defined we would run into the problem of having circular definitions (e.g., idea #1 is defined in terms of idea #2, but idea #2 is defined in terms of idea #1). In this section, we discuss points and lines, and relationships among points and lines.*

DID YOU KNOW? The word *geometry* comes from two Greek words, *ge* meaning "earth", and *metria* meaning "measure", suggesting that, initially, this field of study may have been related to and used for measuring land. Today, geometry is much more than measurement. It has evolved into the study of figures and shapes in two and three dimensions.

9.1.1
Points and Lines

We can describe a **point** as a location. Points do not have any dimension (i.e., no length or width) but they represent a location within the set of all points (called space). We talk about driving from point A to point B, the point of a pencil, or the sharp point of a corner. All of these bring to mind a location in space. We usually represent a point by a dot and we use a capital letter to refer to it, as shown in Figure 9.1.

Figure 9.1

We can describe a **line** as a one-dimensional set of an infinite number of points with direction. A line has no thickness but it has infinite length, because it extends in opposite directions forever. In our everyday talk, we refer to walking in a straight line from here to there, not stepping over the line, or lining up. All of these bring to mind a collection of points stretching out in opposite directions. We usually represent a line, as shown in Figure 9.2, with the arrows at the ends of the line indicating that the set of points goes on indefinitely in opposite directions. A line can be named by using a single lowercase letter (e.g., line *m*) or by using two points that are on the line (e.g., line XY or $\overleftrightarrow{XY}$).

Figure 9.2

9.1.2
Relationships
Among Points And
Lines

Although an infinite number of lines can be drawn through a single point, only one line can be drawn through any two given points. This is an important relationship among two points and a line. Another important relationship is collinearity. Points that are **collinear** are points that lie on the same line. Two points are always collinear, but three or more points are not necessarily collinear. Points that do not lie on the same line are called **noncollinear**.

Points S, T, and R in Figure 9.3 are collinear, but points S, T, and P are noncollinear. We say that point T is **between** points S and R because they are collinear and if we moved along $\overleftrightarrow{SR}$ from point S to point R, we would come to point T before coming to point R.

Figure 9.3

Planes | Line Relationships | Line Segments | Rays and Angles
Cartesian Coordinate System

RELATED TOPICS

TOPIC 9.2 PLANES

CORNERSTONE	Two-dimensional Geometry Basics

INTRODUCTION — *Together with point and line, plane is one of the three foundational undefined ideas in geometry. We use point, line and plane as building blocks on which to build the rest of geometry. In this section, we discuss planes, and relationships among points, lines and planes.*

DID YOU KNOW? — Euclid was a Greek mathematician who lived about 300 B.C. Although no great mathematical discoveries are attributed to him, he is credited with pulling together geometry ideas and putting them together in the thirteen books called *The Elements*. The first six books discuss plane geometry.

For More Information. Bunt, L. N. H., Jones, P. S., & Bedient, J. D. (1988). *The Historical Roots of Elementary Mathematics.* New York: Dover Publications.

9.2.1
Planes

Just as we can describe a line as a one-dimensional set of an infinite number of points with direction, we can describe a **plane** as a two-dimensional set of an infinite number of points extending forever in all directions. A plane has no thickness but it has infinite length and width, because it extends indefinitely as a surface. We can think of a plane as a infinite sheet of paper that is perfectly flat and has no thickness. We usually represent a plane, as shown in Figure 9.4, with a four-sided figure, and we name the plane by using three points in the plane (e.g., Plane *JKL*) or by using a lowercase Greek letter (e.g., Plane α).

Figure 9.4

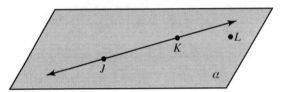

Points that are **coplanar** are points that lie in the same plane. Two points or three points are always coplanar. Four or more points are not necessarily coplanar. Points that do not all lie in the same plane are called **noncoplanar**.

Points *T*, *U*, *V*, and *W* in Figure 9.5 are coplanar, but points *S*, *T*, *U* and *V* are noncoplanar.

Figure 9.5

An infinite number of planes can be drawn through one point and even two points, as shown in Figure 9.6. But for any three points, exactly one plane can contain them. This is an important relationship that can also be stated as: three noncollinear points determine exactly one plane. Another relationship is that a line and a point not on the line determine exactly one plane.

9.2.2
**Relationships
Among Points,
Lines, and Planes**

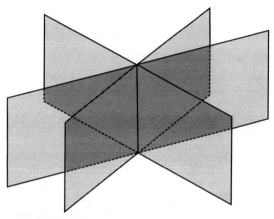

Figure 9.6

A third important relationship among points, lines and planes is that if a line contains two points that are in a plane, then the line is also in the plane.

Line Relationships | Line Segments | Rays and Angles
Cartesian Coordinate System

RELATED TOPICS

TOPIC 9.3 LINE RELATIONSHIPS

CORNERSTONE   Two-dimensional Geometry Basics | Planes

INTRODUCTION   *In geometry, there are special kinds of lines, as well as special relationships between lines and planes. In this section, we discuss coplanar, noncoplanar and skew lines, intersecting and concurrent lines, parallel and perpendicular lines, and relationships among lines and planes.*

DID YOU KNOW?   In *The Elements*, Euclid's systematic account of all the geometry that was known at his time, he based geometry on five postulates. The parallel postulate, as his fifth postulate came to be called, acquired an independent status among the postulates. This postulate stated that two straight lines that meet certain conditions have a point of intersection. One person who challenged this fifth postulate was Nicholai Lobachevsky, a Russian mathematician who lived from 1793-1856. By challenging and rejecting this postulate, Lobachevsky created another set of postulates that were consistent and led to an entirely new kind of geometry. Unlike Euclidean geometry, this geometry was not on a flat surface. In fact, it was based on a spherical surface, and thus could be used to model geometry on the surface of the earth. By the creation of this geometry, Lobachevsky had succeeded in overturning a belief that had been held because the time of Euclid, nearly 2000 years before Lobachevsky—the belief that the fifth postulate was necessary in a geometry system. His success later prompted the creation of other kinds of non-Euclidean geometries that have proved very useful in studying different phenomena in modern times.

For More Information: Sibley, T. Q. (1998). *The Geometric Viewpoint: A Survey of Geometries.* Reading, MA: Addison-Wesley.

9.3.1
Coplanar, Noncoplanar, and Skew Lines

Two lines that can be contained in the same plane are called **coplanar** lines. Two lines that cannot be contained in the same plane are **noncoplanar** lines. In Figure 9.7, lines *m* and *n* are coplanar, and lines *n* and ℓ are coplanar, but lines *m* and ℓ are noncoplanar.

Figure 9.7

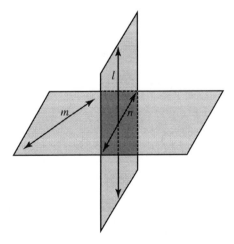

Another name for noncoplanar lines is **skew** lines. Any two lines that cannot lie in the same plane are called skew.

A line in a plane divides the plane into three regions: two half-planes and the line itself. We name a half-plane by using the line that determines the half-plane and a point not on the line that lies in the half-plane. For example, in Figure 9.8, four half-planes are shown: the half-plane determined by $\overleftrightarrow{NO}$ and point D, the half-plane determined by $\overleftrightarrow{NO}$ and point E, the half-plane determined by $\overleftrightarrow{PQ}$ and point D, and the half-plane determined by $\overleftrightarrow{PQ}$ and point E.

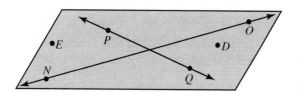

Figure 9.8

9.3.2
Intersecting and Concurrent Lines

Lines are called **intersecting** lines if they share exactly one point. If two lines intersect, they determine a plane. To see why this is true consider Figure 9.9. We know that two points determine a line, so suppose that points A and B determine $\overleftrightarrow{AB}$ and points C and B determine $\overleftrightarrow{CB}$. The two lines are intersecting lines because they have point B in common. Using the fact that three noncollinear points determine a plane, we can see that $\overleftrightarrow{AB}$ and point C determine a plane. Likewise, the same plane is also determined by $\overleftrightarrow{CB}$ and point A.

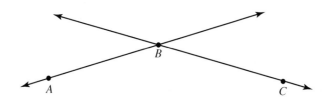

Figure 9.9

Two or more lines that share the same point are called **concurrent** lines. These lines can be coplanar or noncoplanar, as shown in Figure 9.10.

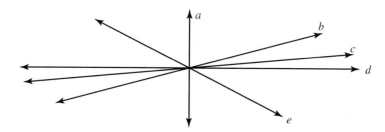

Figure 9.10

9.3.3
Parallel and Perpendicular Lines

Parallel lines are lines that are distinct from each other, are coplanar, and share no common points. Lines r and s in Figure 9.11 are parallel lines. We use the symbol $\parallel$ to say that $r \parallel s$. If two lines are parallel, they determine a plane.

Figure 9.11

Lines are said to be **perpendicular** if they intersect to form right angles. Lines k and ℓ in Figure 9.12 are perpendicular because they form right angles when they intersect. We use the symbol $\perp$ to say that k and ℓ are perpendicular, and we write this relationship, $k \perp \ell$. We also use the symbol $\urcorner$ to show that an angle in a figure is a right angle.

Figure 9.12

9.3.4
Relationships Among Lines and Planes

There are three possible relationships between a line and a plane: (1) A line and a plane can have no points in common. In Figure 9.13, line m and plane β have no points in common; thus, line m is parallel to plane β. (2) A line and a plane can have one point in common. Line n and plane β have one point in common; we say that line n intersects plane β. Because line n does not lie in the plane, it must intersect the plane at exactly one point. (3) If a line and a plane have more than one point in common, the line must lie in the plane. Line p lies in plane β.

Figure 9.13

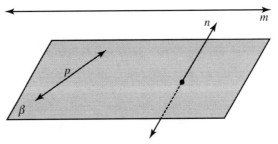

If a line intersects a plane in such a way that a right angle is formed, then the line is perpendicular to the plane; line t is perpendicular to plane λ in Figure 9.14. When a line is perpendicular to a plane, that line is also perpendicular to every line in the plane that passes through the point where the perpendicular line intersects the plane. Thus, line t is perpendicular to every line in plane λ that passes through point C.

Figure 9.14

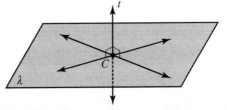

RELATED TOPICS   Line Segments | Rays and Angles | Slope | Cartesian Coordinate System

TOPIC 9.4 LINE SEGMENTS

Line is one of the three foundational ideas upon which geometry is built. Along with point and plane, line is one of the undefined terms in geometry. In this section, we discuss line segments, endpoints and midpoints..   **INTRODUCTION**

Euclid's first postulate, in *The Elements*, states that any point can be connected to any other point by drawing exactly one line segment. The idea of a line segment, as opposed to a line which continues in two directions indefinitely, is very useful because we live in a world where we deal with finite lengths.   **DID YOU KNOW?**

For More Information: Bunt, L. N. H., Jones, P. S., & Bedient, J. D. (1988). *The Historical Roots of Elementary Mathematics.* New York: Dover Publications.

An important part of the concept of a line is that a line is a set of an infinite number of points. A **line segment** is a subset of a line, and consists of two points on the line, called the **endpoints** of the line segment, and all the points on the line that are between the two endpoints. A line segment is named by its two endpoints, and we use a bar over the two capital letters representing the points to show that it is a line segment (e.g., $\overline{AB}$, $\overline{BC}$ and, $\overline{AC}$ are line segments that are subsets of $\overleftrightarrow{AB}$ in Figure 9.15).

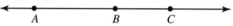

Figure 9.15

Because a line segment has endpoints, it has a finite length. Thus, every line segment also has a **midpoint**, which is the point on the line segment that divides it into two segments of the same length. Point *M* in Figure 9.16 is called the midpoint of $\overline{SR}$ because *M* is between *S* and *R* and the length of $\overline{SM}$ is equal to the length of $\overline{MR}$. Every line segment has exactly one midpoint and we say that the midpoint bisects the line segment.

Figure 9.16

TOPIC 9.5 RAYS AND ANGLES

CORNERSTONE Two-dimensional Geometry Basics

INTRODUCTION *The ideas of rays and angles have many uses, not only in developing further geometrical relationships, but especially in practical matters of constructing and measuring objects. In this section, we discuss rays and angles, including the interior and exterior of an angle.*

DID YOU KNOW? Although we have evidence that early civilizations used the concepts of rays and angles, there is reason to believe that formal discussion and definition of these ideas did not occur until Euclid, a Greek mathematician living around 300 B.C., compiled *The Elements*. These thirteen books pulled together most of the geometry ideas known in Greece at that time.

For More Information: Bunt, L. N. H., Jones, P. S., & Bedient, J. D. (1988). *The Historical Roots of Elementary Mathematics*. New York: Dover Publications.

9.5.1
Rays

Like a line segment, a **ray** is a subset of a line. A ray consists of a point on a line, called the endpoint, and all the points on that line that are on one side of the endpoint. A ray is named by two points; the endpoint is listed first, followed by another point on the ray. It is important that the endpoint is listed first to show in which direction the ray extends. For example, in Figure 9.17, $\overrightarrow{EF}$ and $\overrightarrow{FE}$ are not the same ray.

Figure 9.17

9.5.2
Angles

An **angle** is formed by two rays that have a common endpoint, such as $\overrightarrow{XY}$ an in Figure 9.18. The common endpoint of the rays is called the **vertex** of the angle. An angle is named by a point on one ray, the vertex, and a point on the other ray; thus, the angle in Figure 9.18 can be called $\angle YXZ$ or $\angle ZXY$. If there is only one angle at a vertex, the angle can also be named by the vertex point, such as $\angle X$. However, if there are several angles at a vertex point, three points must be used to name the angle. The rays form the **sides** of an angle, so $\overrightarrow{XY}$ and $\overrightarrow{XZ}$ are the sides of $\angle X$.

Figure 9.18

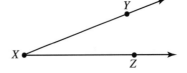

Because three noncollinear points determine a plane, every angle lies in a plane. An angle separates the plane into three disjoint sets of points: the set of points that makes up the interior of the angle, the set of points that makes up the angle, and the set of points that makes up the exterior of the angle. The **interior** of $\angle JKL$, in Figure 9.19, is the set of all points P in the plane that contains $\angle JKL$ such that P and J are on the same side of $\overleftrightarrow{KL}$ and P and L are on the same side of $\overleftrightarrow{JK}$. The **exterior** of $\angle JKL$ is the set of all points in the plane that are neither on the angle nor in its interior.

Figure 9.19

Angle Measurement | Angle Relationships   **RELATED TOPICS**

TOPIC 9.6 ANGLE RELATIONSHIPS

CORNERSTONE Rays and Angles | Angle Measurement | Congruence | Line Relationships

INTRODUCTION *There are a variety of angle relationships that are important to understand because they often play a role in various geometric relationships (e.g., triangle congruence). In this section, we discuss adjacent angles, linear pair angles, and vertical angles, complementary and supplementary angles, angles formed by a transversal and two lines, and angles formed by a transversal and two parallel lines.*

DID YOU KNOW? Some of the relationships that Euclid derived in *The Elements* dealt with angle relationships. These same angle relationships are part of our geometry curriculum today and continue to be useful in proving other relationships and in practical matters, such as cutting congruent shapes out of metal for use in manufacturing.

For More Information: Bunt, L. N. H., Jones, P. S., & Bedient, J. D. (1988). *The Historical Roots of Elementary Mathematics.* New York: Dover Publications.

9.6.1
Adjacent Angles, Linear Pair Angles, and Vertical Angles

Two angles are said to be **adjacent** if they lie in the same plane, share a common side and vertex, and have interiors that do not overlap. Angles *ABC* and *CBD* are adjacent in Figure 9.20, whereas ∠*ABC* and ∠*ABD* are not adjacent.

Figure 9.20

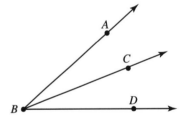

If two adjacent angles have their non-common sides form a straight angle, then the angles are called **linear pair angles**. In Figure 9.21, angles *UVW* and *WVX* are linear pair angles, whereas ∠*WVX* and ∠*XVY* are not. Because linear pair angles form a straight angle, the sum of the two angle measures is 180°.

Figure 9.21

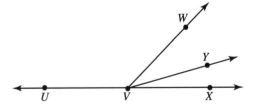

When two lines intersect, they form four angles. Two angles are called **vertical angles** if their sides form two straight angles. In Figure 9.22, ∠1 and ∠3 are vertical angles and ∠2 and ∠4 are vertical angles. An important relationship between vertical angles is that vertical angles are always congruent.

Figure 9.22

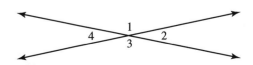

9.6.2
Complementary and Supplementary Angles

If the sum of the measures of two angles is 90°, then the angles are called **complementary angles**. Each angle is said to be a complement of the other. If the sum of the measures of two angles is 180°, then the angles are called **supplementary angles**, and the angles are supplements of each other (see Figure 9.23).

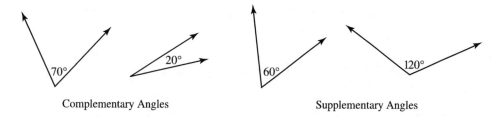

Complementary Angles   Supplementary Angles

Figure 9.23

9.6.3
Angles Formed by a Transversal and Two Lines

A **transversal** of two coplanar lines is a line that intersects the two coplanar lines in two different points. When two coplanar lines are cut by a transversal, eight angles are formed as shown in Figure 9.24. We have special names for these angles, according to their location in relation to the two lines and the transversal. $\angle 3$, $\angle 4$, $\angle 5$, and $\angle 6$ are called **interior** angles because they are contained between the two coplanar lines, while $\angle 1$, $\angle 2$, $\angle 7$, and $\angle 8$ are called **exterior** angles. **Alternate interior angles** are pairs of interior angles on opposite sides of the transversal; $\angle 3$ and $\angle 6$, $\angle 4$ and $\angle 5$ are pairs of alternate interior angles. Likewise, $\angle 1$ and $\angle 8$ as well as $\angle 2$ and $\angle 7$ are pairs of **alternate exterior angles**. **Corresponding angles** are angles that are located in the same place on each line in relation to the transversal; $\angle 1$ and $\angle 5$, $\angle 2$ and $\angle 6$, $\angle 3$ and $\angle 7$, and $\angle 4$ and $\angle 8$ are corresponding angles.

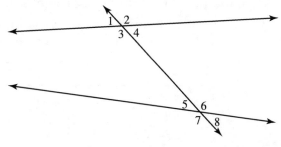

Figure 9.24

If two parallel lines are cut by a transversal, then a pair of (a) alternate interior angles, (b) exterior angles, or (c) corresponding angles must be congruent. The converse is also true. In other words, if two lines are cut by a transversal and a pair of (a) alternate interior angles, (b) exterior angles, or (c) corresponding angles are congruent, then the two lines must be parallel (see Figure 9.25).

9.6.4
Angles Formed by a Transversal and Two Parallel Lines

Figure 9.25

TOPIC 9.7 POLYGONS

CORNERSTONE Line Segments | Rays and Angles | Congruence

INTRODUCTION *All around us, in our everyday lives, there are geometrical figures. Many of these are known to us as triangles, rectangles, squares, pentagons, octagons. These are all types of polygons. In this section, we discuss a polygon and its features, convex and concave polygons, and names of polygons.*

DID YOU KNOW? The word *polygon* comes from Greek: *poly* meaning "many," and *gon* meaning "sides. " Polygons are often thought of as many-sided figures.

**9.7.1
A Polygon and
Its Features**

A **polygon** is a curve composed entirely of line segments that is simple (the curve does not cross itself) and closed. Figure 9.26 shows some examples of polygons and non-polygons.

Figure 9.26

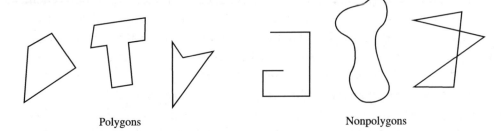

Polygons   Nonpolygons

The line segments that comprise a polygon are called the **sides**, and the point where two sides meet is called a vertex (plural **vertices**). A **diagonal** is a line segment that is drawn between any two non-consecutive vertices in a polygon. A polygon separates the plane into three disjoint subsets. These are the interior of the polygon, the polygon itself, and the exterior of the polygon (see Figure 9.27). A polygon and its interior together make up the set of points known as a **polygonal region**.

Figure 9.27

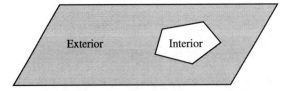

At each vertex, there is an interior angle (or vertex angle) that is formed by the vertex and the two sides that meet at the vertex. There are also exterior angles that can be formed at each vertex by extending sides of the polygon, as shown in Figure 9.28.

Figure 9.28

A polygon is **convex** if and only if for two distinct points in the polygonal region, the segment that joins those points is contained entirely in the polygonal region. If the segment that joins these two points does not lie in the polygonal region, then the polygon is **concave**. Figure 9.29 shows convex and concave polygons.

**9.7.2
Convex and
Concave Polygons**

Convex polygon

Concave polygon

Figure 9.29

Polygons are named by the number of sides or vertices that they have. For example:

**9.7.3
Names of Polygons**

Polygon	Number of Sides or Vertices
Triangle	3
Quadrilateral	4
Pentagon	5
Hexagon	6
Heptagon	7
Octagon	8
Nonagon	9
Decagon	10
n-gon	n

Regular Polygons | Triangles | Quadrilaterals | Symmetry
Area of Regular Polygons and Circles

RELATED TOPICS

TOPIC 9.8 REGULAR POLYGONS

CORNERSTONE | Polygons | Congruence | Angle Measurement | Triangles

INTRODUCTION

In the previous section, we discussed polygons, their features, and particular kinds of polygons. In this section, we discuss what it means for a polygon to be called regular, the sum of the measures of the angles in any convex polygon, and the sum of the measures of the exterior angles in any convex polygon.

DID YOU KNOW?

In 1801, Carl F. Gauss proved which regular polygons could be constructed using only a straightedge and a compass. He found that a regular polygon can be constructed if the number of sides can be expressed as $2^n (2^{2^k} + 1)$, where $2^{2^k} + 1$ is prime. The only known primes of this form are 3, 5, 17, 257, and 65,537. These are called Fermat primes. In 1796, Gauss constructed a regular 17-gon, and in 1837, he and Pierre Wantzel proved that no other regular polygons can be constructed using only a straightedge and compass.

For More Information: Sibley, T. Q. (1998). *The Geometric Viewpoint: A Survey of Geometries*. Reading, MA: Addison-Wesley.

9.8.1
Regular Polygons

A polygon is called **regular** if all of its angles are congruent and all of its sides are congruent. Another way to say this is to say that a regular polygon is one that is **equiangular** (all angles congruent) and **equilateral** (all sides congruent.) The polygons in Figure 9.30 are regular. We use the congruence marks, as shown, to indicate that angles and sides are congruent.

Figure 9.30

9.8.2
Sum of the Measures of Angles in a Convex Polygon

For any convex polygon with n sides, the sum of the measures of the interior angles is $(n - 2)180°$. The $(n - 2)$ represents the number of triangles that can be formed in the polygon by drawing diagonals from one vertex, as shown in Figure 9.31. Because the sum of the measures of the angles in a triangle is 180°, multiplying the number of triangles formed in a polygon in the manner described previously by 180° gives the sum of the measure of the interior angles in the polygon. For example:

Figure 9.31

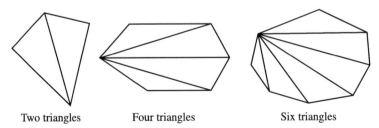

Two triangles   Four triangles   Six triangles

Polygon	Sum of the Measures of the Interior Angles
Triangle	180°
Quadrilateral	360°
Pentagon	540°
Hexagon	720°
Heptagon	900°
Octagon	1080°
Nonagon	1260°
Decagon	1440°

Once you find the sum of the measures of the interior angles in a regular polygon, you can find the measure of each angle by dividing the sum by the number of sides (or angles), because all the angles are congruent. Thus, $\frac{(n-2)180°}{n}$ gives the measure of each angle in a regular n-gon. Some regular polygons and the measure of each of their interior angles is as follows:

Regular Polygon	Measure of Each Interior Angle
Equilateral Triangle	60°
Square	90°
Regular Pentagon	108°
Regular Hexagon	120°
Regular Heptagon	135°

As we discussed in the previous section, exterior angles can be formed at each vertex in a polygon. If we form just one of these exterior angles at each vertex, we can find the sum of these exterior angles no matter how many sides a convex polygon has. Consider the pentagon in Figure 9.32 with one exterior angle at each vertex.

9.8.3
Sum of the Measures of the Exterior Angles in a Convex Polygon

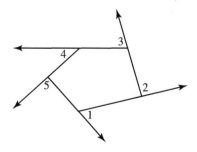

Figure 9.32

Using what we know about linear pair angles, we can see that at each vertex the interior angle and the exterior angle form linear pair angles and, thus, the sum of their measures is 180°. Because a pentagon has five vertices, there are five linear pair angles formed, and so the sum of the pairs of interior and exterior angles is 5(180°). Because we already know that the sum of the interior angles in a convex pentagon is 540°, to find the sum of the measures of just the exterior angles we can subtract the sum of the measures of the interior angles from the sum of the measures of the interior and exterior angles—5(180°) − 3(180°) = 360°. This discussion can be generalized to fit any convex polygon: $n(180°) − (n − 2)180° = 2(180°) = 360°$. Thus, in any convex polygon, the sum of the exterior angles (one at each vertex) is 360°.

RELATED TOPICS   Quadrilaterals | Area of Regular Polygons and Circles

TOPIC 9.9 TRIANGLES

Polygons | Angle Relationships | Congruence | Parallel Line Construction **CORNERSTONE**

Polygons are named by the number of sides they have. Thus, a three-sided polygon is called a triangle. In this section, we discuss features of a triangle, special kinds of triangles, and the sum of the measures of the interior angles in a triangle. **INTRODUCTION**

A triangle is stable in structure. If you form a polygon, with four or more sides, out of cardboard strips and fasten the strips at the vertices, this polygon can be moved so that its shape changes. A triangle, on the other hand, will not change shape once the vertices are fastened. This is why triangles are often used as braces in building structures. **DID YOU KNOW?**

A **triangle** is a polygon that has three sides. An **altitude** in a triangle is a perpendicular segment drawn from a vertex to the line containing the opposite side. Three altitudes can be drawn in any triangle, as shown in Figure 9.33. Any side of a triangle can be the **base** of the triangle; for that base, the **height** of the triangle is the altitude drawn to the line containing that side.

**9.9.1
Features of a
Triangle**

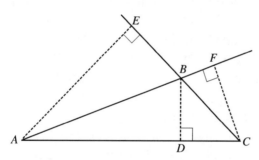

Figure 9.33

We have special names for triangles when classifying them by their angles or by their sides (see Figure 9.34). A triangle with one right angle is called a **right triangle**. A triangle with only acute angles is called an **acute triangle**. A triangle with one obtuse angle is called an **obtuse triangle**.

**9.9.2
Special Kinds of
Triangles**

      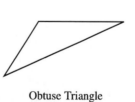

Right Triangle   Acute Triangle   Obtuse Triangle

Figure 9.34

A triangle with no sides congruent is called a **scalene triangle**. A triangle with at least two sides congruent is called an **isosceles triangle**. A triangle with all three sides congruent is called an **equilateral triangle** (see Figure 9.35).

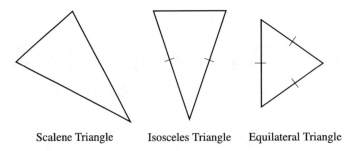

Figure 9.35

Scalene Triangle   Isosceles Triangle   Equilateral Triangle

The relationships among these special kinds of triangles can be illustrated in a hierarchy, as shown in Figure 9.36.

Figure 9.36

Polygon

Triangle

Scalene Triangle   Isosceles Triangle

Equilateral Triangle

**9.9.3
Sum of the
Measures of the
Interior Angles
in a Triangle**

The sum of the measures of the interior angles in a triangle, in a plane, is 180°. To understand why this is true, consider the following proof using triangle *XYZ* with angles 1, 2, and 3, in Figure 9.37. Draw a line *m* through *Y* that is parallel to $\overleftrightarrow{XZ}$. As discussed in the section called Parallel-Line Construction, we know that we can construct a line parallel to another line through a point not on that line. Now consider the angles labeled $\angle 4$ and $\angle 5$ in the figure. Because line $m \parallel \overleftrightarrow{XZ}$, and $\overleftrightarrow{XY}$ and $\overrightarrow{ZY}$ are transversals, $\angle 5 \cong \angle 3$ and $\angle 4 \cong \angle 1$ because they are alternate interior angles. Thus, $m(\angle 5) = m(\angle 1)$ and $m(\angle 4) = m(\angle 3)$ and so because $m(\angle 5) + m(\angle 2) + m(\angle 4) = 180°$ (together they form a line), then $m(\angle 1) + m(\angle 2) + m(\angle 3) = 180°$.

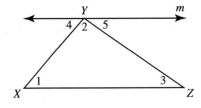

Figure 9.37

RELATED TOPICS   Angle Measurement | Symmetry | Area of Triangles | Quadrilaterals

TOPIC 9.10 QUADRILATERALS

Polygons | Triangles | Congruence **CORNERSTONE**

Quadrilaterals are a specific type of polygon. In this section, we discuss features of a quadrilateral, and special kinds of quadrilaterals. **INTRODUCTION**

In this section, we use the most common definition of a trapezoid. Sometimes another definition is used—a trapezoid is a quadrilateral with exactly one pair of parallel sides. If we use this definition, this changes the relationship among the rest of the special quadrilaterals. For example, a parallelogram would no longer be a trapezoid. **DID YOU KNOW?**

For More Information: Moise, E. E., & Downs, Jr., F. L. (1975). *Geometry.* Menlo Park, CA: Addison-Wesley.

A **quadrilateral** is a polygon that has four sides. Any side of a quadrilateral can be the **base** of the quadrilateral; for that base, the **height** of the quadrilateral is the altitude drawn from the opposite vertex to the line containing that side, as shown in Figure 9.38.

9.10.1
Features of a Quadrilateral

Figure 9.38

We have special names for quadrilaterals that have certain properties (see Figure 9.39). A quadrilateral with at least two distinct pairs of consecutive sides congruent is called a **kite.** A quadrilateral with at least one pair of parallel sides is called a **trapezoid.** An **isosceles trapezoid** is a trapezoid with exactly one pair of opposite sides congruent. A quadrilateral with both pairs of opposite sides parallel is called a **parallelogram.** A **rectangle** is a parallelogram with a right angle. A **rhombus** is a parallelogram with all sides congruent. A **square**

9.10.2
Special Kinds of Quadrilaterals

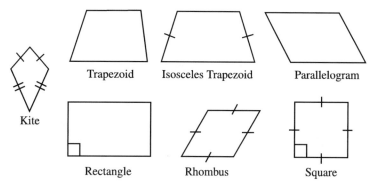

Figure 9.39

is a rectangle with all sides congruent. The relationships among these special kinds of quadrilaterals can be illustrated in a hierarchy, as shown in Figure 9.40.

Figure 9.40

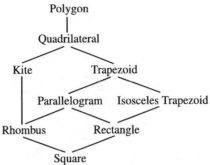

TOPIC 9.11 CIRCLES

Polygons | Regular Polygons

As the number of sides a regular polygon has increases, the polygon becomes closer and closer to the shape of a circle. In this section, we discuss features of a circle, and the compass.

INTRODUCTION

The Babylonians estimated that it takes about 360 days for the sun to travel completely around a circular path. They divided the path into 360 congruent parts. We now call each of these parts a degree and we say that the measure of a circle is 360°.

DID YOU KNOW?

For More Information: Bunt, L. N. H., Jones, P. S., & Bedient, J. D. (1988). *The Historical Roots of Elementary Mathematics.* New York: Dover Publications.

A **circle** is the set of points in a plane that are the same distance from a given point, called the **center**. The **radius** (plural **radii**) of a circle is the length of a segment with an endpoint on the circle and having the center as the other endpoint. The segment is also called a radius. The **diameter** of a circle is the length of a segment that has its endpoints on the circle and passes through the center. The segment is also called a diameter. A **chord** is any line segment that has its endpoints on the circle. Thus, a diameter is a chord (see Figure 9.41).

**9.11.1
Features of a Circle**

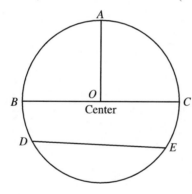

Figure 9.41

An **arc** of a circle is a connected subset of points of the circle. An arc that consists of half of the circle is called a **semicircle**. An arc is named by two points on the circle if the arc is less than half of the circle. If the arc is greater than or equal to half of the circle, we name the arc using three letters, as shown in Figure 9.42.

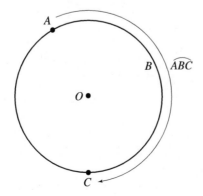

Figure 9.42

9.11.2
The Compass

The ancient Greeks used a straightedge (with no markings) and a collapsible **compass** to construct geometric figures and demonstrate geometric relationships. The modern compass, shown in Figure 9.43, can be used to draw a circle of a given radius, *AB*. Open the compass legs to a length of *AB*, designate a center point, *O*, put the pointed leg of the compass at *O* and move the other leg around *O* to draw the circle. Two circles are congruent if their radii are congruent.

Figure 9.43

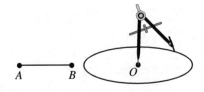

RELATED TOPICS   Symmetry | Linear Measurement | Perimeter | Circumference
Area of Regular Polygons and Circles

TOPIC 9.12 CONGRUENCE

When two geometric objects have the same shape and size, we say that they are **congruent**. *Congruent objects are very common in our world because manufacturing of many objects is done through mass producing objects made out of the same mold. In this section, we discuss congruent segments, angles, and polygons.*

INTRODUCTION

The Greek mathematician, Euclid, did not use the term congruent in his famous volumes, *The Elements*. Rather, he used the idea of equality to describe how equal line segments and equal angles can be moved in the plane until they coincide.

DID YOU KNOW?

For More Information: Bunt, L. N. H., Jones, P. S., & Bedient, J. D. (1988). *The Historical Roots of Elementary Mathematics*. New York: Dover Publications.

Two line segments that have equal lengths are called **congruent segments**. We use the symbol $\cong$ to mean congruent. We say that $\overline{AB} \cong \overline{CD}$ in Figure 9.44 because they are both 5 cm in length.

9.12.1
Congruent Segments

Figure 9.44

Two angles are called **congruent angles** if they have the same measures. In Figure 9.45, $\angle RST \cong \angle JLK$ because they both have measures of 70°.

9.12.2
Congruent Angles

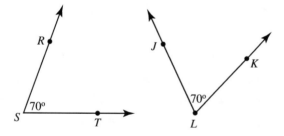

Figure 9.45

Two polygons that are congruent have the same shape and the same size; they can be placed so that they exactly fit one on top of the other. In Figure 9.46, $ABCDE \cong STUVW$.

9.12.3
Congruent Polygons

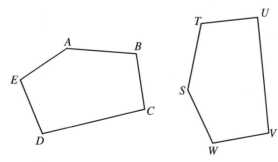

Figure 9.46

TOPIC 9.13 SYMMETRY

| **CORNERSTONE** | Polygons | Triangles |

INTRODUCTION *Repeated patterns occur throughout nature and human-made objects. It is these repeated patterns which underline symmetry. In this section, we discuss reflection, rotational, and plane symmetry.*

DID YOU KNOW? Hermann Weyl, in a classic book *Symmetry* wrote: "Symmetric means something like well-proportioned, well-balanced, and symmetry denotes that sort of concordance of several parts by which they integrate into a whole. Beauty is bound up with symmetry" (1952, p. 3)

For More Information: Weyl, H. (1952). *Symmetry*. Princeton, NJ: Princeton University Press.

9.13.1
Reflection
Symmetry

A figure has **reflection symmetry** (also called **bilateral symmetry** or **line symmetry**) if there is a line (called the **line of symmetry**) such that the reflection of the figure across the line of symmetry is its own image. For example, the figures in Figure 9.47 have reflection symmetry. The second and third figures have more than one line of symmetry.

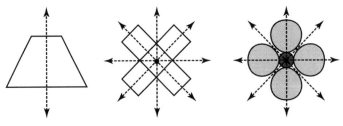

Figure 9.47

9.13.2
Rotational
Symmetry

A figure has **rotational symmetry** if the figure can be rotated less than 360° about some point so that the rotated figure coincides with the original figure. (The reason for the "less than 360°" criterion is that any rotated figure will coincide with its original figure when rotated 360°.) Figure 9.48 shows figures that have 60° rotational symmetry and 90° rotational symmetry, respectively. The equilateral triangle also has 120° rotational symmetry, and the square also has 180° rotational symmetry and 270° rotational symmetry. A figure that has 180° rotational symmetry is said to have **point symmetry**.

Figure 9.48

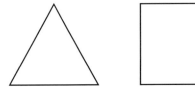

Just as it is possible for a two-dimensional figure to have one or more lines of symmetry, a three-dimensional figure can have one or more **planes of symmetry**. A figure has a plane of symmetry when there is a plane such that the reflection of the figure across the plane of symmetry is its own image. Some three-dimensional figures with plane symmetry are shown in Figure 9.49.

9.13.3
Plane Symmetry

Figure 9.49

Reflections | Rotations   **RELATED TOPICS**

TOPIC 9.14 LINE AND ANGLE CONSTRUCTIONS

CORNERSTONE   Circles | Line Segments

INTRODUCTION   *A geometric construction is a mathematical activity in which we make geometric figures and relationships using only a compass, a straightedge and given geometric figures. In this section, we discuss geometric tools, how to construct a line segment congruent to a given line segment, and how to construct an angle congruent to a given angle.*

DID YOU KNOW?   The Greek mathematician, Euclid, used constructions in three of his five postulates that are the basis of the geometric ideas laid out in *The Elements*. The first three postulates are as follows.

Let the following be postulated:
1. To draw a straight line from any point to any point.
2. To produce a finite straight line continuously in a straight line.
3. To describe a circle with any center and distance.

For More Information: Sibley, T. Q. (1998). *The Geometric Viewpoint: A Survey of Geometries*. Reading, MA: Addison-Wesley.

9.14.1
Geometric Tools

Figure 9.50

The ancient Greeks used two tools to construct geometric objects and relationships: a compass and a straightedge. A **compass** is a tool for constructing circles. The compasses used by the ancient Greeks were collapsible. This means that given two points *A* and *B*, the collapsible compass could be used to draw a circle with center A passing through *B*, but the compass could not be moved to another center *C* to draw a circle of the same radius because the opening of the compass could not be fixed. The type of compass we use today is shown in Figure 9.50. A **straightedge** is a tool for constructing straight lines. It has no markings on it as rulers do.

Other geometric tools that we use today are **rulers** (for measuring lengths of line segments) and **protractors** (for measuring an angle in degrees or radians). Although both of these tools are very useful, we typically use only a compass and a straightedge in making geometric constructions in the study of what is referred to as Euclidean geometry.

9.14.2
Constructing a Line Segment Congruent to a Given Line Segment

To construct a line segment on line *m* congruent to a given line segment, $\overline{FG}$, open the compass so that the pointed end is on *F* and the pencil end is on *G* (or vice versa) as in Figure 9.51.

Label a point *J* on line *m* and place the pointed end of the compass on *J*. Keeping the width of the compass open to a length of *FG*, mark off an arc that intersects line *m*, and label the point of intersection point *K* as in Figure 9.52. Thus, $\overline{JK} \cong \overline{FG}$.

Figure 9.51

Figure 9.52

To construct an angle, with one side on $\overrightarrow{MX}$, congruent to a given angle $\angle P$, place the pointed end of the compass at P and mark off an arc $\overset{\frown}{OQ}$ and then mark off an arc having an equal radius with the center at M (see Figure 9.53). Label the point of the intersection of the arc with $\overrightarrow{MX}$ point N.

**9.14.3
Constructing an
Angle Congruent
to a Given Angle**

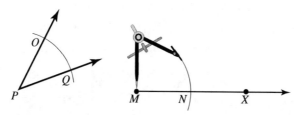

Figure 9.53

Now place the pointed end at Q and open the compass so that the pencil end is at O. Place the pointed end at N and mark off an arc with an equal radius so that this arc intersects the arc that was drawn with center M. Label this point of intersection point L (see Figure 9.54). Draw a ray from M through L. $\angle LMN \cong \angle OPQ$.

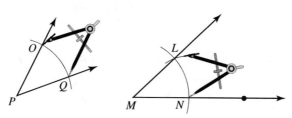

Figure 9.54

Triangle Congruence | Triangle Congruence Properties
Angle Bisector Construction

RELATED TOPICS

TOPIC 9.15 ANGLE BISECTOR CONSTRUCTIONS

CORNERSTONE	Line and Angle Constructions

INTRODUCTION
Sometimes in a geometric construction, we need to separate an angle into two congruent angles. This is known as bisecting an angle. In this section, we discuss what is an angle bisector, and how to bisect an angle.

DID YOU KNOW?
The ancient Greeks were intrigued by challenging geometric constructions. One problem they worked on was trisecting an angle, that is, dividing an angle into three congruent angles. The challenge was to construct one third of a given angle using only compass and straightedge. The Greeks were not able to complete this construction using only these tools, although they did make exact constructions using other methods. In 1837, a mathematician named Pierre Wantzel proved, using algebraic means, that trisecting an angle is an impossible task using only compass and straightedge.

For More Information: Bunt, L. N. H., Jones, P. S., & Bedient, J. D. (1988). *The Historical Roots of Elementary Mathematics.* New York: Dover Publications.

9.15.1
Angle Bisector

An **angle bisector** is a ray that separates an angle into two congruent angles. In Figure 9.55, two angles with their angle bisectors are shown.

Figure 9.55

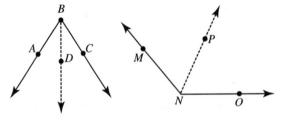

9.15.2
Constructing an Angle Bisector

To bisect a given angle $\angle K$, place the pointed end of the compass at K and mark off an arc $\overset{\frown}{JL}$ as shown in the first drawing in Figure 9.56. Place the pointed end at L and draw an arc as shown in the second drawing in Figure 9.56. Place the pointed end at J and draw an arc having the same radius as shown in the third drawing in Figure 9.56. Label the point of intersection of the two arcs point M and draw $\overrightarrow{KM}$ as shown in the fourth drawing in Figure 9.56. $\overrightarrow{KM}$ is the bisector of $\angle K$, and $\angle JKM \cong \angle MKL$

Figure 9.56

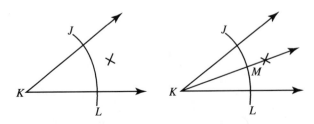

TOPIC 9.16 PERPENDICULAR-LINE-THROUGH-A-POINT CONSTRUCTIONS

Line and Angle Constructions

CORNERSTONE

INTRODUCTION

The distance between a line and a point not on the line is the length of the line segment drawn from the point that is perpendicular to the line. In this section, we discuss how to construct a line perpendicular to a line through a point on the line, how to construct a line perpendicular to a line through a point not on the line, and how to construct a perpendicular bisector of a line segment.

DID YOU KNOW?

Following the Definitions, five Postulates, and Common Notions that Euclid laid out in his geometric work, *The Elements*, he listed Propositions (relationships that could be demonstrated using ones already established). The eleventh and twelfth propositions of Book I state:

> *To draw a straight line at right angles to a given straight line from a given point on it. To a given infinite straight line, from a given point which is not on it, to draw a perpendicular straight line.*

For More Information: Sibley, T. Q. (1998). *The Geometric Viewpoint: A Survey of Geometries.* Reading, MA: Addison-Wesley.

To construct a line perpendicular to a given line n, through a point C on line n, place the pointed end of the compass at C and mark off an arc that intersects line n in two points, as shown in the first drawing in Figure 9.57. Label these two points B and D. Open the compass to a wider setting and draw intersecting arcs with centers at B and D, as shown in the second drawing in Figure 9.57. Label the two points of intersection points E and F. Draw the line through E and F. $\overleftrightarrow{EF}$ is perpendicular to line n through point C.

9.16.1
Constructing a Line Perpendicular to a Line Through a Point on the Line

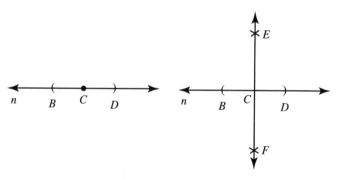

Figure 9.57

To construct a line perpendicular to a given line r, through a point Q not on line r, place the pointed end of the compass at Q and draw an arc that intersects line r in two points, as shown in the first drawing in Figure 9.58. Label these two points R and S. Keeping the compass open to the same width, draw intersecting arcs with centers at R and S, as shown in the second drawing in Figure 9.58. Label the point of intersection T. Draw the line through T and Q. $\overleftrightarrow{TQ}$ is perpendicular to line r through point Q.

9.16.2
Constructing a Line Perpendicular to a Line Through a Point Not on the Line

Figure 9.58

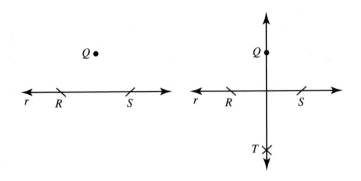

9.16.3
**Constructing a
Perpendicular
Bisector of a
Line Segment**

A **perpendicular bisector** of a line segment is a line that is perpendicular to the line segment at its midpoint. To construct a perpendicular bisector of a given line segment, $\overline{FG}$, draw intersecting arcs with centers at F and G, as shown in the first drawing in Figure 9.59. Label the points of intersection points H and I. Draw the line through H and I as shown in the second drawing in Figure 9.59. Label the point of its intersection wit is the perpendicular bisector of FG and J is the midpoint of $\overline{FG}$.

Figure 9.59

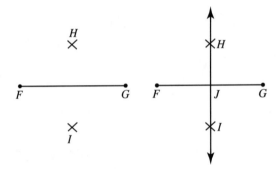

RELATED TOPICS   Parallel Line Construction

TOPIC 9.17 PARALLEL-LINE CONSTRUCTION

Many geometric relationships use parallel lines as a basis for the relationship. In this section, we discuss how to construct a line parallel to a line through a point not on the line.

INTRODUCTION

Using Euclid's first three postulates (listed in Section 9.14) and his fourth postulate—All right angles are equal to one another—allows for the construction of parallel lines.

DID YOU KNOW?

For More Information: Sibley, T. Q. (1998). *The geometric viewpoint: A survey of geometries.* Reading, MA: Addison-Wesley.

To construct a line parallel to a given line *s*, through a point *G* not on line *s*, draw any line *t* through *G* that intersects line *s*, as shown in the first drawing in Figure 9.60. Label the point of intersection point *F*. Place the pointed end of the compass at *F* and draw an arc with radius *FG* that intersects line *s*, as shown in the second drawing in Figure 9.60. Label the point of intersection point *E*. Keeping the compass open to the same width, draw intersecting arcs with centers at *E* and *G*, as shown in the third drawing in Figure 9.60. Label the point of intersection *D*. Draw the line through *G* and *D*. $\overleftrightarrow{GD}$ is parallel to line *s* through point *G*.

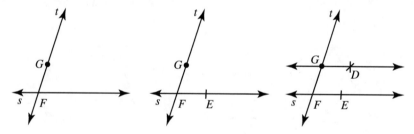

Figure 9.60

TOPIC 9.18 CIRCUMSCRIBED-CIRCLE CONSTRUCTIONS

| **CORNERSTONE** | Circles | Triangles | Perpendicular-Line-Through-a-Point Constructions |

INTRODUCTION

There are some special relationships between circles and triangles. One of these relationships is that every triangle can have a circle circumscribed around it. In this section, we discuss circumscribed circles, and how to circumscribe a circle around a triangle.

DID YOU KNOW?

Another of the famous construction problems from ancient Greece was the task of constructing a square whose area is equal to the area of a given circle using only compass and straightedge. As with the angle trisection problem, the Greeks were able to construct this using other methods but were not able to do the construction using only compass and straightedge. In 1882, the German mathematician Ferdinand Lindemann proved that this task is impossible using only compass and straightedge by proving that the number π is transcendental.

For More Information: Bunt, L. N. H., Jones, P. S., & Bedient, J. D. (1988). *The historical roots of elementary mathematics.* New York: Dover Publications.

**9.18.1
Circumscribed
Circles**

A **circumscribed circle** is a circle that surrounds a polygon such that the vertices of the polygon lie on the circle. The polygons shown in Figure 9.61 are circumscribed by circles.

Figure 9.61

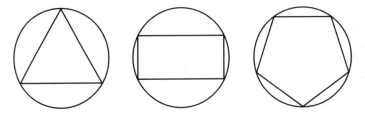

**9.18.2
Constructing a
Circumscribed
Circle About a
Triangle**

To construct the circumscribed circle about a given triangle *XYZ*, we want to construct a point *T* that is equidistant from points *X*, *Y* and *Z*. To accomplish this, construct the perpendicular bisector of each side of triangle *XYZ*, as shown in Figure 9.62.

Figure 9.62

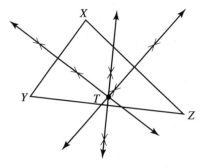

The intersection of these perpendicular bisectors is a point called the **circumcenter** of the triangle. Label this point *T*. Construct the circle with center *T* and radius *TX*, as shown in Figure 9.63. This circle circumscribes triangle *XYZ*.

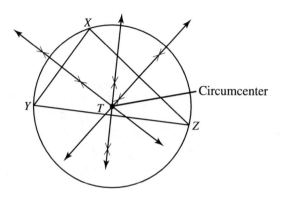

Figure 9.63

Inscribed-Circle Constructions   **RELATED TOPICS**

TOPIC 9.19 INSCRIBED-CIRCLE CONSTRUCTIONS

CORNERSTONE   Circles | Triangles | Perpendicular-Line-Through-a-Point Constructions

INTRODUCTION   *Another special relationship between triangles and circles is that every triangle can have a circle inscribed within it. In this section, we discuss inscribed circles, how to inscribe a circle within a triangle, and orthocenters and centroids.*

DID YOU KNOW?   The third famous construction problem from ancient Greece was the task of constructing the face of a cube whose volume is twice the volume of another cube using only compass and straightedge. As with the angle trisection problem and the squaring-the-circle problem, the Greeks were able to construct this using other methods but were not able to do the construction using only compass and straightedge. In 1837, the mathematician Pierre Wantzel proved that this task, along with the angle-trisection problem, is impossible using only compass and straightedge.

For More Information: Bunt, L. N. H., Jones, P. S., & Bedient, J. D. (1988). *The historical roots of elementary mathematics.* New York: Dover Publications.

9.19.1
Inscribed Circles

   An **inscribed circle** is a circle that is surrounded by a polygon such that the inscribed circle intersects each side of the polygon in exactly one point. The polygons shown in Figure 9.64 have circles inscribed within them.

Figure 9.64

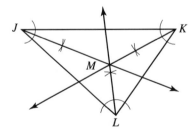

9.19.2
Constructing an Inscribed Circle Within a Triangle

   To construct the circle inscribed within a given triangle *JKL*, we want to construct a point *M* that is equidistant from $\overline{JK}$, $\overline{JL}$ and $\overline{KL}$. To accomplish this, construct the angle bisector of each angle of triangle *JKL*, as shown in Figure 9.65.

Figure 9.65

   The intersection of these angle bisectors is a point called the **incenter** of the triangle. Label this point *M*. Construct a line perpendicular to $\overline{JK}$ that passes through *M*. Label the point of intersection of this line with $\overline{JK}$ point *N*. Construct the circle with center *M* and radius *MN*, as shown in Figure 9.66. This circle is inscribed in triangle *JKL*.

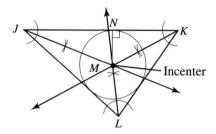

Figure 9.66

Besides circumcenters and incenters, there are two other centers connected with triangles. The **orthocenter** of a triangle is the point of intersection of the triangle's altitudes. The **centroid** of a triangle is the point of intersection of the triangle's medians. The orthocenter and centroid of a triangle are shown in Figure 9.67.

9.19.3
Orthocenters and Centroids

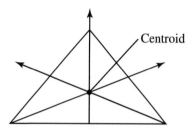

Figure 9.67

Triangle-Congruence Properties

RELATED TOPICS

TOPIC 9.20 TRIANGLE CONGRUENCE

CORNERSTONE	Line and Angle Constructions | Parallel Line Construction | Perpendicular-Line-Through-a-Point Constructions

INTRODUCTION

When two figures are congruent, they must have the same size and shape. In this section, we discuss congruent triangles and their features, and how two triangles may or may not be congruent.

DID YOU KNOW?

Euclid used two senses of equal—equal in measure (angle, length, area or volume) and congruent. He emphasized showing that two figures are congruent from the equal measures of corresponding parts.

For More Information: Sibley, T. Q. (1998). *The Geometric Viewpoint: A Survey of Geometries.* Reading, MA: Addison-Wesley.

9.20.1
Congruent Triangles and Their Features

Two triangles are **congruent** if they coincide when one is placed on the other. In other words, their corresponding angles and corresponding sides are congruent. Corresponding angles and sides are the ones that match when one triangle is placed on a congruent triangle. Two congruent triangles, $\triangle STU$ and $\triangle PQR$, are shown in Figure 9.68. These triangles are congruent because $\angle S \cong \angle P$, $\angle T \cong \angle Q$, $\angle U \cong \angle R$, $\overline{ST} \cong \overline{PQ}$, $\overline{TU} \cong \overline{QR}$, and $\overline{SU} \cong \overline{PR}$.

Figure 9.68

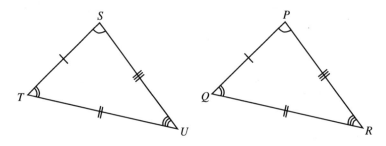

9.20.2
How Two Triangles May or May Not be Congruent

Suppose two triangle, $\triangle ABC$ and $\triangle DEF$, are congruent to each other, as shown in Figure 9.69. The expression $\triangle ABC \cong \triangle DEF$ says not merely that $\triangle ABC$ and $\triangle DEF$ are congruent, but also that they are congruent in a particular way (i.e., under a particular one-to-one correspondence between vertices). Thus, while $\triangle ABC \cong \triangle DEF$, $\triangle ABC$ is not necessarily congruent to this triangle with the vertices listed in another order (e.g., $\triangle DFE$).

Figure 9.69

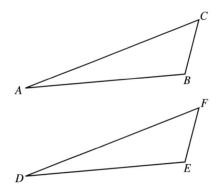

RELATED TOPICS	Triangle-Congruence Properties

TOPIC 9.21 TRIANGLE-CONGRUENCE PROPERTIES

Triangles | Congruence   **CORNERSTONE**

When two triangles are congruent to each other, their corresponding angles   **INTRODUCTION**
and sides are congruent. However, to show that two triangles are congruent,
we do not always need to show that all six corresponding parts are congruent.
There are certain cases when, if three corresponding parts congruent, the other
corresponding parts are forced to be congruent. In this section, we discuss
the side-side-side, side-angle-side, angle-side-angle, angle-angle-side, and
isosceles triangle congruence properties.

A phrase known to almost every student who has completed a course in high school   **DID YOU KNOW?**
geometry is, "Corresponding parts of congruent triangles are congruent."

If three sides of one triangle are congruent to the three corresponding sides   **9.21.1**
of a second triangle, then the triangles are congruent. This property is called   **Side-Side-Side**
the **Side-Side-Side (SSS) Triangle-Congruence Property**, and is illustrated   **Triangle-Congruence**
in Figure 9.70.   **Property**

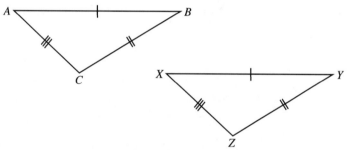

Figure 9.70

Because $\overline{AB} \cong \overline{XY}$, $\overline{BC} \cong \overline{YZ}$, and $\overline{AC} \cong \overline{XZ}$, we know $\triangle ABC \cong \triangle XYZ$.

If two sides and the included angle (the angle formed by these two sides) of   **9.21.2**
one triangle are congruent to the corresponding two sides and included angle of   **Side-Angle-Side**
a second triangle, then the triangles are congruent. This property is called the   **Triangle-Congruence**
Side-Angle-Side (SAS) Triangle-Congruence Property, and is illustrated in   **Property**
Figure 9.71.

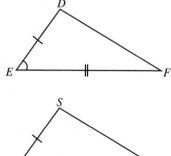

Figure 9.71

Because $\overline{DE} \cong \overline{ST}$, $\overline{EF} \cong \overline{TR}$, and $\angle E \cong \angle T$, we know $\triangle DEF \cong \triangle STR$.

9.21.3
Angle-Side-Angle Triangle-Congruence Property

If two angles and the included side (the side that is common to the two angles) of one triangle are congruent to the corresponding two angles and included side of a second triangle, then the triangles are congruent. This property is called the **Angle-Side-Angle (ASA) Triangle-Congruence Property**, and is illustrated in Figure 9.72.

Figure 9.72

Because $\angle H \cong \angle L$, $\overline{HI} \cong \overline{LM}$, and $\angle I \cong \angle M$, we know $\triangle HIJ \cong \triangle LMN$.

9.21.4
Angle-Angle-Side Triangle-Congruence Property

If two angles and a non-included side of one triangle are congruent to the corresponding two angles and side of a second triangle, then the triangles are congruent. This property is called the **Angle-Angle-Side (AAS) Triangle-Congruence Property**, and is illustrated in Figure 9.73.

Figure 9.73

Because $\angle A \cong \angle U$, $\angle B \cong \angle V$, and $\overline{BC} \cong \overline{VW}$, we know $\triangle ABC \cong \triangle UVW$.

9.21.5
Isosceles-Triangle-Congruence Properties

Isosceles triangles have some properties that are true for every isosceles triangle. (Recall that an isosceles triangle is a triangle with at least two sides congruent.) These are: (a) angles that are opposite congruent sides are congruent, and (b) the altitude drawn from the vertex common to the congruent sides bisects this vertex angle and is the perpendicular bisector of the opposite side. These properties are illustrated in Figure 9.74.

Figure 9.74

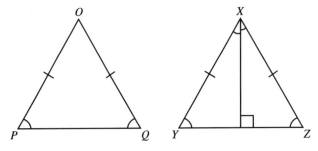

RELATED TOPICS   Quadrilateral Properties

TOPIC 9.22 QUADRILATERAL PROPERTIES

Regular Polygons | Triangle-Congruence Properties

CORNERSTONE

Some special types of quadrilaterals have particular congruence properties, along with other relationships. In this section, we discuss some properties for trapezoids, parallelograms, rectangles, kites, rhombi, and squares.

INTRODUCTION

The series of numbers, 1, 1, 2, 3, 5, 8, 13, . . ., is known as the Fibonacci sequence. The ratio of adjacent numbers in the sequence gets closer and closer to a fixed number known as the Golden Ratio. This number is approximately 1.618. A rectangle that has sides in this ratio is called a Golden Rectangle; many examples of the golden rectangle can be found in ancient Greek architecture.

For More Information: Garland, T. H. (1987). *Fascinating Fibonaccis: Mystery and magic in numbers*. Palo Alto, CA: Dale Seymour.
Runion, G. E. (1990). *The golden section*. Palo Alto, CA: Dale Seymour.

DID YOU KNOW?

Recall that the sum of the measures of the interior angles in any convex quadrilateral is 360°. Because a trapezoid is a quadrilateral with at least one pair of parallel sides, it must be convex. A property of trapezoids is that consecutive angles contained between parallel lines are supplementary. We will prove this relationship.

Given trapezoid $ABCD$ with $\overline{AB} \parallel \overline{DC}$, draw a line through $\overline{AB}$ and $\overline{DC}$ that is perpendicular to these sides (as shown in Figure 9.75). We can draw this line because if a line m is perpendicular to a line n in a plane, line m is perpendicular to all other lines that are parallel to line n. Label the points of intersection E and F (as shown in Figure 9.75). We know that $\angle AEF$ and $\angle EFD$ are right angles because they are formed by perpendicular lines. Thus, $m\angle AEF = 90°$ and $m\angle EFD = 90°$. Because the sum of the measures of the interior angles in $AEFD$ is 360°, then $m\angle FDA + m\angle DAE = 180°$, and thus these angles are supplementary. The same argument can be used to show that $\angle EBC$ and $\angle BCF$ are supplementary.

9.22.1
Properties of Trapezoids

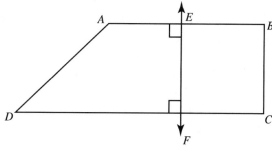

Figure 9.75

9.22.2
Properties of Parallelograms

Certain properties of parallelograms are especially noteworthy in the study of geometry:

- Opposite sides and angles of parallelograms are congruent.
- Diagonals in a parallelogram bisect each other.
- If a quadrilateral has both pairs of opposite sides congruent, it is a parallelogram.
- If a quadrilateral has two sides that are parallel and congruent, it is a parallelogram.
- If the diagonals of a quadrilateral bisect each other, it is a parallelogram.
- Each diagonal of a parallelogram separates it into two congruent triangles.

Because a parallelogram is a trapezoid, properties of a trapezoid are also valid for a parallelogram. We will prove two of these properties.

To prove that opposite sides and angles are congruent in a parallelogram, we will use a triangle congruence property. Given parallelogram $QRST$, draw diagonals $\overline{TR}$ and $\overline{QS}$, and label their intersection point P, as shown in Figure 9.76. Because opposite sides of a parallelogram are parallel, and because alternate interior angles formed by parallel lines cut by a transversal are congruent, then $\angle TRS \cong \angle RTQ$ and $\angle RTS \cong \angle TRQ$. Because $\overline{TR} \cong \overline{TR}$ (every segment is congruent to itself), then $\triangle TRS \cong \triangle RTQ$ by the Angle-Side-Angle Triangle-Congruence Property. Then, because corresponding parts of congruent triangles are congruent, $\overline{TS} \cong \overline{RQ}$, $\overline{QT} \cong \overline{SR}$, and $\angle S \cong \angle Q$. We can use a similar argument to show that $\triangle QTS \cong \triangle SRQ$, and thus, $\angle T \cong \angle R$.

Figure 9.76

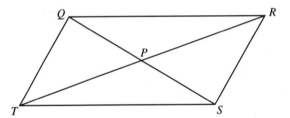

We will also use parallelogram QRST in Figure 9.76 to prove that the diagonals of a parallelogram bisect each other. Consider $\triangle TPS \cong \triangle RPQ$. We know that $\angle PTS \cong \angle PRQ$ and $\angle PST \cong \angle PQR$ because they are alternate interior angles formed by a transversal cutting parallel lines. Because opposite sides in a parallelogram are congruent, $\overline{TS} \cong \overline{RQ}$. Then, $\triangle TPS \cong \triangle RPQ$ by the Angle-Side-Angle Triangle-Congruence Property. Because corresponding parts of congruent triangles are congruent, then $\overline{PS} \cong \overline{PQ}$ and $\overline{PR} \cong \overline{PT}$. Thus, P must be the midpoint of $\overline{QS}$ and $\overline{TR}$, and so we have shown that the diagonals of a parallelogram bisect each other.

9.22.3
Properties of Rectangles

Because rectangles are parallelograms, all the properties that are true for parallelograms are also valid for rectangles. Additionally, rectangles have the following properties:

- A rectangle has four right angles.
- Any quadrilateral with four right angles must be a rectangle.
- The diagonals in a rectangle are congruent.
- Any quadrilateral with diagonals that bisect each other and are congruent is a rectangle.

We will prove the property that the diagonals of a rectangle are congruent.

Given rectangle   with diagonals $\overline{MO}$ and $\overline{NP}$, as shown in Figure 9.77, we know that $\overline{MP} \cong \overline{NO}$ and $\overline{MN} \cong \overline{OP}$ because opposite sides of a rectangle are congruent. We also know that all four angles in a rectangle are right angles, and because all right angles are congruent, $\angle MNO \cong \angle NOP$. Thus, $\triangle MNO \cong \triangle NOP$ by the Side-Angle-Side Triangle-Congruence Property. Because corresponding parts of congruent triangles are congruent, $\overline{MO} \cong \overline{NP}$. This shows that the diagonals in a rectangle are congruent.

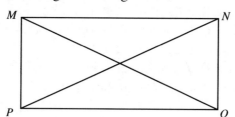

Figure 9.77

9.22.4
Properties of Kites

Some properties of a kite are:

- Diagonals are perpendicular to each other
- Exactly one diagonal is the perpendicular bisector of the other diagonal.

We will prove that the diagonals are perpendicular to each other using kite GHIJ with diagonals $\overline{IG}$ and $\overline{JH}$ as shown in Figure 9.78. Label the point of intersection point K. By definition of a kite, $\overline{JG} \cong \overline{GH}$ and $\overline{JI} \cong \overline{IH}$. Because $\overline{IG} \cong \overline{IG}$, then $\triangle GJI \cong \triangle GHI$ by the Side-Side-Side Triangle-Congruence Property. Because corresponding parts of congruent triangles are congruent, $\angle JGK \cong \angle HGK$. Using the fact that $\overline{GK} \cong \overline{GK}$, then $\triangle GJK \cong \triangle GHK$ by the Side-Angle-Side Triangle-Congruence Property. Because corresponding parts of congruent triangles are congruent, $\angle GKJ \cong \angle GKH$ and because these angles are linear pair angles, they each must be right angles. Thus, the diagonals are perpendicular to each other.

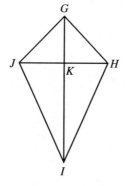

Figure 9.78

9.22.5
Properties of Rhombi

Because a rhombus is both a parallelogram and a kite, all the properties of a parallelogram and a kite also hold for a rhombus. Additionally, a rhombus has the following properties:

- If a quadrilateral has all sides congruent, it is a rhombus.
- Diagonals bisect opposite angles.

We will prove that in a rhombus the diagonals bisect opposite angles. Given rhombus $ABCD$ with diagonals $\overline{AC}$ and $\overline{BD}$, as shown in Figure 9.79, we know from the proof showing that the diagonals in a kite are perpendicular to each other that $\triangle ABC \cong \triangle ADC$. Because corresponding parts of congruent triangles are congruent, we know that $\angle DAC \cong \angle BAC$ and $\angle DCA \cong \angle BCA$. Thus, we know that $\angle DAB$ and $\angle BCD$ are bisected by $\overline{AC}$. A similar argument can be used to show that $\angle ABC$ and $\angle CDA$ are bisected by $\overline{DB}$.

Figure 9.79

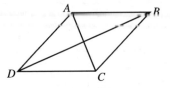

9.22.6
Properties of Squares

Because a square is both a rectangle and a rhombus, it has all the properties of a rectangle and a rhombus.

RELATED TOPICS   Similarity

TOPIC 9.23 SIMILARITY

Triangles | Triangle Congruence Properties

CORNERSTONE

The mathematical ideas of similarity and scale have been studied for thousands of years because they are so useful in solving problems. In this section, we discuss similarity and similar figures, similar triangles, and indirect measurement.

INTRODUCTION

A Greek merchant named Thales, who lived about 600 B.C., is said to have determined the height of a pyramid in Egypt by using the length of its shadow.

DID YOU KNOW?

For More Information: Bunt, L. N. H., Jones, P. S., & Bedient, J. D. (1988). *The Historical Roots of Elementary Mathematics.* New York: Dover Publications.

Informally speaking, two geometric figures are **similar** if they have exactly the same shape, but not necessarily the same size. More precisely, two geometric figures are said to **similar** if their corresponding angles are congruent and their corresponding sides are proportional. The figures shown in Figure 9.80 are similar figures.

9.23.1
Similarity and Similar Figures

Figure 9.80

$\triangle JKL$ is **similar** to $\triangle MNO$ (written $\triangle JKL \sim \triangle MNO$) if and only if $\angle J \cong \angle M$, $\angle K \cong \angle N$, $\angle \Lambda K \cong \angle O$ and $\frac{JK}{MN} = \frac{KL}{NO} = \frac{JL}{MO}$. In other words, two triangles are congruent if and only if their corresponding angles are congruent and their corresponding sides are proportional.

9.23.2
Similar Triangles

In the section called Triangle-Congruence Properties, we discuss how two triangles can be shown to be congruent if minimal congruence relationships are established. Likewise, two triangles can be shown to be similar if minimal conditions are satisfied. There are three similarity properties for triangles:

- If three sides of one triangle are proportional to the three corresponding sides of a second triangle, then the triangles are similar. This property is called the **Side-Side-Side (SSS) Triangle-Similarity Property** and is illustrated in the first drawing in Figure 9.81.

- If two sides of one triangle are proportional to two sides of a second triangle, and the included angles of these triangles are congruent, then the triangles are similar. This property is called the **Side-Angle-Side (SAS) Triangle-Similarity Property** and is illustrated in the second drawing in Figure 9.81.

- If two angles of one triangle are congruent to two angles of a second triangle (which means the third pair of angles is also congruent), then the triangles are similar. This property is called the **Angle-Angle (AA) Triangle-Similarity Property** and is illustrated in the third drawing in Figure 9.81.

Figure 9.81

9.23.3
Indirect
Measurement

Similar triangles can be useful in measuring lengths of objects that cannot be measured directly. We call this indirect measurement. For example, if you wanted to measure the height of a building on a sunny day, you could use your shadow and the building's shadow to determine two triangles, as shown in Figure 9.82.

Figure 9.82

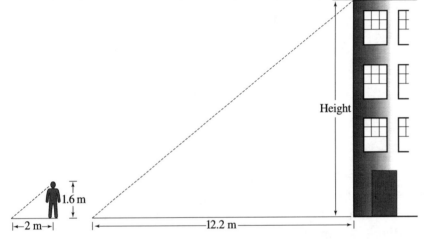

Because both you and the building are (we are assuming) forming right angles with the ground, and the sun is shining down on you and the building at the same angle, the two triangles formed are similar. Thus, we can use the fact that similar triangles have proportional sides to find the height of the building. Suppose you are 1.6 m tall, your shadow is 2.0 m long, and the building's shadow is 12.2 m long. To find the height of the building, we have the proportion:

$$\frac{1.6 \text{ m}}{2.0 \text{ m}} = \frac{\text{height of building}}{12.2 \text{ m}}$$

1.6 m (12.2 m) = 2.0 m (height of the building)

$$\frac{1.6 \text{ m (12.2 m)}}{2.0 \text{ m}} = \text{height of the building}$$

9.76 m = height of the building

RELATED TOPICS   Triangle Proportion Properties | Fractals and Rep-Tiles | Size Transformations

TOPIC 9.24 TRIANGLE PROPORTION PROPERTIES

Similarity   **CORNERSTONE**

There are a number of proportion properties that are relationships within a   **INTRODUCTION**
triangle. In this section, we discuss one of these properties and its converse.

Ideas of proportionality are used in many fields, such as medicine, film, architecture,   **DID YOU KNOW?**
photography, and integrated circuits.

   Two proportion properties for a triangle arise from a line intersecting two sides of a triangle. One property is the converse of the other; this means that one property has the hypothesis and the implication reversed from the other property. To illustrate a statement and its converse, consider the following statement about a square: If a quadrilateral is a square, then it must also be a rectangle. The converse of this statement is: If a quadrilateral is a rectangle, then it must also be a square. In this case, the statement is true, but the converse is not true.

   One of the properties states: If a line parallel to one side of a triangle intersects the other sides, then it divides the intersected sides into proportional segments. We will prove this relationship using ΔDEF and line l parallel to $\overline{EF}$ and intersecting $\overline{DE}$ and $\overline{DF}$ in points G and H, as shown in Figure 9.83. Because $\overline{GH} \parallel \overline{FE}$, then $\angle DGH \cong \angle DFE$ and $\angle DHG \cong \angle DEF$ because they are corresponding angles and $\Delta DGH \sim \Delta DFE$ by the Angle-Angle Triangle-Similarity Property. Thus, $\frac{DF}{DG} = \frac{DE}{DH}$ which can be written as

$$\frac{DG + GF}{DG} = \frac{DH + HE}{DH}$$

$$\frac{DG}{DG} + \frac{GF}{DG} = \frac{DH}{DH} + \frac{HE}{DH}$$

$$1 + \frac{GF}{DG} = 1 + \frac{HE}{DH}$$

$$\frac{GF}{DG} = \frac{HE}{DH}$$

which is the same as $\dfrac{DG}{GF} = \dfrac{DH}{HE}$,

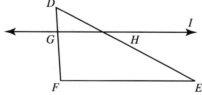

Figure 9.83

and thus the line divides the intersected sides into proportional segments.

   The converse of this property is also true: If a line divides two sides of a triangle into proportional segments, then that line is parallel to the third side. If points G and H in Figure 9.83 are midpoints of $\overline{DF}$ and $\overline{DE}$, respectively, then the segment, $\overline{GH}$, that connects the midpoints of two sides of a triangle is called a **midsegment** of the triangle.

Size Transformations   **RELATED TOPICS**

TOPIC 9.25 FRACTALS AND REP-TILES

CORNERSTONE	Similiarity

INTRODUCTION   *Although the geometry studied in the K-12 curriculum is usually limited to fairly simple, ideal shapes (e.g., circles, polygons, polyhedron), geometric shapes in nature come in a wide variety, often unrelated to the shapes studied in school. In this section, we discuss two especially interesting shapes: fractals and rep-tiles.*

DID YOU KNOW?   Although Benoit Mandelbrot coined the word *fractal* in 1975, mathematicians had begun studying the curves related to fractals before 1900.

For More Information: Sibley, T. Q. (1998). *The Geometric Viewpoint: A Survey of Geometries.* Reading, MA: Addison-Wesley.

9.25.1
Fractals

Figure 9.84

Benôit Mandelbrot used the word **fractal** to describe chaotic curves and surfaces that can be used to represent shapes that occur in nature, such as mountains, coastlines, and even human lungs. These shapes are generally self-similar; in other words, smaller subsets of the shape's outline have the same outline as larger subsets of the shape's outline. A well-known example of a self-similar shape is called the Sierpinski triangle. This triangle is formed by starting with an equilateral triangle and removing equilateral triangles that are one-fourth the size of the original from the centers of the triangles formed in the previous stage. This process is illustrated in Figure 9.84.

Another well-known fractal is called the Koch curve. The construction begins with a segment that we separate into thirds. In the next step, we construct an equilateral triangle "bump" in the middle third of the segment. In the next step, we construct equilateral triangle bumps on the middle third of each side of the big triangle. We now continue to repeat this pattern infinitely many times. (See Figure 9.85.)

Figure 9.85

1st step   2nd step   3rd step   Koch curve snowflake

There are two important aspects to this curve. Firstly, each new triangle that is constructed is similar to the original triangle. It will look exactly the same no matter how many times it is magnified. Secondly, the curve has a finite area—the entire picture can be placed inside a circle. The area of the entire diagram cannot be more than the area of the circle. However, the Koch curve has an infinite perimeter! We thus have an amazing geometric figure here—physically, you may think of it as being a fixed amount of land that needs an infinite amount of wire fencing to cover its boundaries!

9.25.2
Rep-tiles

A **rep-tile** is a figure that serves as a building block for making a larger figure similar to the building block. For example, an equilateral triangle and a square are rep-tiles in the figures shown in Figure 9.86, which are similar to the rep-tiles, respectively.

 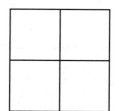

Figure 9.86

Size Transformations   **RELATED TOPICS**

TOPIC 9.26 THREE-DIMENSIONAL GEOMETRY BASICS

CORNERSTONE   Planes | Line Relationships | Rays and Angles

INTRODUCTION   *An important part of the study of geometry deals with three-dimensional geometry. After all, the world in which we live is three-dimensional. In this section, we discuss plane relationships, and dihedral angles.*

DID YOU KNOW?   The Greek philosopher Plato (427-347 B.C.) is said to have had a sign over the entrance to his academy that read: "Let no one ignorant of geometry enter here."

**9.26.1
Plane
Relationships**

When planes intersect each other, they have various possible points of intersection. Two planes may not have any points in common, and would be parallel planes. Think of the plane of a door intersecting the plane of a wall; those two planes intersect and have many points in common. In fact, if two distinct planes intersect, they intersect in a line, as in Figure 9.87.

Figure 9.87

There are four possible ways that three distinct planes can relate to each other. They could have no points in common and, thus, be parallel to each other. They could have exactly one point in common among all three planes, as shown in Figure 9.88 in the illustration of the box. They could have a line in common, as shown in the illustration of a booklet where each page represents a plane. And two planes could be parallel to each other and the third plane intersects each of the other two planes.

Figure 9.88

When two planes intersect, they form an angle. This angle is called a **dihedral angle** and is formed by the line of intersection of the two planes and the union of the two half-planes. Whenever two planes intersect, there are four dihedral angles formed, as shown in Figure 9.89.

9.26.2
Dihedral Angles

Figure 9.89

Angle Measurement | Polyhedra, Prisms, and Pyramids | Regular Polyhedra   **RELATED TOPICS**
Cylinders, Cones, and Spheres

TOPIC 9.27 POLYHEDRA, PRISMS, AND PYRAMIDS

CORNERSTONE   Three-dimensional Geometry Basics

INTRODUCTION   *All around us, in our everyday world, are types of three-dimensional figures. Many of these figures are polyhedra. In this section, we discuss a simple closed surface, a polyhedron and its features, convex and concave polyhedra, prisms, and pyramids.*

DID YOU KNOW?   Leonard Euler (1707–1783), a Swiss mathematician, developed a formula showing the relationship among the number of vertices, edges and faces for many polyhedra, including all convex ones. This relationship has a number of applications in geometry, graph theory and topology.

For More Information: Sibley, T. Q. (1998). *The Geometric Viewpoint: A Survey of Geometries.* Reading, MA: Addison-Wesley.

9.27.1
A Simple Closed Surface

A **simple closed surface** is a three-dimensional surface that is closed and has exactly one interior, no holes and is hollow. In the same way that a polygon separates the plane into three disjoint sets, a simple closed surface separates space into three disjoint sets. These are the interior of the surface, the surface, and the exterior of the surface (see Figure 9.90). A simple closed surface and its interior together make up the set of points known as a **solid**.

Figure 9.90

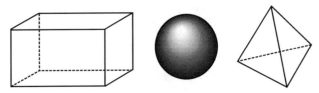

9.27.2
A Polyhedron and its Features

A **polyhedron** is a simple closed surface composed entirely of polygonal regions. The word *polyhedron* comes from poly meaning "many" and *hedron* meaning "flat surfaces." Figure 9.91 shows some examples of polyhedra and non-polyhedra. The non-polyhedra are not polyhedra because they either have holes, are not closed, or are not composed entirely of polygonal regions.

Polyhedra

Figure 9.91

Nonpolyhedra

The polygonal regions that comprise a polyhedron are called the **faces** and the vertices of the faces are called the **vertices** of the polyhedron. The line segment where two faces meet is called an **edge** (see Figure 9.92).

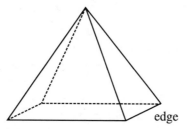

Figure 9.92

A polyhedron is **convex** if and only if for two distinct points in the interior of the polyhedron, the segment that joins those points is contained entirely in the interior of the polyhedron. If the segment that joins these two points does not lie in the interior of the polyhedron, then the polyhedron is **concave**. Figure 9.93 shows convex and concave polyhedra.

9.27.3
Convex and Concave Polyhedra

Convex Polyhedra   Concave Polyhedra

Figure 9.93

A **prism** is a polyhedron comprised of two congruent faces that are in parallel planes and parallelograms for the remaining faces. The two congruent faces that are parallel to each other are called the **bases** of the prism, and the remaining parallelogram faces are called the **lateral faces** of the prism, as shown in Figure 9.94.

9.27.4
Prisms

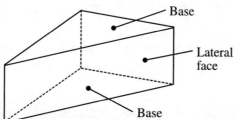

Base
Lateral face
Base

Figure 9.94

If the lateral faces are all rectangles, then the prism is called a **right** prism. If all the lateral faces are not rectangles, the prism is called an **oblique prism**. A prism is also named by its bases, as shown in Figure 9.95.

Figure 9.95

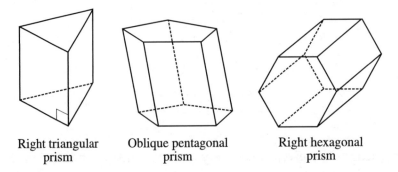

Right triangular prism   Oblique pentagonal prism   Right hexagonal prism

9.27.5 Pyramids

A **pyramid** is a polyhedron comprised of a polygon with n edges for its **base**, a point not in the plane of the base called the **apex**, and n triangular faces that are determined by the apex and the n edges of the base. The triangular faces are called the **lateral faces**. If the base of a pyramid is a regular polygon, and the lateral faces are congruent isosceles triangles, the pyramid is called a **right regular pyramid**. If the pyramid's base is regular but the lateral faces are not isosceles triangle, the pyramid is called an **oblique regular pyramid**. A pyramid is also named by its base, as shown in Figure 9.96.

Figure 9.96

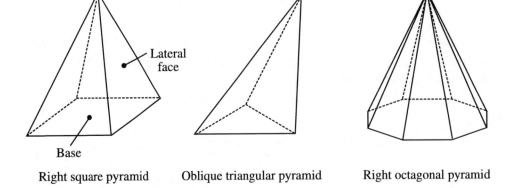

Right square pyramid   Oblique triangular pyramid   Right octagonal pyramid

RELATED TOPICS   Regular Polyhedra | Cylinders, Cones, and Spheres | Cavalieri's Principle
Surface Area of Prisms and Cylinders
Surface Area of Pyramids, Cones, and Spheres
Volume of Prisms and Cylinders | Volume of Pyramids, Cones, and Spheres

TOPIC 9.28 REGULAR POLYHEDRA

Three-dimensional Geometry Basics | Polyhedra, Prisms, and Pyramids   **CORNERSTONE**

Regular polyhedra are particular kinds of polyhedra and, as we will see, there are a limited number of regular polyhedra. In this section, we discuss regular and semiregular polyhedra.   **INTRODUCTION**

One of the marks of the Greek philosopher Plato's influence on the development of mathematics is the fact that the regular polyhedra are often called the Platonic solids, due to his fascination with these solids. Plato's writings about the regular polyhedra are among the oldest writings about polyhedra that survive.   **DID YOU KNOW?**

For More Information: Bunt, L. N. H., Jones, P. S., & Bedient, J. D. (1988). *The Historical Roots of Elementary Mathematics.* New York: Dover Publications.

A **regular polyhedron** is a convex polyhedron comprised of congruent regular polygons where at each vertex of the polyhedron there are the same number of edges meeting. There are exactly five regular polyhedra, as shown in the following figure.   **9.28.1**
Regular Polyhedra

Polyhedron	Polygon Used	Number of faces, F	Number of vertices, V	Number of edges, E	Figure
Tetrahedron	Triangle	4	4	6	
Octahedron	Triangle	8	6	12	
Icosahedron	Triangle	20	12	30	
Cube	Square	6	8	12	
Dodecahedron	Pentagon	12	20	30	

Figure 9.97

A **semiregular polyhedron** is a convex polyhedron comprised of regular polygons but not necessarily with the same number of sides. Some semiregular polyhedra are shown in Figure 9.98.   **9.28.2**
Semiregular Polyhedra

 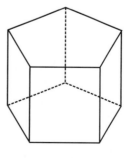

Triangular prism   Cube octahedron   Pentagonal prism

Figure 9.98

Cylinders, Cones, and Spheres | Cavalieri's Principle   **RELATED TOPICS**
Surface Area of Prisms and Cylinders | Surface Area of Pyramids, Cones, and Spheres
Volume of Prisms and Cylinders | Volume of Pyramids, Cones, and Spheres

TOPIC 9.29 CYLINDERS, CONES, AND SPHERES

CORNERSTONE	Three-dimensional Geometry Basics

INTRODUCTION	*Not all simple closed surfaces are polyhedra. In this section, we discuss cylinders, cones, and spheres.*

DID YOU KNOW? Astronomy and navigational needs have pushed the study of the geometry of the sphere. The inside surface of a sphere is used by astronomers to locate stars, planets and other objects. Navigators use a sphere to represent the earth in seeking the most direct shipping or flying routes, where following the curved surface of the Earth is more direct than a straight line on a planar map of the earth.

For More Information: Sibley, T. Q. (1998). *The Geometric Viewpoint: A Survey of Geometries.* Reading, MA: Addison-Wesley.

9.29.1
Cylinders

A **cylinder** is a simple closed surface comprised of two congruent simple closed non-polygonal curves that are in parallel planes, their interiors, and the line segments that connect corresponding points on the curves. The two non-polygonal curves are called the **bases** of the cylinder. The remaining points of the cylinder compose the **lateral surface** of the cylinder, as shown in Figure 9.99.

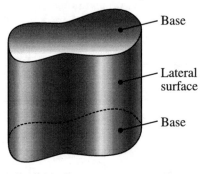

Figure 9.99

A particular kind of cylinder is a **circular cylinder**, which has two congruent circles for bases. If the line segments joining corresponding points on the bases are perpendicular to the bases, the cylinder is a **right cylinder**. An **oblique cylinder** is a cylinder that is not a right cylinder. Some examples of cylinders are shown in Figure 9.100.

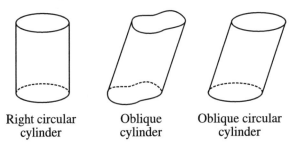

Figure 9.100

Right circular cylinder   Oblique cylinder   Oblique circular cylinder

A **cone** is a simple closed surface comprised of a simple closed non-polygonal curve, its interior, and the line segments that connect each point of the curve to a point not in the plane of the curve. The non-polygonal curve is called the **base** of the cone, and the point not in the plane of the curve is called the **apex**.

The **altitude** of the cone is the line segment from the apex that is perpendicular to the base, as shown in Figure 9.101.

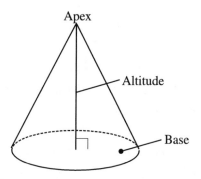

Figure 9.101

A cone with a circular base is called a **circular cone**. A circular cone whose altitude intersects the base at the center of the circular base is called a **right circular cone**. An **oblique circular cone** is one that is not a right circular cone, as shown in Figure 9.102.

Right circular   Oblique   Oblique circular
   cone   cone   cone

Figure 9.102

A **sphere** is a simple closed surface comprised of all the points that are a given distance from a given point called the **center**, as shown in Figure 9.103. The **radius** of a sphere is the length of a segment with an endpoint on the sphere and having the center as the other endpoint. The segment is also called a radius. The **diameter** of a sphere is the length of a segment that has its endpoints on the sphere and passes through the center. The segment is also called a diameter.

Figure 9.103

Polyhedra, Prisms, and Pyramids | Regular Polyhedra   **RELATED TOPICS**
Cavalieri's Principle | Surface Area of Prisms and Cylinders
Surface Area of Pyramids, Cones, and Spheres | Volume of Prisms and Cylinders
Volume of Pyramids, Cones, and Spheres

TOPIC 9.30 VAN HIELE LEVELS

CORNERSTONE   Two-dimensional Geometry Basics

INTRODUCTION   *The study of geometry has been an important part of the school mathematics curriculum for a long time, but it has suffered from being poorly defined. Work done by Pierre van Hiele and Dina van Hiele-Geldof of the Netherlands has helped to better determine what geometry ideas should be included in the school curriculum, and when they should be included. The van Hieles' work, conducted primarily in the 1950s, suggests that children move through developmental stages as they grow in their understanding of geometry ideas.*

DID YOU KNOW?   Although the van Hieles' work was given much attention in the 1960s and 1970s in what was then the Soviet Union, their work was largely ignored in the United States for nearly two decades. Now, however, their work has become very influential in determining the pre-college geometry curriculum.

For More Information: Fuys, D., Geddes, D., & Tischler, R. (1988). The van Hiele model of thinking in geometry among adolescents. *Journal for Research in Mathematics Education Monograph No. 3.*

**9.30.1
Coplanar,
Noncoplanar,
and Skew Lines**

A central part of the van Hieles' model is a five-level developmental hierarchy of geometric thinking. The five levels describe the thinking processes that the van Hieles propose people use in geometric situations. Learners, according to the van Hieles, pass through the five levels assisted by appropriate instructional experiences, and cannot reach a particular level of thinking without having gone through the previous levels. The descriptions provided here are only a brief overview of the van Hiele levels of geometric thinking and are taken from a monograph written by Fuys, Geddes and Tischler (1988).

Level 0: The student identifies, names, compares and operates on geometric figures (e.g., triangles, angles, intersecting or parallel lines) according to their appearance.

Level 1: The student analyzes figures in terms of their components and relationships among components and discovers properties/rules by giving or following informal arguments.

Level 2: The student logically interrelates previously discovered properties/rules by giving or following informal arguments.

Level 3: The student proves theorems deductively and establishes interrelationships among networks of theorems.

Level 4: The student establishes theorems in different postulational systems and analyzes/compares these systems. (p. 5)

RELATED TOPICS   Polyhedra, Prisms, and Pyramids | Regular Polyhedra
Cavalieri's Principle | Surface Area of Prisms and Cylinders
Surface Area of Pyramids, Cones, and Spheres
Volume of Prisms and Cylinders | Volume of Pyramids, Cones, and Spheres

IN THE CLASSROOM

While this chapter focuses on the *Geometry Content Standard*, it also emphasizes the *Communication Process Standard* (NCTM, 2000). All students should be enabled to "analyze characteristics and properties of two- and three- dimensional shapes and develop mathematical arguments about geometric relationships" (p. 41), and "use the language of mathematics to express mathematical ideas precisely" (p. 60). To enable your students in this manner, we believe you should explore the following in the context of geometry: (a) the importance of language and representation in mathematics (Activities 9.1-9.6), (b) the logic of classification and inherited properties and results (Activities 9.7-9.11), and (c) mathematical connections, proof, and changing assumptions (Activities 9.12-9.17).

How Activities 9.1-9.17 help you develop an adult-level perspective on the above expectations.

- By working with two-dimensional shapes you discuss the importance of precise language and communication while exploring properties of shapes. You discuss the concept of necessary and sufficient attributes and analyze various ways of defining a single shape.

- By making geometric constructions you continue to explore definitions while also making connections with ideas in number and measurement.

- By working with quadrilaterals you further classify shapes according to their attributes.

- By working with triangles, you continue to make connections with measurement and number ideas. In particular, you focus on the measure of line segments and angles and on the ratios of sides of triangles in discussing the concepts of congruence and similarity.

- By initially making and testing conjectures about triangles and quadrilaterals, you develop logical arguments to justify your conclusions. Later you build on these conclusions to prove simple results about more complex geometric shapes while learning to write your justifications in precise mathematical language.

- By exploring spherical geometry, you begin to describe and interpret shapes as the space and distance measures change from the familiar Euclidean and extend your thinking about definitions, geometry, and measurement.

Some expectations of your future students

Pre-K-2 (NCTM, 2000, p. 96)	recognize, name, build, draw, compare, and sort two- and three-dimensional shapes
	describe attributes and parts of two- and three-dimensional shapes
	describe, name, and interpret direction and distance in navigating space and apply ideas about direction and distance
	relate ideas in geometry to ideas in number and measurement
Grades 3-5 (NCTM, 2000, p. 164)	classify two- and three-dimensional shapes according to their properties and develop definitions of classes of shapes such as triangles and pyramids
	explore congruence and similarity
	make and test conjectures about geometric properties and relationships and develop logical arguments to justify conclusions
	build and draw geometric objects

BIBLIOGRAPHY

Arithmetic Teacher. (1990, February). Focus issue on spatial sense, 37.

Battista, M. T. (1998). *Shape makers: Developing geometric reasoning with the Geometer's Sketchpad*. Emeryville, CA: Key Curriculum Press.

Bennett, D. (1999). *Exploring geometry with the Geometer's Sketchpad* (2nd ed.). Emeryville, CA: Key Curriculum Press.

Brahier, D. J., & Speer, W. R. (1997). Worthwhile tasks: Exploring mathematical connections through geometric solids. *Mathematics Teaching in the Middle School, 3*, 20-28.

Bright, G. W., & Harvey, J. G. (1988). Learning and fun with geometry games. *Arithmetic Teacher, 35*, 22-26.

Bruni, V., & Seidenstein, R. B. (1990). Geometric concepts and spatial sense In J. N. Payne (Ed.), *Mathematics for the young child* (pp 203-207). Reston, VA: National Council of Teachers of Mathematics.

Cangelosi, J. S. (1985). A "fair" way to discover circles. *Arithmetic Teacher, 33* 11 - 13.

Carroll, W. M. (1988). Cross sections of clay solids. *Arithmetic Teacher, 35, 6-11*.

Carroll, W. M. (1998). Middle school students' reasoning about geometric situations. *Mathematics Teaching in the Middle School, 3*, 398-403.

Chazan, D. (1990). Implementing the *Standards*: Students' microcomputer-aided exploration in geometry. *Mathematics Teacher, 83*, 628-635.

Clements, D. H. (1999). Geometric and spatial thinking in young children. In J. V. Copley (Ed.), *Mathematics in the early years* (pp. 66-79). Reston, VA: National Council of Teachers of Mathematics.

Clements, D. H., & Battista. M. (1986). Geometry and geometric measurement. *Arithmetic Teacher, 33, 29-32*.

Confer, C. (1994). *Math by all means: Geometry, grade 2*. Sausalito, CA: Math Solutions Publications.

Craine, T. V., & N. Rubenstein, R. N. (1993). A quadrilateral hierarchy to facilitate learning in geometry. *Mathematics Teacher, 86 , 30-36*.

Dana, M. E. (1987). Geometry: A square deal for elementary teachers. In M. M Lindquist (Ed.), *Learning and teaching geometry K-12* (pp. 113-125). Reston, VA: National Council of Teachers of Mathematics.

de Villiers, M. D. (1999). *Rethinking proof with the Geometer's Sketchpad*. Emeryville, CA: Key Curriculum Press.

Del Grande, J. (1993). *Geometry and spatial sense: Addenda series, grades K-6*. Reston, VA: National Council of Teachers of Mathematics.

Ellington, B. (1983). Star Trek: A construction problem using compass and straightedge. *Mathematics Teacher, 76*, 329-332.

Enderson, M. C., & Manouchehri, A. (1998). Technology-based geometric explorations for the middle grades. In L. P. Leutzinger (Ed.), *Mathematics in the middle* (pp. 193-200). Reston, VA: National Council of Teachers of Mathematics.

Evered, L. J. (1992). Folded fashions: Symmetry in clothing design. *Arithmetic Teacher, 40*, 204-206.

Flores, A. (1993) Pythagoras meets van Hiele. *School* Science and Mathematics, 93, 152-157.

Fuys, D J., & Liebov, A K. (1993). Geometry and spatial sense In R J Jensen (Ed.), *Research ideas for the classroom: Early childhood mathematics* (pp 195-222) Old Tappan, NJ: Macmillan.

Geddes, D. (1992). *Geometry in the middle grades. Addenda series, grades 5-8*. Reston. VA: National Council of Teachers of Mathematics.

Hill, J. M. (Ed.) (1987). *Geometry for grades K-6: Readings from The Arithmetic Teacher*. Reston, VA. National Council of Teachers of Mathematics.

Hoffer, A. R., & Hoffer, S. A. K. (1992). Geometry and visual thinking. In T R. Post (Ed.), *Teaching mathematics in grades K-8: Research-based methods* (2nd ed.) (pp. 249-277). Needham Heights, MA: Allyn & Bacon.

Johnson, A., & Boswell, L. (1992). Geographic constructions. *Mathematics Teacher, 85*, 184-187.

Krause, E. F. (1986). *Taxicab geometry: An adventure in non-Euclidean geometry*. New York: Dover Publications, Inc.

Kriegler, S. (1991). The Tangram: It's more than an ancient puzzle. *Arithmetic Teacher, 38*, 38-43.

Lappan, G., & Even, R. (1988). Similarity in the middle grades. *Arithmetic Teacher, 35*, 32-35.

Lappan, G., Phillips, E. A., & Winter, M. J. (1984). Spatial visualization. *Mathematics Teacher 77,* 618-625.

Lehrer, R., & Curtis, C. L. (2000). Why are some solids perfect? Conjectures and experiments by third graders. *Teaching Children Mathematics, 6*, 324-329.

Malloy, C. (1999). Perimeter and area through the van Hiele model. *Mathematics Teaching in the Middle School, 5*, 87-90.

Manouchehri, A., Enderson, M. C., & Pugnucco, L. A. (1998). Exploring geometry with technology. *Mathematics Teaching in the Middle School, 3*, 436-442.

Masingila, J. O. (1993). Secondary geometry: A lack of evolution. *School Science and Mathematics, 93* (1), 38-44.

Mercer, S., & Henningsen, M.A. (1998). The Pentomino project: Moving students from manipulatives to reasoning and thinking about mathematical ideas. In L. P. Leutzinger (Ed.), *Mathematics in the middle* (pp. 184-192). Reston, VA: National Council of Teachers of Mathematics.

Morrow, L. J. (1991). Implementing the *Standards*: Geometry through the *Standards*. *Arithmetic Teacher, 38*, 21 -25.

Nowlin, D. (1993). Practical geometry problems: The case of the Ritzville pyramids. *Mathematics Teacher, 86*, 198-200.

Rowan, T. E. (1990). Implementing the *Standards*: The geometry standards in K-8 mathematics. *Arithmetic Teacher, 37*, 24-28.

Rubenstein, R. N., Lappan, G., Phillips, E., & Fitzgerald, W. (1993). Angle sense: A valuable connector. *Arithmetic Teacher, 40*, 352-358.

Rubenstein. R. N., & Thompson, D R. (1995). Making connections with transformations in grades K-8. In P. A. House (Ed). Connecting mathematics across the curriculum (pp. 65-78). Reston, VA: National Council of Teachers of Mathematics.

Sandberg, S. E. (1998). A plethora of polyhedra. *Mathematics Teaching in the Middle School, 3*, 388-391.

Thiessen, D., & Matthias, M. (1989). Selected children's books for geometry. *Arithmetic Teacher, 37*, 47-51.

Wilson, P. S. (1990). Understanding angles: Wedges to degrees. *Mathematics Teacher, 83*, 294-300.

Winter, J J., Lappan, G., Phillips, E., & Fitzgerald, W. (1986). *Middle grades mathematics project: Spatial visualization*. Menlo Park, CA: Addison-Wesley.

Woodward, E., Gibbs, V., & Shoulders, M. (1992). A fifth-grade similarity unit. *Arithmetic Teacher, 39*, 22-26.

Yeshurun, S. (1985). An improvement of the congruent angles theorem. *Mathematics Teacher, 78*, 53-54.

MEASUREMENT 10

TOPIC

10.1	Angle Measurement
10.2	Linear Measurement
10.3	Perimeter
10.4	Circumference
10.5	Measuring Area
10.6	Area of Quadrilaterals
10.7	Area of Triangles
10.8	Area of Regular Polygons and Circles
10.9	Surface Area of Prisms and Cylinders
10.10	Surface Area of Pyramids, Cones and Spheres
10.11	Measuring Volume
10.12	Volume of Prisms and Cylinders
10.13	Volume of Pyramids, Cones and Spheres
10.14	Cavalieri's Principle
10.15	Mass and Temperature
10.16	Pythagorean Theorem and Other Triangle Relationships
10.17	Distance Formula
10.18	Tessellations
10.19	Tessellations of Regular Polygons
10.20	Transformations
10.21	Translations
10.22	Rotations
10.23	Reflections and Glide Reflections
10.24	Size Transformations
	In the Classroom
	Bibliography

CHAPTER OVERVIEW

Perhaps no part of mathematics is more clearly applicable to everyday life than measurement. As a consequence of the practicality of measurement in the real world, it is a very important strand in the elementary school mathematics curriculum. In particular, students learn extremely useful measurement skills (e.g., how to use a ruler), concepts (e.g., the concepts of area and perimeter), and key formulas (e.g., $A = \ell \cdot w$). Just as important is the fact that making measurements can be a source of many, very interesting problems. For example, did you know that two shapes can have the same perimeter, but different areas? One natural question that follows from this is "Can two shapes have the same area, but different perimeters?" In this chapter you can learn some interesting facts about measurement, and examine some concepts and procedures involving measurement ideas.

BIG MATHEMATICAL IDEAS

- Problem-solving Strategies
- Conjecturing
- Verifying
- Generalizing

NCTM PRINCIPLES & STANDARDS LINKS

Measurement
Problem Solving
Reasoning
Communication
Connections
Representation

311

TOPIC 10.1 ANGLE MEASUREMENT

CORNERSTONE Planes | Rays and Angles | Three-dimensional Geometry Basics

INTRODUCTION *Angles are essential parts of many geometric figures, and often it is important for us to be able to measure angles. In this section, we discuss angle measurement and notation, how to use a protractor, angle classification, and dihedral angle measurement.*

DID YOU KNOW? The Babylonians determined that there were approximately 360 days in one year, and so divided a circle into 360 equal parts. This is how we have come to measure angles, in terms of degrees, where each degree is $\frac{1}{360}$ of a circle.

For More Information: Bunt, L. N. H., Jones, P. S., & Bedient, J. D. (1988). *The Historical Roots of Elementary Mathematics.* New York: Dover Publications.

10.1.1
Angle Measurement and Notation

An angle is **measured** by considering the rotation needed to move one ray to fit on the other ray. A common way to measure this rotation is to use **degree units**. There are 360 degree units (or **degrees**) in a full circular rotation. We use the symbol ° to stand for degrees. The angles shown in Figure 10.1 have measures of 50° and 135°, respectively.

Figure 10.1

10.1.2
How to Use a Protractor

A geometric tool we use to measure angles is called a **protractor**, as shown in Figure 10.2. The unit of measurement on the protractor is the **degree**. Each degree is divided into 60 equal parts called **minutes**, and each minute is divided into 60 equal parts called **seconds**. If an angle has a measurement of 65 degrees, 30 minutes, 15 seconds, we write that as 60°30'15".

Figure 10.2

To use a protractor to measure an angle, first place the center mark of the protractor on the vertex of the angle so that one ray of the angle lies on the zero degree (0°) line on the protractor (see the first drawing in Figure 10.3). Then see where the other ray of the angle crosses the protractor's scale. Make sure that the number corresponds to the rotation needed to move the one ray (at 0°) to fit on top of the second ray, as shown in the second drawing in Figure 10.3.

Figure 10.3

Angles are usually classified as one of five type of angles: acute, right, obtuse, straight, or reflex. An **acute** angle is an angle that has a measure greater than 0° and less than 90°. An angle that measures 90° is called a **right** angle. An **obtuse** angle is one that has a measure greater than 90° and less than 180°. An angle that measures 180° is called a **straight** angle. An angle that measures more than 180° is called a **reflex** angle. In the drawings in Figure 10.4, *x* represents the measure of the angle.

10.1.3
Angle Classification

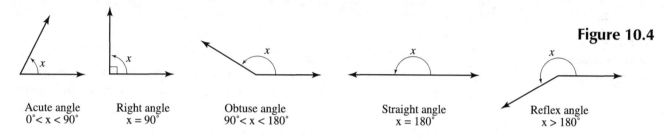

Figure 10.4

As discussed in section 9.26.2, a dihedral angle is formed by the line of intersection of two planes and the union of the two half-planes. To determine the measure of a dihedral angle, we form a planar angle that is on the dihedral angle by choosing a point *B* on the line of intersection of the two planes, and drawing a ray in each half-plane that is perpendicular to the line of intersection, as shown in Figure 10.5. An infinite number of planar angles can be formed for any dihedral angle, each having the same measure. The measure of a dihedral angle is the measure of any of its planar angles.

10.1.4
Dihedral Angle Measurement

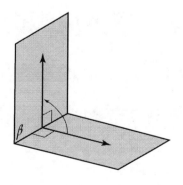

Figure 10.5

TOPIC 10.2 LINEAR MEASUREMENT

CORNERSTONE	Line Segments

INTRODUCTION

Throughout history, humans have chosen various units to measure length or distance. These non-standard units evolved into standard units of measure. In this section, we discuss length and how to measure it, the English system of linear measurement, and the metric system of linear measurement.

DID YOU KNOW?

The earliest recorded linear unit of measurement is the *cubit*, the distance from the point of the elbow to the outstretched tip of the middle finger. *Foot* was another early unit of measure, and its length was likely based on the length of the foot of Charlemagne, Emperor of the Holy Roman Empire. In the 10th century, King Edgar I of England decreed that the *yard* would be the distance from the tip of *his* nose to the top of the middle finger of *his* outstretched arm. This decree was to regulate trade in textiles, so that one yard of cloth would be the same throughout England.

For More Information: Bunt, L. N. H., Jones, P. S., & Bedient, J. D. (1988). *The Historical Roots of Elementary Mathematics*. New York: Dover Publications.

10.2.1
Length and How to Measure It

The **length** of a segment is the number of units that fit into the segment. In order to measure a segment, we must choose a unit of measure. Historically, groups of people developed various units of measure in order to be able to trade goods and record quantities. However, these measurements were not standardized, and eventually two main systems of measurement emerged. The English system is quite complicated, whereas the metric system is based on powers of ten and is easier to remember and to convert among measures within the system.

10.2.2
The English System of Linear Measurement

The basic units of linear measure in the **English system** (also called the U.S. customary system) are inch, foot, yard, and mile. The length of a pencil might be measured in inches, the length of a room might be measured in feet, a playing field might be measured in yards, and the distance between two cities might be measured in miles. Table 10.1 shows the equivalent values of one unit in terms of other units.

Table 10.1

UNIT	EQUIVALENT
1 inch (in)	1/12 ft
1 foot (ft)	12 in; 1/3 yd
1 yard (yd)	3 ft; 36 in
1 mile (mi)	5280 ft; 1760 yd

Almost all countries in the world, except the United States, use the **metric system** of measurement. The metric system is based on powers of ten. The basic unit of linear measure in the metric system is the **meter**, and the most commonly used linear measures are millimeter, centimeter, meter, and kilometer. The thickness of a pencil point might be measured in millimeters, the length of a piece of paper might be measured in centimeters, the distance a ball is thrown might be measured in meters, and the distance traveled in a vehicle might be measured in kilometers. Table 10.2 shows the equivalent values of one unit in terms of other units.

**10.2.3
The Metric
System of Linear
Measurement**

UNIT	EQUIVALENT
1 millimeter (mm)	1/10 cm
1 centimeter (cm)	10 mm; 1/100 yd
1 meter (m)	100 cm; 1000 mm
1 kilometer (km)	1000 m

Table 10.2

The prefixes used are shown in Table 10.3. Different units are obtained by multiplying the basic unit by a power of ten.

PREFIX	FACTOR
milli	0.001 (10^{-3})
centi	0.01 (10^{-2})
deci	0.1 (10^{-1})
basic unit	1 (10^{0})
deka	10 (10^{1})
hecto	100 (10^{2})
kilo	1000 (10^{3})

Table 10.3

Measuring Area | Distance Formula | Perimeter | Circumference   **RELATED TOPICS**

TOPIC 10.3 PERIMETER

CORNERSTONE	Linear Measurement	Distance Formula

INTRODUCTION

Knowing the distance around a figure is important information when constructing a building, putting up a fence, or laying out a garden. In this section, we discuss the perimeters of polygons, that is the distance around polygons.

DID YOU KNOW?

The Romans divided one foot into 12 equal units, called unciae from which we get the word inch.

For More Information: Bunt, L. N. H., Jones, P. S., & Bedient, J. D. (1988). *The Historical Roots of Elementary Mathematics.* New York: Dover Publications.

10.3.1
Perimeter

The length of a simple closed curve, or the distance around the curve, is called the **perimeter**. Perimeter is a type of linear measure. A figure could have a perimeter of, for example, 8 cm or 10 ft or 135 km.

10.3.2
Perimeters of Polygons

The perimeter of a polygon is the sum of the lengths of the sides of the polygon. For example, for a pentagon with sides of length s_1, s_2, s_3, s_4, and s_5, the perimeter is $P = s_1 + s_2 + s_3 + s_4 + s_5$. The perimeters of the polygons in Figure 10.6 can be found by adding up the lengths of the sides.

Figure 10.6

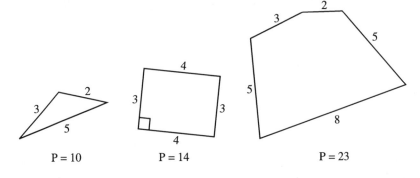

P = 10   P = 14   P = 23

For some special polygons, we can simplify the perimeter formula. For an **equilateral triangle, P = 3s**, where s is the length of a side. For a **square, P = 4s**; for a **rectangle, P = 2l + 2w**, where *l* is the length of one side and *w* is the length of a consecutive side, as shown in Figure 10.7.

Figure 10.7

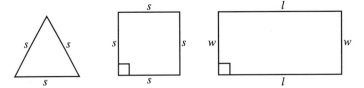

RELATED TOPICS	Circumference

TOPIC 10.4 CIRCUMFERENCE

CORNERSTONE

INTRODUCTION

While the distance around a circle is its perimeter, we have a special name for the perimeter of a circle. In this section, we discuss circumference and π, and arc length.

DID YOU KNOW?

The quest for more accurate estimates of π began as early as with the ancient Egyptians. A problem from the Ahmes Papyrus asks: A circular field has diameter 9 khet. What is its area? In solving this problem, the Egyptians used an implicit estimate of π of approximately 3.1605.

For More Information: Joseph, G. G. (1991). *The Crest of the Peacock: Non-European Roots of Mathematics*. London, England: Penguin Books.

The distance around a circle is called the **circumference**. In other words, for The distance around a circle is called the **circumference**. In other words, for a circle the perimeter is known as the circumference. The ratio of the circumference (C) of a circle to its diameter (d) has been found to be approximately 3.14 or $\frac{22}{7}$. This ratio is the irrational number pi (π). In other words, the circumference of a circle divided by its diameter will always equal π. Thus, the formula for the circumference of any circle is: $\frac{C}{d} = \pi$ or $C = \pi d$. Because the length of the diameter in a circle is twice the length of a radius in the same circle, this can also be written: $C = 2\pi r$, where r is the radius. The circumferences of the circles shown in Figure 10.8 can be found by using these formulas.

**10.4.1
Circumference
and π**

$C = 2\pi \approx 6.28$ $C = 14\pi \approx 21.98$

Figure 10.8

The length of an arc on a circle is determined by the radius of the circle and the **central angle** forming the arc. A central angle is an angle that has the center of a circle as its vertex, and has sides intersecting the circle, as shown in Figure 10.9. When a central angle intersects the circle, two arcs are formed. For example, in Figure 10.9, $\overarc{AB}$ and $\overarc{ACB}$ are formed by ∠AOB intersecting circle O.

**10.4.2
Arc Length**

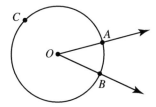

Figure 10.9

A central angle with a measure of 180° forms two arcs that are semicircles. Because the circumference of a circle is 2πr, where r is the radius of the circle, the arc length of a semicircle is half of the circumference, or πr, as shown in Figure 10.10.

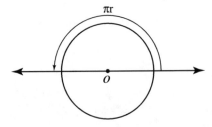

Figure 10.10

Any arc length can be determined by using the fact that a circle has 360° and an arc length is formed by a central angle having a particular measure, say $\theta°$. Because an arc is a portion of a circle, we can set up a proportion to find the arc length of an arc formed by a central angle with a measure of $\theta°$: $\frac{\text{arc length}}{2\pi r} = \frac{\theta°}{360°}$ or arc length $= \frac{\pi r \theta°}{180°}$ (see Figure 10.11).

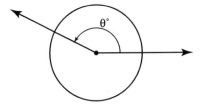

Figure 10.11

RELATED TOPICS   Perimeter

TOPIC 10.5 MEASURING AREA

Linear Measurement

INTRODUCTION

Measuring the area of a region is important in many situations, such as laying carpet, sewing, and designing a brochure. In this section, we discuss area and how to measure it, the English system of area measurement, and the metric system of area measurement.

DID YOU KNOW?

Historically, an acre was the amount of land that a farmer and two oxen could plow in one day. This varied from place to place. Eventually, King Henry VIII of England standardized the area of an acre as 40 poles long by 4 poles wide. A pole equals 16.5 feet.

For More Information: Bunt, L. N. H., Jones, P. S., & Bedient, J. D. (1988). *The Historical Roots of Elementary Mathematics.* New York: Dover Publications.

The **area** of a planar shape is the number of square units enclosed by the shape. If we use a square as the basic unit, the area of a figure is the number of squares that is required to cover the region enclosed by the shape with no squares overlapping and no gaps (this is called *tessellating the plane* and is discussed in the section called Tessellations). Area is measured in square units, such as square inches, square meters, or square miles.

To measure the area of a planar shape, we can place a grid comprised of squares over the shape and estimate the number of square units needed to cover the shape. If we use a finer grid, we can arrive at a better estimate of the area, as illustrated in Figure 10.12.

10.5.1
Area and How to Measure It

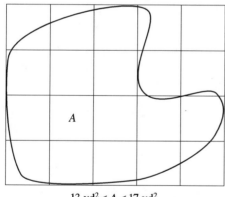

13 yd² < A < 17 yd²
which is 71.7 ft² < A < 153ft²

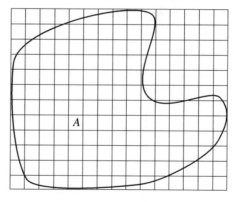

143 ft² < A < 149 ft²

Figure 10.12

In the English system of measurement, area is usually measured in square inches, square feet, square yards, acres, or square miles. Table 10.4 shows these units and their equivalents in other units in the English system.

10.5.2
The English System of Area Measurement

UNIT	EQUIVALENT	
1 square inch (1in²)	1/144 ft²	Table 10.4
1 square foot (1ft²)	144 in²; 1/9 yd²	
1 square yard (1yd²)	9 ft²	
1 acre (1 A)	43,560 ft²	
1 square mile (1mi²)	27,878,400 ft²; 3,097,600 yd²	

Figure 10.13

2 ft

10.5.3
**The Metric
System of Area
Measurement**

To convert from one area measure to another within the system, we need to remember that we are using square units. For example, a square with each side having a length of 2 feet would have an area of 4 ft², as shown in Figure 10.13. To determine what the area would be in terms of square inches, we substitute 24 inches for the length of each side because 2 ft = 24 in. Then the number of square inches that it would take to cover the region enclosed by the square would be 24 · 24 or 576. Thus, 4 ft² = 576 in².

In the metric system of measurement, area is usually measured by square millimeters, square centimeters, square decimeters, square meters, square dekameters (called ares), square hectometers (called hectares), and square kilometers. Table 10.5 shows these units and their equivalents in other units in the metric system.

Table 10.1

UNIT	EQUIVALENT
1 square millimeter (1 mm²)	0.000001 m²
1 square centimeter (1 cm²)	0.0001 m²
1 square decimeter (1 dm²)	0.01 m²
1 square meter (1 m²)	10,000 cm²
1 are (1 a)	100 m²
1 hectare (1 ha)	10,000 m²
1 square kilometer (1 km²)	1,000,000 m²

We can convert from one area measure to another within the system by substituting equivalent quantities. For example, to determine how many 1-mm squares are in a square centimeter, we replace the length of each side (1 cm) with 10 millimeters, as shown in Figure 10.14, because 1 cm = 10 mm. Then we can see that it takes 100 1-mm squares to equal 1 cm², and thus, 100 mm² = 1 cm².

Figure 10.14

1 cm

RELATED TOPICS   Area of Triangles | Area of Quadrilaterals | Tessellations
Area of Regular Polygons and Circles

TOPIC 10.6 AREA OF QUADRILATERALS

CORNERSTONE

Because area is measured in square units, the square is the foundational building   **INTRODUCTION**
block we can use to determine area formulas for many polygonal figures. In this
section, we discuss the areas of various quadrilaterals; in particular, square,
rectangle, parallelogram and trapezoid.

The early Egyptians had ways to calculate the areas of certain planar figures. Their   **DID YOU KNOW?**
procedures for calculating the area of a rectangle, a triangle and a trapezoid were correct.
However, they calculated the area of an arbitrary quadrilateral as the product of half the
sum of two opposite sides and half the sum of the other two, which is valid for only some
quadrilaterals.

For More Information: Bunt, L. N. H., Jones, P. S., & Bedient, J. D. (1988). *The Historical*
Roots of Elementary Mathematics. New York: Dover Publications.

The area of a square is the number of square units required to cover the re-   **10.6.1**
gion enclosed by the square. Consider the square in Figure 10.15 with each side   **Area of a Square**
of length 4 units. If we place 1-unit squares inside the 4-unit square, we can see
that there are four 1-unit squares along each dimension of the 4-unit square, and
there are a total of 16 1-unit squares inside the 4-unit square. Thus, the area of
the 4-unit square is 16 square units, or 16 units^2. This is the same as the product
of the length of the square's sides, or the square of the length of one side. The
formula for the area of a square is: $A = s^2$.

Figure 10.15

Using what we derived for the area of a square, we can see that if we place   **10.6.2**
1-unit squares inside a rectangle, we find that the area of the rectangle is equal   **Area of a Rectangle**
to the product of the number of unit squares along the base and the number of
unit squares along the height, as illustrated in Figure 10.16. This is the same as
the product of the rectangle's base and height (also called the length and width).

Figure 10.16

The formula for the area of a rectangle is: $A = bh$ (or $A = lw$).

10.6.3
Area of a Parallelogram

We can use what we know about finding the area of a rectangle to find the area of a parallelogram. Consider the parallelogram shown in A in Figure 10.17. If we draw the altitude from one vertex to the opposite side, as shown in the second drawing in Figure 10.17, and then take the right triangle formed by drawing this altitude and move it to the opposite side of the parallelogram, we see that we now have, B, a rectangle with a base of b and a height of h as shown in the second drawing in Figure 10.17.

Figure 10.17

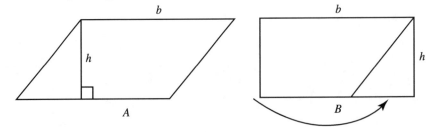

Thus, the formula for the area of a parallelogram is: $A = bh$.

10.6.4
Area of a Trapezoid

To find the area of a trapezoid, we can use what we know about finding the area of a parallelogram. Consider the trapezoid in A in Figure 10.18 with bases of length b_1 and b_2. Take a trapezoid that is congruent to A and position it as shown in B in Figure 10.18. We can see that a parallelogram is formed with a base of $b_1 + b_2$, and a height of h. Because this parallelogram is comprised of two congruent trapezoids, the area of the trapezoid must be half the area of the parallelogram.

Figure 10.18

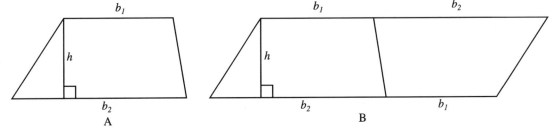

Because the area of the parallelogram is bh, which in this case is $(b_1 + b_2)h$, then the formula for the area of a trapezoid is: $A = \frac{1}{2}(b_1 + b_2)h$.

RELATED TOPICS   Area of Triangles | Area of Regular Polygons and Circles

TOPIC 10.7 AREA OF TRIANGLES

Measuring Area | Area of Quadrilaterals | Triangles

CORNERSTONE

The formula for the area of a triangle can be derived from the formula for the area of a parallelogram. In this section, we discuss the area of a triangle.

INTRODUCTION

The name of Heron, a Greek mathematician, is connected with a formula for finding the area of a triangle using its side lengths (a, b, c): $A = \sqrt{s(s-a)(s-b)(s-c)}$, where $s = \frac{1}{2}(a + b + c)$. Although this algorithm may actually be the work of Archimedes, Heron's proof of the relationship is the oldest one that exists.

DID YOU KNOW?

For More Information: Bunt, L. N. H., Jones, P. S., & Bedient, J. D. (1988). *The Historical Roots of Elementary Mathematics.* New York: Dover Publications.

Consider $\triangle ABC$ in Figure 10.19. Place a congruent triangle, $\triangle A'B'C'$ so that B and C' are the same vertex and C and B' are the same vertex, as shown in the second drawing in Figure 10.19. We will now prove that the quadrilateral formed by these two triangles is a parallelogram.

10.7.1
Area and How to Measure It

 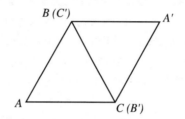

Figure 10.19

We know that $\triangle ABC \cong \triangle A'CB$. Because corresponding parts of congruent triangles are congruent, $\angle ABC \cong \triangle BCA'$ and $\angle ACB \cong \triangle CBA'$. Because these angles are alternate interior angles, then $\overline{AB} \parallel \overline{CA'}$ and $\overline{AC} \parallel \overline{BA'}$. Because both pairs of opposite sides are parallel, ABA' is a parallelogram.

This proof is valid for any triangle. Because any two congruent triangles can form a parallelogram, the area of a triangle is half the area of a parallelogram. Thus, the formula for the area of a triangle is: $A = \frac{1}{2}bh$.

Area of Regular Polygons and Circles

RELATED TOPICS

TOPIC 10.8 AREA OF REGULAR POLYGONS AND CIRCLES

CORNERSTONE	Measuring Area	Regular Polygons	Area of Triangles	Circles Circumscribed Circle Constructions	Circumference

INTRODUCTION	*Using what we know about finding the area of a triangle, we can find the area of any regular polygon and the area of a circle. In this section, we discuss the areas of regular polygons, circles, and sectors of circles.*

DID YOU KNOW?	The ancient Egyptians used a procedure that was equivalent to $A = (\frac{8}{9}d)^2$, where d is the length of the diameter, to find the area of a circular region. The Babylonians used a procedure equivalent to $A = \frac{1}{12}C^2$, where C is the circumference of the circle. Both of these procedures produced results that are very good approximations to the results produced by the algorithm we use today.
	For More Information: Sibley, T. Q. (1998). *The Geometric Viewpoint: A Survey of Geometries*. Reading, MA: Addison-Wesley.

10.8.1
Area of a Regular Polygon

The area of a regular polygon can be found by dividing the polygon into congruent triangles and finding the sum of the areas of those triangles. Consider the regular pentagon with sides of length s shown in the first drawing in Figure 10.20. Divide the pentagon into five congruent triangles as shown in the second drawing in Figure 10.20. The point that is a common vertex for the five triangles is the center of the circle that could circumscribe the pentagon.

Figure 10.20

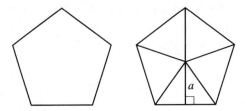

The height of the congruent triangles formed in a regular polygon, each with a vertex at the center, is called the *apothem* and is denoted by a. Thus, the area of each of these triangles is $\frac{1}{2}as$. Because there are five triangles, the area of the regular pentagon is $5(\frac{1}{2})as$. But $5s$ is the perimeter of the pentagon, so the area of the regular pentagon is $\frac{1}{2}ap$, where p is the perimeter. This same procedure can be used to derive the area of any regular polygon. Thus, the formula for the area of a regular polygon is: $A = \frac{1}{2}ap$, where a is the height of one of the congruent triangles and p is the perimeter of the polygon.

10.8.2
Area of a Circle

We can use what we know about finding the area of a regular polygon to derive the formula for the area of a circle. As the number of sides of a regular polygon increases, the perimeter and the area of the regular polygon get closer and closer to the circumference and area of a circle circumscribed about the polygon, as shown in Figure 10.21.

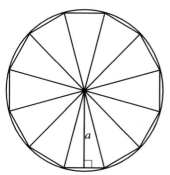

Figure 10.21

If we form the congruent triangles, each with a vertex at the center, we can see that the apothem in each triangle is approximately equal to the radius of the circle and the perimeter of the polygon is approximately equal to the circumference of the circle. Thus, the formula for the area of a regular polygon can be used to derive the formula for the area of a circle: $A = \frac{1}{2}r(2\pi r) = \pi r^2$. The justification for this derivation is beyond the scope of this book. The interested reader is referred to the references noted through this topic.

A **sector** of a circle is a region of the circle formed by a central angle, as shown in Figure 10.22. If the central angle has a measure of 180°, the sector is half of the circle and so the area of the sector is half the area of the circle. If the central angle has a measure of 90°, the area of the sector is one fourth the area of the circle. In general, the formula for the area of a sector with a central angle of $\theta°$ is: $A = \frac{\theta}{360}(\pi r^2)$.

10.8.3
Area of a Sector

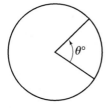

Figure 10.22

Surface Area of Prisms and Cylinders
Surface Area of Pyramids, Cones, and Spheres

RELATED TOPICS

TOPIC 10.9 SURFACE AREA OF PRISMS AND CYLINDERS

CORNERSTONE	Measuring Area | Polyhedra, Prisms, and Pyramids Cones, Cylinders, and Spheres | Area of Regular Polygons and Circles
INTRODUCTION	*Package designers need to know the dimensions and shapes of package surfaces. The surface area of a package is important in designing the package. In this section, we discuss surface area, surface area of a right prism, and surface area of a right circular cylinder.*
DID YOU KNOW?	The world's largest oil tanks are located in Ju'ayman, Saudi Arabia. The five cylindrical tanks are each 72 feet tall and have a diameter of 386 feet. **For More Information:** Guinness Book of Records

10.9.1
Surface Area

The **surface area** of an object is literally the area of its surface. We can find the surface area of three-dimensional geometric figures by separating the surface into planar figures for which we can find the area, and then summing the areas of all the regions. We can represent the surface of a three-dimensional figure by using a two-dimensional pattern called a **net**. Recall that prisms, cylinders, pyramids and cones all have at least one base, and their remaining surfaces are called the lateral surface. Thus, for these figures, their nets are comprised of their bases and their lateral surfaces.

10.9.2
Surface Area of a Right Prism

Recall from section 9.27.4, that a prism is a polyhedron comprised of two congruent faces that are in parallel planes and parallelograms for the remaining faces. If the lateral faces are all rectangles, then the prism is called a right prism. We will discuss how to find the surface area for right prisms only.

To find the surface area of a right prism, we sum the areas of the bases and the lateral faces (called the **lateral surface area**). Figure 10.23 shows two right prisms, one with a triangular base and the other with a rectangular base. Figure 10.24 shows nets for these two prisms.

Figure 10.23

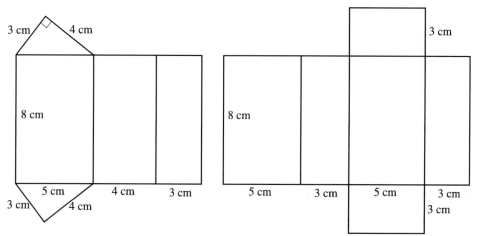

Figure 10.24

To find the surface area of the right triangular prism, we find the area of the bases [$2(\frac{1}{2} \cdot 3 \cdot 4)$, or 12 cm²] and the lateral surface area [$(3 \cdot 8 + 4 \cdot 8 + 5 \cdot 8)$, or 96 cm²]. Thus, the surface area of the right triangular prism is 12 cm² + 96 cm², or 108 cm².

To find the surface area of the right rectangular prism, we find the area of the bases [$2(3 \cdot 5)$, or 30 cm²] and the lateral surface area [$2(3 \cdot 8) + 2(5 \cdot 8)$, or 128 cm²]. Thus, the surface area of the right rectangular prism is 30 cm² + 128 cm², or 158 cm². The formula for the surface area of a prism is: S.A. = 2B + L.A., where S.A. is the surface area, B is the base area, and L.A. is the lateral surface area.

We can use what we know about finding the surface area of a prism to find the surface area of a cylinder because as the number of edges of a prism's bases increases, the prism moves closer to approximating a cylinder. We find the surface area of a right circular cylinder by summing the area of its bases and its lateral surface area. Figure 10.25 shows a right circular cylinder and a net. This net can be obtained by cutting off the bases and cutting the lateral surface along a line perpendicular to the bases. When flattened, we can see that the lateral surface is a rectangle.

To find the surface area of this cylinder, we find the area of the bases [$2(\pi$

10.9.3
Surface Area of a Right Circular Cylinder

Figure 10.25

· 4^2) or 32π cm^2] and the lateral surface area [$2 \cdot \pi \cdot 4 \cdot 7$, or 56π cm^2]. Thus, the surface of this right circular cylinder is 88π cm^2. In general, the formula for the surface area of a right circular cylinder is: S.A. $= 2\pi r^2 + 2\pi rh = 2\pi(r^2 + h)$, where each base has area πr^2, the length of the rectangular lateral surface is the circumference of a base—$2\pi r$, and h is the height of the rectangular lateral surface.

Recall from section 9.27.5, that a pyramid is a polyhedron comprised of a

RELATED TOPICS   Surface Area of Pyramids, Cones, and Spheres

TOPIC 10.10 SURFACE AREA OF PYRAMIDS, CONES, AND SPHERES

Measuring Area | Polyhedra, Prisms, and Pyramids | Cones, Cylinders, and Spheres | Area of Regular Polygons and Circles | Area of Triangles

CORNERSTONE

Some packages are in the form of pyramids, cones and spheres. Thus, manufacturers need to be able to find the surface area of these three-dimensional figures in designing and producing these containers. In this section, we discuss surface area of a right regular pyramid, surface area of a right circular cone, and surface area of a sphere.

INTRODUCTION

The early Egyptians may have derived an algorithm for finding the surface area of a hemisphere (half of a sphere), which is equivalent to the modern formula with a different value for π. However, some scholars have suggested that a term used in the Egyptian problem should be interpreted differently, and what the Egyptians actually derived was a counterpart for the modern formula for the area of the curved surface of a semi-cylinder.

For More Information: Joseph, G. G. (1991). *The crest of the peacock: Non-European roots of mathematics.* London, England: Penguin Books.

DID YOU KNOW?

polygon with *n* edges for its base, a point not in the plane of the base called the apex, and *n* triangular faces that are determined by the apex and the *n* edges of the base. The triangular faces are called the lateral faces. If the base of a pyramid is a regular polygon, and the lateral faces are congruent isosceles triangles, the pyramid is called a right regular pyramid. We will discuss how to find the surface for right regular pyramids only.

Because a pyramid has one base, the surface area of a pyramid is the sum of the base area and the lateral surface area. Figure 10.26 shows a right square pyramid and its net. The area of its base is 6^2 cm², or 36 cm². To find the lateral surface area, we need to find the area of one of the isosceles triangles that is a lateral face, and then multiply that area by the number of lateral faces (which is the number of edges of the base). Each of these congruent isosceles triangles has an altitude of length 8 cm. The altitude on a lateral face of a pyramid is called the **slant height**. The lateral surface area for this pyramid is $4 \cdot \frac{1}{2} \cdot 6 \cdot 8$, or 96

10.10.1
Surface Area of a Right Regular Pyramid

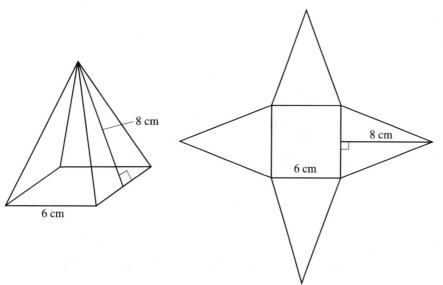

Figure 10.26

cm². Thus, the surface area of the right triangular prism is 36 cm² + 96 cm², or 132 cm². Thus, the formula for the surface area of a pyramid is: S.A. = B + n · $\frac{1}{2}$ · b · ℓ where B is the area of the base, n is the number of edges of the base, b is the length of each side of the base, and ℓ is the slant height.

10.10.2
Surface Area of a Right Circular Cone

As the number of edges of a pyramid's base increases, the pyramid moves closer to approximating a cone. Thus, we can use what we know about finding the surface area of a pyramid to find the surface area of a cone. Figure 10.27 shows a pyramid having a base with many edges, and its net, as a way of approximating a cone.

Figure 10.27

The surface area of a right circular cone is the sum of the base area (πr^2) and the lateral surface area. In a pyramid, the lateral surface area is n · $\frac{1}{2}$ · b · ℓ (as discussed in section 10.10.1). However, n · b, the number of edges times the length of each side of the base, is equal to the perimeter of the base; in a cone, this would be the circumference of the circular base. Thus, the formula for the surface area of a right circular cone is: S.A. = B + $\frac{1}{2}$(2πr)ℓ = πr^2 + πrℓ = πr(r + ℓ).

10.10.3
Surface Area of a Sphere

The formula for the surface area of a sphere can be derived using methods of calculus; however, that derivation is beyond our scope in this book. We will, however, discuss the formula, and to do so we need to define a great circle. A **great circle** is a circle on a sphere that is formed by the intersection of the sphere and a plane passing through the center of the sphere, as shown in Figure 10.28. The surface area of a sphere is four times the area of a great circle of the sphere. Thus, the formula for the surface area of a sphere is: S.A. = $4\pi r^2$.

Figure 10.28

RELATED TOPICS   Surface Area of Prisms and Cylinders

TOPIC 10.11 MEASURING VOLUME

Measuring Area | Area of Triangles | Area of Quadrilaterals
Area of Regular Polygons and Circles

CORNERSTONE

Knowing the volume or capacity of a container is often very useful in real-world problem solving. In this section, we discuss volume and how to measure it, the English system of volume measurement, and the metric system of volume measurement.

INTRODUCTION

One of the major achievements of the ancient Egyptian mathematicians was deriving a formula for calculating the volume of a truncated pyramid (a pyramid with the top portion sliced off by a plane parallel to the base).

For More Information: Joseph, G. G. (1991). *The crest of the peacock: Non-European roots of mathematics*. London, England: Penguin Books.

DID YOU KNOW?

The **volume** of a three-dimensional shape is the number of cubic units enclosed by the shape. A **cubic unit** is the amount of space enclosed by a cube that is 1 unit in length along each edge. If we use a cube as the basic unit, the volume of a figure is the number of cubes required to fill the space enclosed by the shape with no cubes overlapping and no gaps (this is called *tessellating the space* and is discussed in the section called Tessellations). Volume is measured in cubic units, such as cubic centimeters, cubic feet, or cubic meters.

10.11.1
Volume and How to Measure It

In the English system of measurement, dry volume is usually measured in cubic inches, cubic feet, and cubic yards, whereas liquid volume is usually measured in cups, pints, quarts, and gallons. We will discuss the units for dry measure only. Table 10.6 shows these units and their equivalents in other units in the English system.

10.11.2
The English System of Volume Measurement

Unit	Equivalent
1 cubic inch (1 in.^{3})	$\dfrac{1}{1,728}$ ft^3
1 cubic foot (1 ft^3)	1,728 in.^{3}; $\dfrac{1}{27}$ yd^3
1 cubic yard (1 yd^3)	27 ft^3

Table 10.6

To convert from one volume measure to another within the system, we need to remember that we are using cubic units. For example, a cube with each side having a length of 2 feet would have a volume of 8 ft^3, as shown in Figure 10.29. To determine what the volume would be in terms of cubic inches, we substitute 24 inches for the length of each side because 2 ft = 24 in. Then the number of cubic inches that it would take to fill the space enclosed by the cube would be $24 \cdot 24 \cdot 24$ or 13,824. Thus, 8 ft^3 = 13,824 in^3.

Figure 10.29

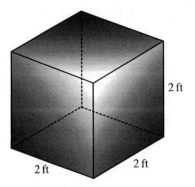

10.11.3
The Metric System of Volume Measurement

In the metric system of measurement, volume is usually measured by cubic centimeters and cubic meters, or milliliters and liters, depending on the type of measure. These units can be used for either dry or wet measure, but milliliters and liters are the metric units typically used for liquid measure. Table 10.7 shows these units and their equivalents in other units in the metric system.

Table 10.7

Unit	Equivalent
1 cubic centimeter (1 cm³)	0.000001 m³
1 cubic meter (1 m³)	1,000,000 cm³
1 milliliter (1 mL)	0.001 L; 1 cm³
1 liter (1 L)	1 dm³

We can convert from one volume measure to another within the system by substituting equivalent quantities. For example, to determine how many 1-cm cubes are in a cube measuring 2 m on a side, we replace the length of each side (2 m) with 200 centimeters, as shown in Figure 10. 30, because 2 m = 200 cm. We can see that it takes 1,000,000 1-cm cubes to equal 1 m³, and thus, 8,000,000 cm³ = 8 m³, which is the volume of the cube measuring 2 m on a side.

Figure 10.30

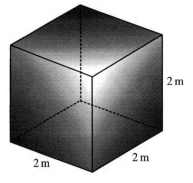

RELATED TOPICS   Volume of Prisms and Cylinders | Volume of Pyramids, Cones, and Spheres
Cavalieri's Principle

TOPIC 10.12 VOLUME OF PRISMS AND CYLINDERS

Measuring Volume | Polyhedra, Prisms, and Pyramids
Cones, Cylinders, and Spheres

CORNERSTONE

If we were designing a container to hold as much of a product as possible for a certain amount of packaging material, we would need to be able to determine the volume of the container. In this section, we discuss the volume of a right prism and the volume of a right circular cylinder.

INTRODUCTION

A typical drinking straw is 19.4 cm high with a diameter of 0.6 cm. Because 1 mL of water occupies 1 cm³, then a typical straw can contain approximately 5.48 mL of water.

DID YOU KNOW?

The volume of a prism is the number of cubic units that are needed to fill the space enclosed by the prism. We will discuss the volume of a right prism in this section, while the volume of any prism is discussed in the section called Cavalieri's Principle. Consider the right rectangular prism shown in Figure 10.31. We can see that one layer of cubes that is ℓ units long and w units wide will cover the base of the prism. If we have h layers, we can fill the space enclosed by the prism.

**10.12.1
Volume of a
Right Prism**

Figure 10.31

Thus, the formula for the volume of a right rectangular prism is: $V = \ell wh$. We can extend this to a right prism with any polygonal base, using the fact that ℓw is the area of the base of the right rectangular prism. Thus, the formula for the volume of a right prism is: $V = Bh$, where B is the area of the base. (Note: A right rectangular prism for which $\ell = w = h$ is commonly called a **cube**.)

We can use what we know about finding the volume of a right prism to find the volume of a right circular cylinder because as the number of edges of a prism's bases increases, the prism moves closer to approximating a cylinder. Because the base is a circle, its area is $B = \pi r^2$, where r is the radius. If the cylinder is h units tall, the formula for the volume of a right circular cylinder is: $V = Bh = \pi r^2 h$. Thus, the right circular cylinder shown in Figure 10.32 has a volume of 192 cm³.

**10.12.2
Volume of a
Right Circular
Cylinder**

Figure 10.32

RELATED TOPICS   Volume of Pyramids, Cones, and Spheres | Cavalieri's Principle

TOPIC 10.13 VOLUME OF PYRAMIDS, CONES, AND SPHERES

Measuring Volume | Polyhedra, Prisms, and Pyramids   **CORNERSTONE**
Cones, Cylinders, and Spheres | Volume of Prisms and Cylinders

The relationships between the volumes of a right prism and a right pyramid   **INTRODUCTION**
with congruent bases and equal heights, and the volumes of a right circular cylinder and a right cone with congruent bases and equal heights are very interesting. In this section, we discuss volumes of right pyramids, right circular cones, and spheres.

The Greek mathematician Archimedes derived a formula for finding the volume of a   **DID YOU KNOW?**
sphere by demonstrating that the volume of a sphere is equal to the volume of a cylinder
circumscribed about the sphere minus the volume of the cone inscribed in the cylinder.
His proof involved slicing the three solids with planes and comparing the slices.

For More Information: Bunt, L. N. H., Jones, P. S., & Bedient, J. D. (1988). *The Historical Roots of Elementary Mathematics.* New York: Dover Publications.

The volume of a right pyramid is one third the volume of a right prism with   **10.13.1**
congruent bases and equal height; in other words, three right pyramids could fit   **Volume of a**
into one right prism with congruent bases and equal height, as shown in Figure   **Right Pyramid**
10.33. Thus, the formula for the volume of a right pyramid is: $V = \frac{1}{3} Bh$, where
B is the base area and h is the height.

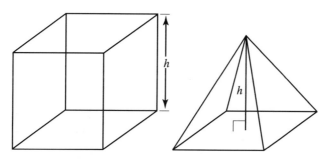

Figure 10.33

The volume of a right circular cone is one third the volume of a right circu-   **10.13.2**
lar cylinder with congruent bases and equal height; in other words, three right   **Volume of a**
circular cones could fit into one right circular cylinder with congruent bases and   **Right Circular**
equal height, as shown in Figure 10.34. Thus, the formula for the volume of a   **Cone**
right circular cone is: $V = \frac{1}{3}\pi r^2 h$ where h is the height.

Figure 10.34

10.13.3
Volume of a Sphere

To better understand the volume formula for a sphere, think of a sphere as having a very large number of congruent pyramids having their apexes at the center of the sphere and with their vertices of the base touching the sphere, as shown in Figure 10.35. If the bases of the pyramids are small, then the radius, r, of the sphere is approximately equal to the height of each pyramid. Because we know that the volume of each pyramid is $\frac{1}{3}Bh$ or $\frac{1}{3}Br$, then the volume of all the pyramids is $n \cdot \frac{1}{3}Br$, where n is the number of pyramids. Now, $n \cdot B$ is the area of all the bases of the pyramids, and because this approximates the surfaces area of the sphere (which is $4\pi r^2$), the formula for the volume of a sphere is: $V = \frac{1}{3}(4\pi r^2)r = \frac{4}{3}\pi r^3$.

Figure 10.35

RELATED TOPICS   Cavalieri's Principle

TOPIC 10.14 CAVALIERI'S PRINCIPLE

Measuring Volume | Polyhedra, Prisms, and Pyramids   **CORNERSTONE**
Cones, Cylinders, and Spheres | Volume of Prisms and Cylinders
Volume of Pyramids, Cones, and Spheres

We can derive the formulas for the volumes of various three-dimensional figures   **INTRODUCTION**
using the formula for the volume of a right prism. In this section, we discuss
Cavalieri's Principle which details this.

Bonaventura Cavalieri (1598–1647) was an Italian mathematician and one of Galileo's   **DID YOU KNOW?**
students. His ideas were used to find volumes before calculus techniques were invented.

For More Information: Sibley, T. Q. (1998). *The geometric viewpoint: A survey of geometries.*
Reading, MA: Addison-Wesley.

Cavalieri developed a principle for finding the volume of many three-dimensional figures given a particular relationship. His principle states: Let A
and B be two solids included between two parallel planes (as shown in Figure
10.36). If every plane parallel to the given planes intersects A and B in sections
with the same area, then A and B have the same volume.

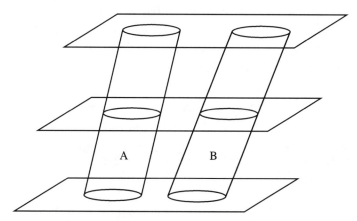

Figure 10.36

Figure 10.37 illustrates another example of solids with the same volume. If two
pyramids have the same height and their bases have the same area, then the two
pyramids have the same volume.

 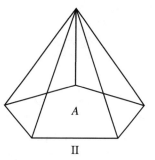

Figure 10.37

Pyramid I and pyramid II have the same volume because their bases have the
same area.

TOPIC 10.15 MASS AND TEMPERATURE

CORNERSTONE	Linear Measure

INTRODUCTION	*We measure a wide variety of things besides length, area and volume. Two common characteristics that are measured are mass and temperature. In this section, we discuss mass and weight, and temperature.*

DID YOU KNOW?	The gram is the basic unit of mass in the metric system. One gram is officially equal to the weight of one cubic centimeter of distilled water at 4°C.
	For More Information: Webster's New World Dictionary

10.15.1
Mass and Weight

Mass and weight are two quantities that are often confused. **Mass** is a quantity of matter; **weight** is a force exerted by gravitational pull. This is why the weight of astronauts changes when measured on the earth and when measured on the moon, but their masses remain the same.

In everyday usage, we interchange the quantities of mass and weight but we use different units of measure to quantify them. We measure mass in metric units, with the **gram** being the basic unit. Table 10.8 shows metric units for measuring mass and their equivalents in other units in the metric system.

Conversions between different units of mass measure within the metric system are calculated in the same way that we did when working with metric units for linear measures in section 10.2.3.

In the English system of measurement, weight is measured in avoirdupois units such as ounces, pounds, and tons. Table 10.9 shows these units and their equivalents.

Table 10.7	Unit	Equivalent
	1 miligram (1 mg)	0.001 g
	1 centigram (1 cg)	0.01 g
	1 decigram (1 dg)	0.1 g
	1 gram (1 g)	1,000 mg
	1 dekagram (1 dg)	10 g
	1 hectogram (1 hg)	100 g
	1 kilogram (1 kg)	1,000 g
	1 ton (metric) (1 t)	1,000,000 g

Table 10.8	Unit	Equivalent
	1 ounce (1 oz)	$\frac{1}{16}$ lb
	1 pound (1 lb)	16 oz; $\frac{1}{2,000}$ t
	1 ton (English) (1 t)	2,000 lb

10.15.2
Temperature

Temperature, the characteristic that indicates how cold or how hot something is, can be measured using either the metric system or the English system. In the metric system, the **degree Kelvin** is used for scientific measurements; the temperature for the freezing point of water on the Kelvin scale is 273°.

The more common unit of measure in the metric system is the **degree Celsius**. This scale is named after the Swedish scientist Anders Celsius who invented it. The Celsius scale is marked off in 100 equal parts between 0 degrees Celsius (0°C), which is the freezing point of water, and 100 degrees Celsius

(100°C), which is the boiling point of water.

In the English system of measurement, the Fahrenheit scale is used to measure temperature. This scale is named after Gabriel Fahrenheit, a German instrument maker who made the first mercury thermometer in 1714. He labeled the lowest temperature that he could create in his laboratory as 0° and the normal temperature of the body as 98°. The Fahrenheit scale is marked off in 180 equal parts between 32°F, which is the freezing point of water, and 212°F, which is the boiling point of water.

To convert from temperature measures using a Celsius scale to those using a Fahrenheit scale, or vice versa, we can derive a conversion formula. Because the Celsius scale has 100 equal parts between the freezing point and boiling point of water, and the Fahrenheit scale has 180 equal parts, the ratio is 100 to 180, or 5 to 9. Thus, for every 5 degree increase on the Celsius scale, there is a 9 degree increase on the Fahrenheit scale. Because the scales have the freezing point of water at different values, we must also adjust for that. The formulas for converting from the Celsius scale to the Fahrenheit scale, and the Fahrenheit scale to the Celsius scale are, respectively:

$$°F = \frac{9}{5}°C + 32° \text{ and } °C = \frac{5}{9}(°F - 32°).$$

Thus, if we have a temperature of 25°C that we want to convert to the Fahrenheit scale, we have: $F = \frac{9}{5}(25) + 32 = 45 + 32 = 77$. So, 25°C = 77°F. Likewise, if we have a temperature of 50°F that we want to convert to the Celsius scale, we have: $C = \frac{5}{9}(50 - 32) = \frac{5}{9}(18) = 10$. So, 50°F = 10°C.

TOPIC 10.16 PYTHAGOREAN THEOREM AND OTHER TRIANGLE RELATIONSHIPS

CORNERSTONE	Triangles	Measuring Area

INTRODUCTION *Quite possibly the most famous theorem in all of mathematics—known to school children and mathematicians alike—is what is known as the Pythagorean Theorem. In this section, we discuss the Pythagorean Theorem, its converse, special right triangles, and the triangle inequality.*

DID YOU KNOW? Pythagoras was a Greek mathematician who lived about 570–500 B.C. He and his followers, called the Pythagoreans, divided mathematics into four parts: music, arithmetic (what is commonly known today as number theory), astronomy, and geometry. These four subjects were called the *quadrivium*, and were later adopted by Plato and Aristotle, and became the school curriculum up until the Renaissance period.

For More Information: Bunt, L. N. H., Jones, P. S., & Bedient, J. D. (1988). *The historical roots of elementary mathematics.* New York: Dover Publications.

10.16.1
The Pythagorean Theorem

Long before the time of the Pythagoreans, people knew about and used the relationship we call the Pythagorean theorem. Before discussing the theorem, we need to identify some parts of a right triangle. In a right triangle, the side opposite the right angle is called the **hypotenuse**, and the two sides that form the right angle are called the **legs**, as illustrated in Figure 10.38.

Figure 10.38

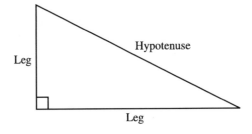

The Pythagorean theorem, as stated in Euclid's *Elements* is: In right-angled triangles the square on the side subtending the right angle is equal to the squares on the sides containing the right angle. In textbooks today, we are more likely to find it stated as: If a right triangle has legs of length a and b and hypotenuse of length c, then $a^2 + b^2 = c^2$, as illustrated in Figure 10.39.

Figure 10.39

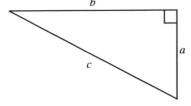

The illustration in Figure 10.39 shows the relationship among the sides of the right triangle, but the original statement of the Pythagorean theorem demonstrates the relationship among the area of the squares formed on the sides of a right triangle, as illustrated in Figure 10.40.

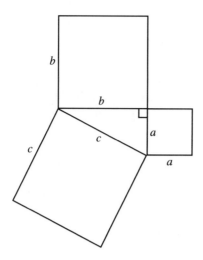

Figure 10.40

The converse of the Pythagorean Theorem is also true. Euclid stated the converse as: If in a triangle the square on one of the sides be equal to the squares on the remaining two sides of the triangle, the angle contained by the remaining two sides of the triangle is right. Textbooks today might state the converse as: If a triangle with sides of lengths a, b, and c has the relationship $a^2 + b^2 = c^2$, then the triangle is a right triangle with the right angle opposite the side of length c.

10.16.2
The Converse of the Pythagorean Theorem

Besides the Pythagorean Theorem, there are other relationships that exist in right triangles. We will discuss two special kinds of right triangles and the relationships that exist within these triangles.

10.16.3
Special Right Triangles

The first triangle we will discuss is called a **45°-45°-90° right triangle**. This triangle is a right triangle with two 45° angles and two congruent legs, and can be formed by drawing a diagonal of a square, as shown in Figure 10.41. Using the relationship discussed in the Pythagorean Theorem, we can see that if each leg in this triangle has length a, then the hypotenuse must have length a because $a^2 + a^2 = c^2$ gives us $2a^2 = c^2$, which gives us $c = a\sqrt{2}$. Thus, a property of a 45°-45°-90° triangle is that if the legs have length a, then the hypotenuse will have length $a\sqrt{2}$.

Figure 10.41

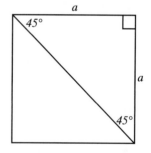

Another special right triangle is a **30°-60°-90° right triangle**. This triangle is a right triangle with a 30° angle and a 60° angle, and can be formed by dividing an equilateral triangle in half, as shown in Figure 10.42.

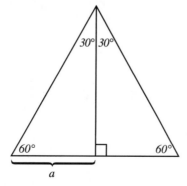

Figure 10.42

From the equilateral triangle in Figure 10.42, we can see that the side opposite the 30° angle will be half the length of the hypotenuse. Suppose the side opposite the 30° angle has length a, then the hypotenuse has length $2a$. Using the Pythagorean Theorem relationship, we can see then that the side opposite the 60° angle must have length $a\sqrt{3}$, because $a^2 + b^2 = (2a)^2$ gives us $b^2 = 3a^2$ which gives us $b = a\sqrt{3}$. Thus, a property of a 30°-60°-90° triangle is that the length of the hypotenuse is twice as long as the leg opposite the 30° angle, and the leg opposite the 60° angle is $\sqrt{3}$ times the length of the leg opposite the 30° angle.

**10.16.4
The Triangle
Inequality**

To construct a triangle using three segment lengths, there has to be a particular relationship among the lengths of the segments or sides. This relationship is known as the **Triangle Inequality**. The Triangle Inequality theorem states: the sum of the lengths of any two sides of a triangle is greater than the length of the third side. In other words, in any triangle, $\triangle XYZ$, $XY + YZ > XZ$ and $XY + XZ > YZ$ and $YZ + XZ > XY$ (see Figure 10.43).

Figure 10.43

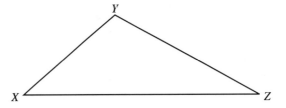

RELATED TOPICS   Distance Formula

TOPIC 10.17 DISTANCE FORMULA

Line Segments | Cartesian Coordinate System

CORNERSTONE

There is a common saying that the shortest distance between any two points is a straight line. In this section, we discuss distance and how to find the distance between two points.

INTRODUCTION

Before standardized units of measure were adopted, distance was measured in various ways by various peoples. In some African societies, long distances were measured by the number of days it would take to travel between two points, or by time between meals.

For More Information: Zaslavsky, C. (1979). *Africa counts: Number and pattern in African culture.* Brooklyn, NY: Lawrence Hill Books.

DID YOU KNOW?

The **distance postulate** states: to every pair of different points there corresponds a unique positive number. In other words, for every two points that are different, we can assign a unique positive value that is the distance between those two points.

If two points are on the coordinate axes and lie on a horizontal or vertical line, then to find the distance between these two points we simply count the number of units in the horizontal or vertical direction. In Figure 10.44, we can see that A and B are 5 units apart, so $AB = 5$, while C and D are 4 units apart, so $CD = 4$. We can generalize counting units to say that (a) the distance between two points that lie on a horizontal line is the absolute value of the difference of their x-coordinates ($|x_2 - x_1|$), and (b) the distance between two points that lie on a vertical line is the absolute value of the difference of their y-coordinates ($|y_2 - y_1|$). Furthermore, the distance between any two points, X and Y, is the same as the distance between Y and X. Thus, in Figure 10.44, $BA = 5$ and $DC = 4$, as well.

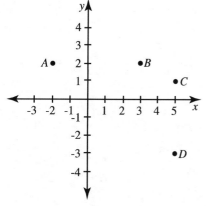

Figure 10.44

Using the Pythagorean theorem relationship, we can derive the formula to find the distance between any two points, regardless of where they are located on the coordinate axes. Consider point J with ordered pair (x_1, y_1) and point K with ordered pair (x_2, y_2) in Figure 10.45. We can draw a horizontal line through J and a vertical line through K, labeling the point of intersection of the two lines as L. Notice that L corresponds to the ordered pair (x_2, y_1), and we have formed a right triangle, $\triangle JKL$.

Figure 10.45

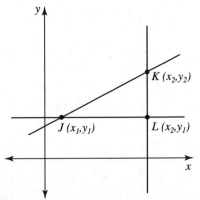

We know that $(JL)^2 + (KL)^2 = (JK)^2$, from the Pythagorean theorem. Substituting in the values of these lengths, we have $(x_2 - x_1)^2 + (y_2 - y_1)^2 = (JK)^2$. Thus, we find that $JK = \sqrt{(x_2 - x_1)^2 + (y_2 - y_1)^2}$. This is formula is called the **distance formula** and we can state it as: The distance between the points (x_1, y_1) and (x_2, y_2) is $\sqrt{(x_2 - x_1)^2 + (y_2 - y_1)^2}$.

One other formula that is related to the distance between two points is the **midpoint formula**. We know that every segment has a unique midpoint, and that this midpoint is equal distance from both endpoints of the segment. The midpoint formula gives us the coordinates of the midpoint of a segment. It states: given A with ordered pair (x_1, y_1) and B with ordered pair (x_2, y_2), the midpoint of $\overline{AB}$ is the point M with ordered pair $\left(\frac{x_1 + x_2}{2}, \frac{y_1 + y_2}{2}\right)$.

RELATED TOPICS   Slope | Coordinate Geometry
Pythagorean Theorem and Other Triangle Relationships

TOPIC 10.18 TESSELLATIONS

Polygons | Regular Polygons | Planes | Angle Measurement

CORNERSTONE

There are tessellations all around us—from tile floors, to brick buildings, to patterns on fabric. In this section, we discuss what is a tessellation, how any triangle can tessellate the plane, and how any quadrilateral can tessellate the plane.

INTRODUCTION

Some of the most celebrated examples of tessellations are found in Islamic designs. These designs often use geometric figures and floral designs.

For More Information: Zaslavsky, C. (1996). *The multicultural math classroom: Bringing in the world.* Portsmouth, NH: Heinemann.

DID YOU KNOW?

A **tessellation** has been defined in different ways. Here are the two most common definitions:

I. A tessellation is a filling of the plane with repetitions of polygonal regions (polygons and their interiors), without gaps and overlapping of regions and where all corners meet at a vertex.

II. A tessellation is a filling of the plane with repetitions of polygonal regions, without gaps and overlapping of regions and where corners do not necessarily meet at a vertex.

We can see that a *tiling of the plane* (filling the plane) that fits the first definition also fits the second definition, but a tiling of the plane that fits the second definition does not necessarily fit the first definition. The first drawing in Figure 10.46 shows a tessellation that fits both the first and second definition, whereas the second drawing shows a tessellation that fits only the second definition.

10.18.1
What is a Tessellation?

Figure 10.46

Any triangle can tessellate the plane; in other words—any triangle can repeatedly be used to fill the plane without gaps and overlapping. Figure 10.47 illustrates the process of tessellating the plane with a scalene triangle whose angles have been labeled $\angle 1$, $\angle 2$, and $\angle 3$. To fill the plane, we rotate the triangle so that congruent sides are placed against each other. Notice that at any vertex where the corners of the triangles meet, there are six angles that meet at the vertex ($\angle 1$, $\angle 2$, $\angle 3$, $\angle 1$, $\angle 2$, $\angle 3$). Because we know that the sum of the measures of the three interior angles of a triangle is $180°$, we can see that the sum of the measures of the angles at any vertex in this tessellation is $360°$. Because one complete revolution about a point is $360°$, we can see that this triangle is filling the plane without gaps or overlapping. This is true for any type of triangle.

10.18.2
Any Triangle Can Tessellate the Plane

Figure 10.47

10.18.3
Any Quadrilateral Can Tessellate the Plane

Using what we learned about any triangle tessellating the plane, we can see that any quadrilateral can tessellate the plane. Figure 10.48 illustrates the process of tessellating the plane with a quadrilateral whose angles have been labeled ∠1, ∠2, ∠3, and ∠4. To fill the plane, we rotate the quadrilateral so that congruent sides are placed against each other. Notice that at any vertex where the corners of the quadrilaterals meet, there are four angles that meet at the vertex (∠1, ∠2, ∠3, ∠4). Because we know that the sum of the measures of the four interior angles of a quadrilateral is 360°, then we can see that the sum of the measures of the angles at any vertex in this tessellation is 360°. Because one complete revolution about a point is 360°, we can see that this quadrilateral is filling the plane without gaps or overlapping. This is true for any type of quadrilateral.

Figure 10.48

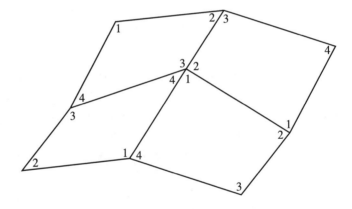

RELATED TOPICS   Tessellations of Regular Polygons

TOPIC 10.19 TESSELLATIONS OF REGULAR POLYGONS

Tessellations | Regular Polygons

INTRODUCTION

We can find tessellations of some regular polygons in nature. Two examples are the tessellation of a regular hexagon in any honeycomb, and the tessellation of regular polygons in the molecular structures of some crystals. In this section, we discuss which regular polygons can tessellate the plane, and semi-regular tessellations. There are other types of tessellations that we will not address here.

DID YOU KNOW?

The twentieth-century Dutch artist Maurits Cornelis Escher created tessellations using design elements such as fish, reptiles, birds, and humans. Some of his inspiration came from observing the Islamic designs in the Alhambra in Granada, Spain.

For More Information: Schattschneider, D. (1990). *Visions of symmetry: Notebooks, periodic drawings, and related work of M. C. Escher.* New York: W. H. Freeman and Company.

**10.19.1
Which Regular
Polygons Can
Tessellate the
Plane?**

In order for any polygon to tessellate the plane, with repetitions of the same polygon, the measures of the angles that come together must sum to 360°, because a complete revolution about a point is 360°. If the measures of the angles that come together did not sum to 360°, then there would be gaps (if the sum of the angle measures was less than 360°) or overlapping (if the sum of the angle measures was more than 360°).

We can determine which regular polygons can tessellate the plane because we know that in a regular polygon all the interior angles have the same measure, and thus, the measure of an interior angle must be a factor of 360 in order for the sum of the angle measures to equal 360°. Table 10.10 shows the regular polygons from $n = 3$ to 10 sides, and the measure of each interior angle in these polygons.

Polygon	Measure of Each Interior Angle
Equilateral Triangle	60°
Square	90°
Regular Pentagon	108°
Regular Hexagon	120°
Regular Heptagon	about 128.6°
Regular Octagon	135°
Regular Nonagon	140°
Regular Decagon	144°

Table 10.10

We can see that the equilateral triangle, the square, and the regular hexagon all have interior angle measures that are factors of 360. These, in fact, are the only regular polygons that have this characteristic, and thus, an equilateral triangle, a square, and a regular hexagon are the only regular polygons that will tessellate the plane. Figure 10.49 shows tessellations made from each of these three regular polygons.

Figure 10.49

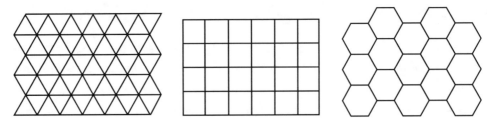

An interesting observation is that when we were determining which regular polygons will tessellate the plane, we could have stopped checking at a regular hexagon (where $n = 6$) because for that polygon the measure of each interior angle is 120°. The only factor of 360 that is larger than 120, is 180. However, the measure of each angle in a regular polygon must be less than 180°. Thus, no regular polygon with more than six sides could tessellate the plane.

10.19.2
Semiregular
Tessellations

A **semiregular tessellation** is a tessellation comprised of more than one regular polygon such that each vertex has the same polygonal arrangement. Combining squares and regular octagons, as shown in the first drawing in Figure 10.50, is an example of a semi-regular tessellation. The second drawing in Figure 10.50 shows another semi-regular tessellation, formed by equilateral triangles and squares.

Figure 10.50

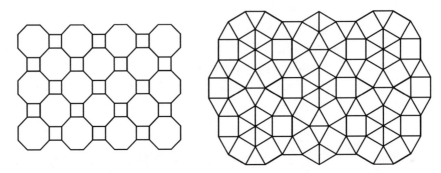

RELATED TOPICS   Transformations

TOPIC 10.20 TRANSFORMATIONS

Congruence | Line Segments   **CORNERSTONE**

The study of geometry concerns not only geometric figures, but also the movement **INTRODUCTION**
of geometric figures. In this section, we discuss the meaning of a transformation
and the different types of transformations.

M. C. Escher (1889–1972), a Dutch artist, identified ten foundational systems (or types) **DID YOU KNOW?**
of tessellations. The first nine involve quadrilaterals and the tenth uses triangles. Escher
described these ten systems in a chart that lists the transformations for each system.

For More Information: Schattschneider, D. (1990). *Visions of symmetry: Notebooks, periodic
drawings, and related work of M. C. Escher.* New York: W. H. Freeman and Company.

If we have a geometric figure in a plane and we move all the points of the
figure in certain ways, we form a new geometric figure called the **image** of the
original figure. A **transformation** is a correspondence between all the points
of a geometric figure in a plane and all the points of its image such that each
point of the figure can be matched with exactly one point of its image, and each
point of the image can be matched with exactly one point of the original figure.
Figure 10.51 shows some figures and their images formed by transformations.

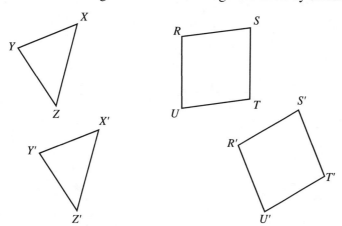

Figure 10.51

When we move all the points of a planar figure, we represent the points of
the image using the corresponding letters with a special notation. Figure 10.52
shows figure *ABCD* and its image *A′B′C′D′*.

Figure 10.52

A transformation that preserves the size and shape of the original figure is called an **isometry**, or a **rigid transformation**. There are three types of transformations that are isometries: translation (slide), rotation (turn), and reflection (flip). Because an isometry does not change the size or shape from the original figure to the image, the figure and its image are congruent. Not all transformations preserve both size and shape. For example, size transformations preserve the shape of a figure but either reduce or enlarge the size.

RELATED TOPICS   Translations | Rotations | Reflections | Size Transformations

TOPIC 10.21 TRANSLATIONS

INTRODUCTION

A translation is often thought of as a slide, like the sliding action involved in playing checkers or chess. In this section, we discuss translations and their features.

DID YOU KNOW?

Felix Klein (1849–1925) gave his inaugural address as a professor of mathematics at the University of Erlangen in 1872 at the age of 23. The presentation is now known as Klein's Erlanger Programm. In his address, he defined geometry by using groups of transformations: Geometry is the study of those properties of a set that are preserved under a group of transformations on that set.

For More Information: Sibley, T. Q. (1998). *The geometric viewpoint: A survey of geometries.* Reading, MA: Addison-Wesley.

One transformation that is an isometry is a **translation**. Formally, a translation is a transformation on a plane in which every point in a set is moved the same number of units in the same direction. Thus, a translation involves both distance and direction. Figure 10.53 shows a rectangle (*UVWX*) and its image (*U′V′W′X′*) under a translation. The translation is determined by the **directed line segment** from *J* to *K* (denoted by $\overrightarrow{JK}$). A directed line segment is a line segment that has a direction, in this case from *J* to *K*. In Figure 10.63, the image of a point *U* in the plane, is the point *U′* which results from moving *U* along a line that is parallel to $\overrightarrow{JK}$ a distance of *JK* in the direction from *J* to *K*. Because a translation is an isometry, the image is congruent to the original figure (i.e., congruence is preserved).

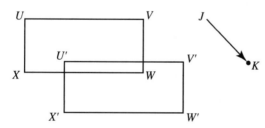

Figure 10.53

Thus, we obtain the image of *UVWX* by moving each point in the set of points that comprise *UVWX* along a line parallel to $\overrightarrow{JK}$ a distance of *JK* in the direction from *J* to *K*.

On a coordinate plane, we can specify a translation using the horizontal and vertical movements in the plane. For example, $\overline{EF}$ is shown with its image $\overline{E'F'}$ in Figure 10.54. We can see that each point of $\overline{EF}$ has been moved four units to the right and two units down. We can denote this translation symbolically by writing $(x, y) \rightarrow (x + 4, y - 2)$.

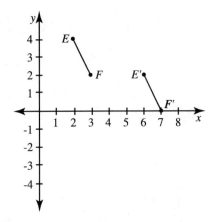

Figure 10.54

RELATED TOPICS   Rotations | Reflections

TOPIC 10.22 ROTATIONS

A rotation is often thought of as a turn, like the turning of a steering wheel or of a screw. In this section, we discuss rotations and their features.

INTRODUCTION

Because one complete revolution around a point is 360°, if you rotate any figure 360° the image will match the original figure. In basketball or skateboarding, this motion is called "doing a 360."

DID YOU KNOW?

Like a translation, a **rotation** is a transformation that is an isometry. Formally, a rotation is a transformation on a plane in which every point in a set is moved the same number of units (e.g., degrees) in the same direction by rotating about a point. Thus, a rotation involves both the amount of the turn and direction. The point in the plane about which the set of points is rotated is called the **center of rotation**. The direction of the rotation can be either clockwise or counterclockwise. In any rotation, three key elements are the center of rotation, the amount of the turn, and the direction.

Figure 10.55 shows a triangle (ABC) and its image ($A'B'C'$) under a rotation about point A through 45° in a clockwise direction.

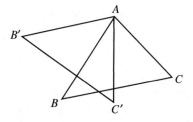

Figure 10.55

Figure 10.56 shows a triangle (ABC) and its image ($A'B'C'$) under a rotation about point K through 60° in a counterclockwise direction. Because a rotation is an isometry, the image is congruent to the original figure (i.e., congruence is preserved).

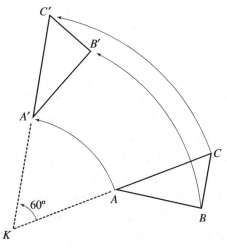

Figure 10.56

TOPIC 10.23 REFLECTIONS AND GLIDE REFLECTIONS

CORNERSTONE | Transformations | Translations | Perpendicular Bisector Construction

INTRODUCTION | *A reflection is often thought of as a flip, like a tree reflected in the water of a pond. In this section, we discuss reflections, including glide reflections, and their features.*

DID YOU KNOW? | Although we may think that the human face is symmetrical—with one side being a reflection of the other side over a line dividing the face vertically—in reality, the human face is rarely symmetrical and computer-generated photos of human faces that are symmetrical have been found to be less attractive than photos of the original human faces.

Another transformation that is an isometry is a **reflection**. Formally, a reflection is a transformation on a plane in which every point in a set is paired with a point in the image such that there is a line that is the perpendicular bisector of the line segment joining a point and its image. The line that is the perpendicular bisector of the line segments joining points and their images is called the **line of reflection**. If a point of the set being reflected happens to lie on the line of reflection, the point will be paired with itself under the reflection.

Figure 10.57 shows a pentagon (*DEFGH*) and its image (*D'E'F'G'H'*) under a reflection in line *m*. Because a reflection is an isometry, the image is congruent to the original figure (i.e., congruence is preserved).

Figure 10.57

By combining two transformations, we can obtain another transformation. If we slide a figure and then flip it, we can perform a glide reflection. A **glide reflection** is a transformation on a plane in which every point in a set is translated and then reflected in a line parallel to the directed line segment. Figure 10.58 shows a parallelogram *STUV* and its image (*S'T'U'V'*) under a glide reflection, where *STUV* is first translated from *A* to *B*, and then reflected in line *n*, which is parallel to $\overrightarrow{AB}$. Because a glide reflection consists of a translation and a reflection, it is an isometry, and thus the image is congruent to the original figure (i.e., congruence is preserved).

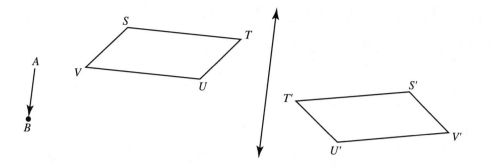

Figure 10.58

Rotations | Symmetry   **RELATED TOPICS**

TOPIC 10.24 SIZE TRANSFORMATIONS

CORNERSTONE	Transformations

INTRODUCTION   *A size transformation is often thought of as shrinking or enlarging, such as enlarging a photo. In this section, we discuss size transformations and their features.*

DID YOU KNOW?   Overhead projectors and photocopy machines are common machines that make use of size transformations.

One type of transformation that is not an isometry is a **size transformation**. A size transformation can be thought of as a reduction or an enlargement; formally, a size transformation is a transformation on a plane to the plane with center O and scale factor s ($s > 0$) in which every point P in a set is paired with a point P', such that $OP' = s \cdot OP$ and O, P and P' are collinear with O not between P and P'.

Figure 10.59 shows a triangle (XYZ) and its image ($X'Y'Z'$) under a size transformation with a scale factor of 2.5.

Figure 10.59

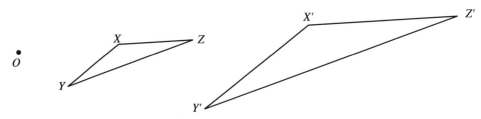

Figure 10.60 shows a rectangle ($JKLM$) and its image ($J'K'L'M'$) under a size transformation with a scale of 0.5. If the scale factor is greater than 1, the image will be an enlargement of the original figure. If the scale factor is less than 1, the image will be a reduction of the original figure. If the scale factor is equal to 1, the image will be congruent to the original figure. Unless the scale factor is 1, a size transformation is not an isometry and the image will not be congruent to the original figure (i.e., congruence is not preserved). However, the shape of the original figure is preserved.

Figure 10.60

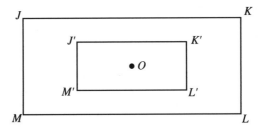

RELATED TOPICS	Translations | Rotations | Reflections | Fractals and Rep-tiles

IN THE CLASSROOM

This chapter emphasizes standards from both *Measurement* and *Geometry Content Standards* as well as the *Connections Process Standard*. In order to prepare instruction that enables your students to "understand measurable attributes of objects and the units, systems, and processes of measurement [and to] apply appropriate techniques, tools, and formulas to determine measurements" (NCTM, 2000, p. 44), we believe you should (a) work with measures of objects in ways that extend your current thinking by challenging your misconceptions and by rethinking familiar results in multiple ways (Activities 10.1-10.12), and (b) use measurement to explore new concepts and ways of reasoning (Activities 10.13-10.17).

How Activities 10.1-10.18 help you develop an adult-level perspective on the above expectations.

- By working with area and perimeter of polygons, you understand the importance of units of measurement and using appropriate tools for measuring as well as their limitations.

- By developing strategies for measuring irregular objects, you continue to work with the big idea of decomposition. You draw, construct, or model ways to make indirect measurements by building formulae that enable calculation of the required measurement.

- By exploring a number proofs of Pythagoras' Theorem, you realize that length and area measurements are the theorem's conceptual basis, while developing reasoning strategies.

- By investigating the circumference to diameter ratio of a circle, you work with the idea that physical measurement is an estimation and make important connections to concepts from number, geometry, data analysis, and algebra. You use your knowledge from these content areas to argue for the existence of the irrational number p and to develop a formula for calculating the circumference and area of a circle in terms of its radius.

- By working with *Geometer's Sketchpad*™ you continue to associate the attribute being measured with the analogous physical object(s) while exploring the geometric concepts of translations, rotations, and reflections all which depend on well defined measures.

- By investigating three-dimensional shapes and coordinate geometry, you explore the concepts of perspective, volume, surface area, and systems to specify locations.

Some expectations of your future students

Pre-K-2 (NCTM, 2000, pp. 96, 102)	recognize and apply slides, flips, and turns
	recognize and represent shapes from different perspectives
	select an appropriate unit and tool for the attribute being measured
	use repetition of a single unit to measure something larger than the unit
Grades 3-5 (NCTM, 2000, pp. 164, 170)	make and use coordinate systems to specify locations and to describe paths
	predict and describe the results of sliding, flipping, and turning two-dimensional shapes
	explore what happens to measurements of a two-dimensional shape such as its perimeter and area when the shape is changed in some way
	develop strategies for estimating the perimeters, areas, and volumes of irregular shapes and to determine the surface areas and volumes of rectangular solids
	develop, understand, and use formulas to find the area of rectangles and related triangles and parallelograms

BIBLIOGRAPHY

Battista, M. T. (1999). Fifth graders' enumeration of cubes in 3D arrays: Conceptual progress in an inquiry-based classroom. *Journal for Research in Mathematics Education, 30*, 417-448.

Beaumont, V., Curtis, R., & Smart, J. (1986). *How to teach perimeter, area, and volume*. Reston, VA: National Council of Teachers of Mathematics.

Binswanger, R. (1988). Discovering perimeter and area with Logo. *Arithmetic Teacher, 36*, 18-24.

Bledsoe, G. (1987). Guessing geometric shapes. *Mathematics Teacher, 80*, 78-80.

Bright, G. W., & Hoeffner. K. (1993). Measurement, probability, statistics, and graphing. In D. T. Owens (Ed.), *Research ideas for the classroom: Middle grades mathematics* (pp. 7~98) Old Tappan, NJ: Macmillan.

Clemens, S. R. (1985). Applied measurement: Using problem solving. *Mathematics Teacher, 78*, 176- 180.

Clopton, E. L. (1991). Area and perimeter are independent *Mathematics Teacher, 84*, 33-35.

Clopton, E. L. (1991). Sharing teaching ideas: Area and perimeter are independent. *Mathematics Teacher, 84*, 33-35.

Coburn, T. G., & Shulte, A. P. (1986). Estimation in measurement. In H. L. Schoen (Ed.), *Estimation and mental computation* (pp. 195-203). Reston, VA: National Council of Teachers of Mathematics.

Corwin, R. B., & Russell, S. J. (1990). Measuring: *From* paces to feet. (A unit of study for grades 3-5 from *Used numbers: Real data in the classroom*) Palo Alto, CA: Dale Seymour.

Fay, N., & Tsairides, C. (1989). Metric mall. *Arithmetic Teacher, 37*, 6- 11.

Fosnaugh, L. S., & Harrell, M E. (1996). Covering the plane with reptiles. *Mathematics Teaching in the Middle School, 1*, 666-670.

Gerver, R. (1990). Discovering pi: Two approaches. *Arithmetic Teacher, 37*, 18-22.

Giganti. P., Jr., & Cittadino, M. J. (1990). The art of tessellation. *Arithmetic Teacher, 3l*(7), 6-16.

Harrison, W. R. (1987). What lies behind measurement? *Arithmetic Teacher, 34*, 19-21.

Hart, K. (1984). Which comes first—length, area, or volume? *Arithmetic Teacher, 31*, 16- 18, 26-27.

Hawkins, V. J. (1989). Applying Pick's theorem to randomized areas. *Arithmetic Teacher, 36*, 47-49.

Hawkins, V. J. (1984). The Pythagorean theorem revisited: Weighing the results. *Arithmetic Teacher , 32*, 36-37.

Hiebert, J. (1984). Why do some children have trouble learning measurement concepts? *Arithmetic Teacher, 31*(7), 19-24.

Jensen, R. (1984). Multilevel metric games. *Arithmetic Teacher, 32*, 36-39.

Kaiser, B. (1988). Explorations with tessellating polygons. *Arithmetic Teacher, 36*, 19-24.

Kastner, B. (1989). Number sense: The role of measurement applications. *Arithmetic Teacher, 36*, 40-46.

Kennedy, J. B. (1993). Activities: Area and perimeter connections. *Mathematics Teacher, 86*, 218-221, 23 1 -232.

Liedtke, W. W. (1990). Measurement. In J. N. Payne (Ed.), *Mathematics for the young* child (pp. 229—249). Reston, VA: National Council of Teachers of Mathematics.

Lindquist, M. M. (1989). Implementing the *Standards*: The measurement standards. *Arithmetic Teacher, 37*, 22-26.

Marche, M. M. (1984). A Pythagorean curiosity. *Mathematics Teacher, 77*, 611-613.

Masingila, J. O. (1995). Carpet laying: An illustration of everyday mathematics. In P.A. House (Ed.), *Connecting mathematics across the curriculum* (pp. 163-169). Reston, VA: National Council of Teachers of Mathematics.

McClain, K., Cobb, P., Gravemeijer, K., & Estes, B. (1999). Developing mathematical reasoning within the context of measurement. In L. V. Stiff (Ed.), *Developing mathematical reasoning in grades K-12* (pp. 93-106). Reston, VA: National Council of Teachers of Mathematics.

McLaughlin, H. (1992). Activities: Determining area and calculating cost: A "model" application. *Mathematics Teacher, 85*, 360-361, 367-370.

Miller, L. D., & Miller, J. (1989). Metric week—The capitol way. *Mathematics Teacher, 82*, 454-458.

Miller, W. A., & Wagner, L. (1993). Activities: Pythagorean dissection puzzles. *Mathematics Teacher, 86*, 302-308, 313-314

Neufeld, K. A. (1989). Body measurement. *Arithmetic Teacher, 36*, 12- 15.

Parker, J., & Widmer, C. C. (1993). Teaching mathematics with technology: Patterns in measurement. *Arithmetic Teacher, 40*, 292-295.

Rectanus, C. (1998). *Math by all means: Area and perimeter, grades 5-6*. Sausalito, CA: Math Solutions Publications.

Renshaw, B. S. (1986). Symmetry the trademark way. *Arithmetic Teacher, 34*, 6-12.

Rhone, L. (1995). Measurement in a primary-grade integrated curriculum. In P. A. House (Ed.) *Connecting mathematics across the curriculum* (pp. 124-133). Reston, VA: National Council of Teachers of Mathematics.

Schultz, J. E. (1991). Area models: Spanning the mathematics of grades 3-9. *Arithmetic Teacher, 39*, 42-46.

Shaw, J. M (1983). Student-made measuring tools. *Arithmetic Teacher, 31*(3), 12- 15.

Shaw, J. M., & Cliatt, M. J. P. (1989). Developing measurement sense. In P. R. Trafton (Ed.), *New directions for elementary school mathematics* (pp. 149-155). Reston, VA: National Council of Teachers of Mathematics.

Smith, R. F. (1986). Let's do it: Coordinate geometry for third graders. *Arithmetic Teacher, 36*, 6- 11.

Souza, R. (1988). Golfing with a protractor. *Arithmetic Teacher, 35*, 52-56.

Szetela, W., & Owens, D. T. (1986). Finding the area of a circle: Use a cake pan and leave out the pi. *Arithmetic Teacher, 33*(9), 12-18.

Terc, M. (1985). Coordinate geometry: Art and mathematics. *Arithmetic Teacher, 33*, 22-24.

Thompson, C. S., & Van de Walle, J. A. (1985). Learning about rulers and measuring. *Arithmetic Teacher, 32*(8), 8-12.

Vissa, J. M. (1987). Coordinate graphing: Shaping a sticky situation. *Arithmetic Teacher, 35*, 6-10.

Whitman, N. (1991). Activities: Line and rotational symmetry. *Mathematics Teacher, 84*, 296-302.

Wilson, P. S., & Adams, V. M. (1992). A dynamic way to teach angle and angle measure. *Arithmetic Teacher, 39*, 6-13.

Wilson, P. S., & Rowland, R. E. (1993). Teaching measurement In R. J. Jensen (Ed.), *Research ideas for the classroom: Early childhood mathematics* (pp. 171-194). Old Tappan, NJ. Macmillan.

Wilson. P. S., & Osbome, A. (1992). Foundational ideas in teaching about measure. In T. R. Post (Ed.), *Teaching mathematics in grades K-8: Research-based methods* (2nd ed.) (pp. 89-121). Needham Heights, MA: Allyn & Bacon.

Zaslavsky, C. (1990). Symmetry in American folk art. *Arithmetic Teacher, 38,* 6- 12.

Zweng, M. J. (1986). Introducing angle measurement through estimation In H. L. Schoen (Ed.), *Estimation and mental computation* (pp 212-219). Reston, VA: National Council of Teachers of Mathematics.

APPENDIX A
Resources and Tools

Helpful Resources/Websites

Contact Information for *Standards*-based Curricula

NCTM *Standards*

Black-line Masters

Organizations:

www.awm-math.org/	Association for Women in Mathematics
www.nctm.org	National Council of Teachers of Mathematics
www.nsf.gov/nsb/documents/	National Science Board
www.nsf.gov/home/ehr/start.htm	National Science Foundation: Education and Human Resources

Math Lessons and Resources:

www.aplusmath.co/	Aplus Math—Interactive activities for teaching and reinforcing math skills
www.coolmath.com	Cool Math—Collection of activities, games and lessons
www.enc.org/	Eisenhower National Clearinghouse (ENC)—Classroom activities and databases
www.forum.swarthmore.edu/	Math Forum—Mathematics Internet Library, discussion groups, and classroom activities
www.mathgoodies.com	Math Goodies—Collection of lessons, puzzles and professional networking
www.mcrel.org/resources/links/hotlinks.asp	McRel Educator Resources—Math activities and lessons
www.scienceu.com/geometry/	Science U—Interactive activities and classroom lessons

Math Competitions and Projects:

www.unl.edu/amc/	American Mathematical Competitions
www.figurethis.org/index40.htm	Figure This!—Math challenges for grades 5–8 and families
www.kidlink.org/KIDPROJ/math00/	Kidlink—Collaborative project designed to make students aware of the math around them
www.mathcounts.org/	MATHCOUNTS—Annual mathematics competition

Calculator Activities:

www.ti.com	Texas Instruments—Newsletter for grades K–8, calculator activities

Research Support:

www.showmecenter.missouri.edu/ShowMe/RelatedLinks.html	Links to National Science Foundation Curriculum Implementation Projects
www.middleweb.com/	MiddleWeb: Exploring Middle School Reform
www.terc.edu/index.cfm	TERC—Research and Development of Math, Science and Technology Teaching
www.ustimss.msu.edu/	Third International Mathematics and Science Study

Software:

www.clearinghouse.k12.ca.us/	Clearinghouse—Educators Guide to high quality instructional technology resources
www.handygraph.com	Handygraph—Create and edit grids, blank graphs and number lines with Microsoft Word
www.mathforum.com/mathed/math.software.reviews.html	Internet Math Library for catalog of software reviews
www.keypress.com	Key Curriculum Press—Dynamic Geometry software
www.mathgoodies.com/software/	Math goodies—Mathematics software referrals
www.mathtype.com/	Math Type—create mathematical notation
www.terc.edu/mathequity/gw/html/gwhome.html	NSF Funded research projects describes 50 games and criteria for evaluating mathematical games
www.superkids.com	Superkids Educational Software Review
www.math.ucalgary.ca/~laf/colorful/colorful.html	U of Calgary—Mathematics Computer Games

Buyer's Guide:

www.nctm.org/buyersguide/	Buyer's Guide and information on math education vendors, consultation and software producers.

Standards-based curricula:

Investigations in number, Data, and Space—Grades K–5

Phone: (617) 547-0430
Email: tasha_morris@terc.edu   **www.terc.edu/byterc/invest.html**

Publisher: Dale Seymour Publications
PO Box 5026
White Plains, NY 10602
(800) 872-1100 ext. 5237   **www.aw.com/dsp/**

University of Chicago School Mathematics Project (UCSMP)—Grades K–6

To receive more information, including a project brochure and recent newsletters,
e-mail UCSMP at ucsmp@uchicago.edu

Publisher: Everyday Learning Corporation
(800) 382-7670   **www.Everydaylearning.com/index.html**

The Connected Mathematics Project (UCSMP)—Grades 6–8

Michigan State University
8715 Wells Hall
East Lansing, MI 48824
(517) 353-3835
E-mail: *ephillips@math.msu.edu*   **www.ns.msu.edu/CMP/cmp.html**

Publisher: Dale Seymour Publications
10 Bank Street
White Plains, NY 10602
Phone: (800) 872-1100

Seeing and Thinking Mathematically: Mathscape—Grades 6–8

Phone: (617) 969-7100

Publisher: Creative Publications
5623 West 115th Street
Alsip, Illinois 60482
Phone: (800) 624-0822

Mathematics in Context: A Connected Curriculum—Grades 6–8

(608) 263-4285

Publisher: Encyclopedia Britannica Educational Corporation
310 South Michigan Ave.
Chicago, Illinois 60604
(800) 554-9862 Ext. 7007
E-mail: info@ebec.com

Number and Operations

Standard	Pre-K–2	Grades 3–5	Grades 6–8
Instructional programs from prekindergarten through grade 12 should enable all students to—	**Expectations** In prekindergarten through grade 2 all students should—	**Expectations** In grades 3–5 all students should—	**Expectations** In grades 6–8 all students should—
Understand numbers, ways of representing numbers, relationships among numbers, and number systems	• count with understanding and recognize "how many" in sets of objects; • use multiple models to develop initial understandings of place value and the base-ten number system; • develop understanding of the relative position and magnitude of whole numbers and of ordinal and cardinal numbers and their connections; • develop a sense of whole numbers and represent and use them in flexible ways, including relating, composing, and decomposing numbers; • connect number words and numerals to the quantities they represent, using various physical models and representations; • understand and represent commonly used fractions, such as 1/4, 1/3, and 1/2.	• understand the place-value structure of the base-ten number system and be able to represent and compare whole numbers and decimals; • recognize equivalent representations for the same number and generate them by decomposing and composing numbers; • develop understanding of fractions as parts of unit wholes, as parts of a collection, as locations on number lines, and as divisions of whole numbers; • use models, benchmarks, and equivalent forms to judge the size of fractions; • recognize and generate equivalent forms of commonly used fractions, decimals, and percents; • explore numbers less than 0 by extending the number line and through familiar applications; • describe classes of numbers according to characteristics such as the nature of their factors.	• work flexibly with fractions, decimals, and percents to solve problems; • compare and order fractions, decimals, and percents efficiently and find their approximate locations on a number line; • develop meaning for percents greater than 100 and less than 1; • understand and use ratios and proportions to represent quantitative relationships; • develop an understanding of large numbers and recognize and appropriately use exponential, scientific, and calculator notation; • use factors, multiples, prime factorization, and relatively prime numbers to solve problems; • develop meaning for integers and represent and compare quantities with them.
Understand meanings of operations and how they relate to one another	• understand various meanings of addition and subtraction of whole numbers and the relationship between the two operations; • understand the effects of adding and subtracting whole numbers; • understand situations that entail multiplication and division, such as equal grouping of objects and sharing equally.	• understand various meanings of multiplication and division; • understand the effects of multiplying and dividing whole numbers; • identify and use relationships between operations, such as division as the inverse of multiplication, to solve problems; • understand and use properties of operations, such as the distributivity of multiplication over addition.	• understand the meaning and effects of arithmetic operations with fractions, decimals, and integers; • use the associative and commutative properties of addition and multiplication and the distributive property of multiplication over addition to simplify computations with integers, fractions, and decimals; • understand and use the inverse relationships of addition and subtraction, multiplication and division, and squaring and finding square roots to simplify computations and solve problems.

Algebra

Standard	Pre-K–2	Grades 3–5	Grades 6–8
Instructional programs from prekindergarten through grade 12 should enable all students to—	**Expectations** In prekindergarten through grade 2 all students should—	**Expectations** In grades 3–5 all students should—	**Expectations** In grades 6–8 all students should—
Understand patterns, relations, and functions	• sort, classify, and order objects by size, number, and other properties; • recognize, describe, and extend patterns such as sequences of sounds and shapes or simple numeric patterns and translate from one representation to another; • analyze how both repeating and growing patterns are generated.	• describe, extend, and make generalizations about geometric and numeric patterns; • represent and analyze patterns and functions, using words, tables, and graphs.	• represent, analyze, and generalize a variety of patterns with tables, graphs, words, and, when possible, symbolic rules; • relate and compare different forms of representation for a relationship; • identify functions as linear or nonlinear and contrast their properties from tables, graphs, or equations.
Represent and analyze mathematical situations and structures using algebraic symbols	• illustrate general principles and properties of operations, such as commutativity, using specific numbers; • use concrete, pictorial, and verbal representations to develop an understanding of invented and conventional symbolic notations.	• identify such properties as commutativity, associativity, and distributivity and use them to compute with whole numbers; • represent the idea of a variable as an unknown quantity using a letter or symbol; • express mathematical relationships using equations.	• develop an initial conceptual understanding of different uses of variables; • explore relationships between symbolic expressions and graphs of lines, paying particular attention to the meaning of intercept and slope; • use symbolic algebra to represent situations and to solve problems, especially those that involve linear relationships; • recognize and generate equivalent forms for simple algebraic expressions and solve linear equations.
Use mathematical models to represent and understand quantitative relationships	• model situations that involve the addition and subtraction of whole numbers, using objects, pictures, and symbols.	• model problem situations with objects and use representations such as graphs, tables, and equations to draw conclusions.	• model and solve contextualized problems using various representations, such as graphs, tables, and equations.
Analyze change in various contexts	• describe qualitative change, such as a student's growing taller; • describe quantitative change, such as a student's growing two inches in one year.	• investigate how a change in one variable relates to a change in a second variable; • identify and describe situations with constant or varying rates of change and compare them.	• use graphs to analyze the nature of changes in quantities in linear relationships.

Number and Operations (continued)

Standard	Pre-K–2	Grades 3–5	Grades 6–8
Instructional programs from prekindergarten through grade 12 should enable all students to—	**Expectations** In prekindergarten through grade 2 all students should—	**Expectations** In grades 3–5 all students should—	**Expectations** In grades 6–8 all students should—
Compute fluently and make reasonable estimates	• develop and use strategies for whole-number computations, with a focus on addition and subtraction; • develop fluency with basic number combinations for addition and subtraction; • use a variety of methods and tools to compute, including objects, mental computation, estimation, paper and pencil, and calculators.	• develop fluency with basic number combinations for multiplication and division and use these combinations to mentally compute related problems, such as 30 × 50; • develop fluency in adding, subtracting, multiplying, and dividing whole numbers; • develop and use strategies to estimate the results of whole-number computations and to judge the reasonableness of such results; • develop and use strategies to estimate computations involving fractions and decimals in situations relevant to students' experience; • use visual models, benchmarks, and equivalent forms to add and subtract commonly used fractions and decimals; • select appropriate methods and tools for computing with whole numbers from among mental computation, estimation, calculators, and paper and pencil according to the context and nature of the computation and use the selected method or tool.	• select appropriate methods and tools for computing with fractions and decimals from among mental computation, estimation, calculators or computers, and paper and pencil, depending on the situation, and apply the selected methods; • develop and analyze algorithms for computing with fractions, decimals, and integers and develop fluency in their use; • develop and use strategies to estimate the results of rational-number computations and judge the reasonableness of the results; • develop, analyze, and explain methods for solving problems involving proportions, such as scaling and finding equivalent ratios.

Reproduced with permission from "Principles and Standards for School Mathematics," copyright © 2004 by the National Council of Teachers of Mathematics, Inc. www.nctm.org. All rights reserved.

Geometry

Standard	Pre-K–2	Grades 3–5	Grades 6–8
Instructional programs from prekindergarten through grade 12 should enable all students to—	**Expectations** In prekindergarten through grade 2 all students should—	**Expectations** In grades 3–5 all students should—	**Expectations** In grades 6–8 all students should—
Analyze characteristics and properties of two- and three-dimensional geometric shapes and develop mathematical arguments about geometric relationships	• recognize, name, build, draw, compare, and sort two- and three-dimensional shapes; • describe attributes and parts of two- and three-dimensional shapes; • investigate and predict the results of putting together and taking apart two- and three-dimensional shapes.	• identify, compare, and analyze attributes of two- and three-dimensional shapes and develop vocabulary to describe the attributes; • classify two- and three-dimensional shapes according to their properties and develop definitions of classes of shapes such as triangles and pyramids; • investigate, describe, and reason about the results of subdividing, combining, and transforming shapes; • explore congruence and similarity; • make and test conjectures about geometric properties and relationships and develop logical arguments to justify conclusions.	• precisely describe, classify, and understand relationships among types of two- and three-dimensional objects using their defining properties; • understand relationships among the angles, side lengths, perimeters, areas, and volumes of similar objects; • create and critique inductive and deductive arguments concerning geometric ideas and relationships, such as congruence, similarity, and the Pythagorean relationship.
Specify locations and describe spatial relationships using coordinate geometry and other representational systems	• describe, name, and interpret relative positions in space and apply ideas about relative position; • describe, name, and interpret direction and distance in navigating space and apply ideas about direction and distance; • find and name locations with simple relationships such as "near to" and in coordinate systems such as maps.	• describe location and movement using common language and geometric vocabulary; • make and use coordinate systems to specify locations and to describe paths; • find the distance between points along horizontal and vertical lines of a coordinate system.	• use coordinate geometry to represent and examine the properties of geometric shapes; • use coordinate geometry to examine special geometric shapes, such as regular polygons or those with pairs or parallel or perpendicular sides.
Apply transformations and use symmetry to analyze mathematical situations	• recognize and apply slides, flips, and turns; • recognize and create shapes that have symmetry.	• predict and describe the results of sliding, flipping, and turning two-dimensional shapes; • describe a motion or a series of motions that will show that two shapes are congruent; • identify and describe line and rotational symmetry in two- and three-dimensional shapes and designs.	• describe sizes, positions, and orientations of shapes under informal transformations such as flips, turns, slides, and scaling; • examine the congruence, similarity, and line or rotational symmetry of objects using transformations.
Use visualization, spatial reasoning, and geometric modeling to solve problems	• create mental images of geometric shapes using spatial memory and spatial visualization; • recognize and represent shapes from different perspectives; • relate ideas in geometry to ideas in number and measurement; • recognize geometric shapes and structures in the environment and specify their location.	• build and draw geometric objects; • create and describe mental images of objects, patterns, and paths; • identify and build a three-dimensional object from two-dimensional representations of that object; • identify and build a two-dimensional representation of a three-dimensional object; • use geometric models to solve problems in other areas of mathematics, such as number and measurement; • recognize geometric ideas and relationships and apply them to other disciplines and to problems that arise in the classroom or in everyday life.	• draw geometric objects with specified properties, such as side lengths or angle measures; • use two-dimensional representations of three-dimensional objects to visualize and solve problems such as those involving surface area and volume; • use visual tools such as networks to represent and solve problems; • use geometric models to represent and explain numerical and algebraic relationships; • recognize and apply geometric ideas and relationships in areas outside the mathematical classroom, such as art, science, and everyday life.

Measurement

Standard	Pre-K–2	Grades 3–5	Grades 6–8
Instructional programs from prekindergarten through grade 12 should enable all students to—	**Expectations** In prekindergarten through grade 2 all students should—	**Expectations** In grades 3–5 all students should—	**Expectations** In grades 6–8 all students should—
Understand measurable attributes of objects and the units, systems, and processes of measurement	• recognize the attributes of length, volume, weight, area, and time; • compare and order objects according to these attributes; • understand how to measure using nonstandard and standard units; • select an appropriate unit and tool for the attribute being measured.	• understand such attributes as length, area, weight, volume, and size of angle and select the appropriate type of unit for measuring each attribute; • understand the need for measuring with standard units and become familiar with standard units in the customary and metric systems; • carry out simple unit conversions, such as from centimeters to meters, within a system of measurement; • understand that measurements are approximations and understand how differences in units affect precision; • explore what happens to measurements of a two-dimensional shape such as its perimeter and area when the shape is changed in some way.	• understand both metric and customary systems of measurement; • understand relationships among units and convert from one unit to another within the same system; • understand, select, and use units of appropriate size and type to measure angles, perimeter, area, surface area, and volume.
Apply appropriate techniques, tools, and formulas to determine measurements	• measure with multiple copies of units of the same size, such as paper clips laid end to end; • use repetition of a single unit to measure something larger than the unit, for instance, measuring the length of a room with a single meterstick; • use tools to measure; • develop common referents for measures to make comparisons and estimates.	• develop strategies for estimating the perimeters, areas, and volumes of irregular shapes; • select and apply appropriate standard units and tools to measure length, area, volume, weight, time, temperature, and the size of angles; • select and use benchmarks to estimate measurements; • develop, understand, and use formulas to find the area of rectangles and related triangles and parallelograms; • develop strategies to determine the surface areas and volumes of rectangular solids.	• use common benchmarks to select appropriate methods for estimating measurements; • select and apply techniques and tools to accurately find length, area, volume, and angle measures to appropriate levels of precision; • develop and use formulas to determine the circumference of circles and the area of triangles, parallelograms, trapezoids, and circles and develop strategies to find the areas of more-complex shapes; • develop strategies to determine the surface area and volume of selected prisms, pyramids, and cylinders; • solve problems involving scale factors, using ratio and proportion; • solve simple problems involving rates and derived measurements for such attributes as velocity and density.

Data Analysis and Probability

Standard	Pre-K–2	Grades 3–5	Grades 6–8
Instructional programs from prekindergarten through grade 12 should enable all students to—	**Expectations** In prekindergarten through grade 2 all students should—	**Expectations** In grades 3–5 all students should—	**Expectations** In grades 6–8 all students should—
Formulate questions that can be addressed with data and collect, organize, and display relevant data to answer them	• pose questions and gather data about themselves and their surroundings; • sort and classify objects according to their attributes and organize data about the objects; • represent data using concrete objects, pictures, and graphs.	• design investigations to address a question and consider how data-collection methods affect the nature of the data set; • collect data using observations, surveys, and experiments; • represent data using tables and graphs such as line plots, bar graphs, and line graphs; • recognize the differences in representing categorical and numerical data.	• formulate questions, design studies, and collect data about a characteristic shared by two populations or different characteristics within one population; • select, create, and use appropriate graphical representations of data, including histograms, box plots, and scatterplots.
Select and use appropriate statistical methods to analyze data	• describe parts of the data and the set of data as a whole to determine what the data show.	• describe the shape and important features of a set of data and compare related data sets, with an emphasis on how the data are distributed; • use measures of center, focusing on the median, and understand what each does and does not indicate about the data set; • compare different representations of the same data and evaluate how well each representation shows important aspects of the data.	• find, use, and interpret measures of center and spread, including mean and interquartile range; • discuss and understand the correspondence between data sets and their graphical representations, especially histograms, stem-and-leaf plots, box plots, and scatterplots.
Develop and evaluate inferences and predictions that are based on data	• discuss events related to students' experiences as likely or unlikely.	• propose and justify conclusions and predictions that are based on data and design studies to further investigate the conclusions or predictions.	• use observations about differences between two or more samples to make conjectures about the populations from which the samples were taken; • make conjectures about possible relationships between two characteristics of a sample on the basis of scatterplots of the data and approximate lines of fit; • use conjectures to formulate new questions and plan new studies to answer them.
Understand and apply basic concepts of probability		• describe events as likely or unlikely and discuss the degree of likelihood using such words as *certain, equally likely,* and *impossible*; • predict the probability of outcomes of simple experiments and test the predictions; • understand that the measure of the likelihood of an event can be represented by a number from 0 to 1.	• understand and use appropriate terminology to describe complementary and mutually exclusive events; • use proportionality and a basic understanding of probability to make and test conjectures about the results of experiments and simulations; • compute probabilities for simple compound events, using such methods as organized lists, tree diagrams, and area methods.

Problem Solving

Standard
Instructional programs from prekindergarten through grade 12 should enable all students to—

- Build new mathematical knowledge through problem solving
- Solve problems that arise in mathematics and in other contexts
- Apply and adapt a variety of appropriate strategies to solve problems
- Monitor and reflect on the process of mathematical problem solving

Reasoning and Proof

Standard
Instructional programs from prekindergarten through grade 12 should enable all students to—

- Recognize reasoning and proof as fundamental aspects of mathematics
- Make and investigate mathematical conjectures
- Develop and evaluate mathematical arguments and proofs
- Select and use various types of reasoning and methods of proof

Communication

Standard
Instructional programs from prekindergarten through grade 12 should enable all students to—

- Organize and consolidate their mathematical thinking through communication
- Communicate their mathematical thinking coherently and clearly to peers, teachers, and others
- Analyze and evaluate the mathematical thinking and strategies of others
- Use the language of mathematics to express mathematical ideas precisely

Connections

Standard
Instructional programs from prekindergarten through grade 12 should enable all students to—

- Recognize and use connections among mathematical ideas
- Understand how mathematical ideas interconnect and build on one another to produce a coherent whole
- Recognize and apply mathematics in contexts outside of mathematics

Representation

Standard
Instructional programs from prekindergarten through grade 12 should enable all students to—

- Create and use representations to organize, record, and communicate mathematical ideas
- Select, apply, and translate among mathematical representations to solve problems
- Use representations to model and interpret physical, social, and mathematical phenomena

Centimeter Grid Paper

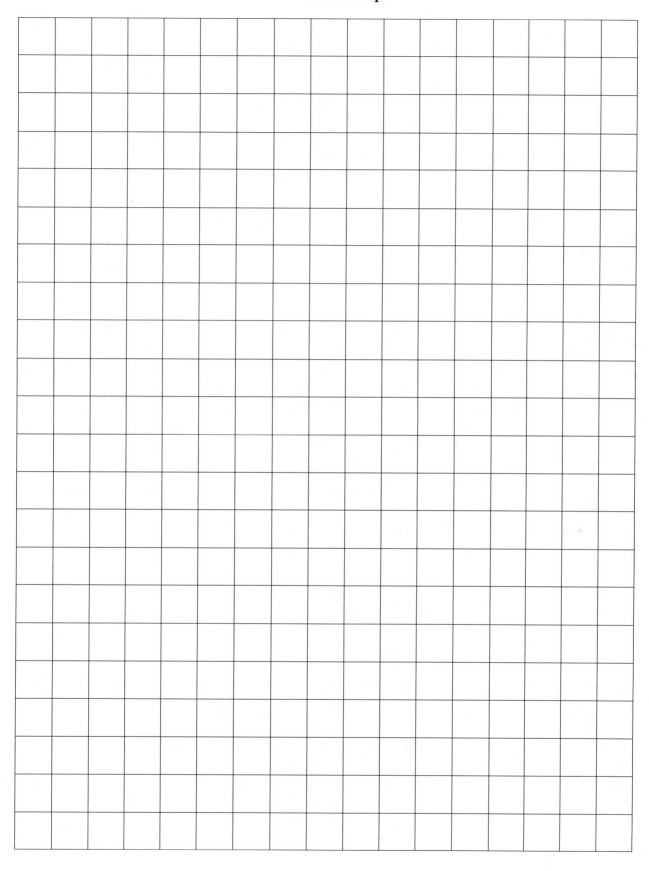

Inch Grid Paper

Half-Inch Grid Paper

Quarter-Inch Grid Paper

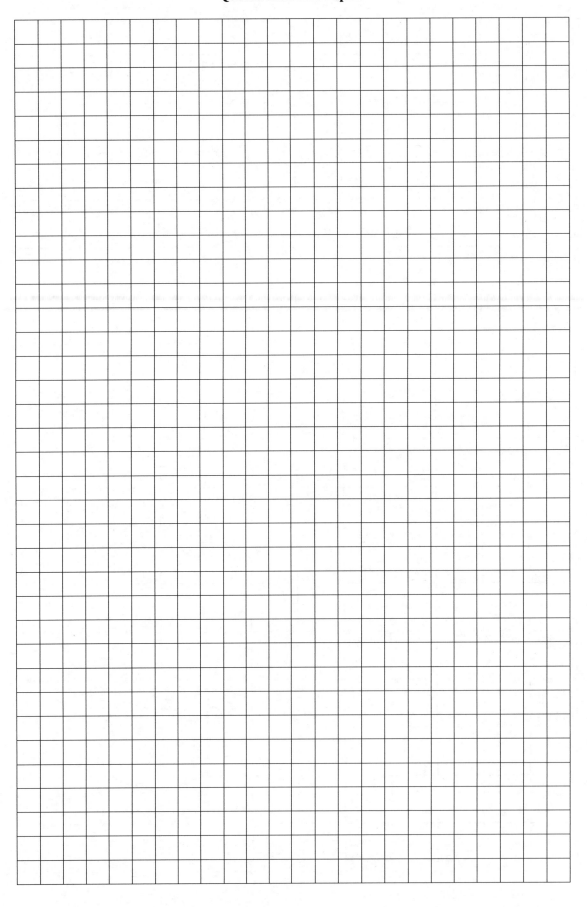

Isometric Dot Paper

Geoboard Dot Paper

Hundreds Charts

1	2	3	4	5	6	7	8	9	10
11	12	13	14	15	16	17	18	19	20
21	22	23	24	25	26	27	28	29	30
31	32	33	34	35	36	37	38	39	40
41	42	43	44	45	46	47	48	49	50
51	52	53	54	55	56	57	58	59	60
61	62	63	64	65	66	67	68	69	70
71	72	73	74	75	76	77	78	79	80
81	82	83	84	85	86	87	88	89	90
91	92	93	94	95	96	97	98	99	100

0	1	2	3	4	5	6	7	8	9
10	11	12	13	14	15	16	17	18	19
20	21	22	23	24	25	26	27	28	29
30	31	32	33	34	35	36	37	38	39
40	41	42	43	44	45	46	47	48	49
50	51	52	53	54	55	56	57	58	59
60	61	62	63	64	65	66	67	68	69
70	71	72	73	74	75	76	77	78	79
80	81	82	83	84	85	86	87	88	89
90	91	92	93	94	95	96	97	98	99

Variations of Hundreds Charts: A

1	2	3	4	5	6	7	8	9	10
11	12	13	14	15	16	17	18	19	20
21	22	23	24	25	26	27	28	29	30
31	32	33	34	35	36	37	38	39	40
41	42	43	44	45	46	47	48	49	50
51	52	53	54	55	56	57	58	59	60
61	62	63	64	65	66	67	68	69	70
71	72	73	74	75	76	77	78	79	80
81	82	83	84	85	86	87	88	89	90
91	92	93	94	95	96	97	98	99	100

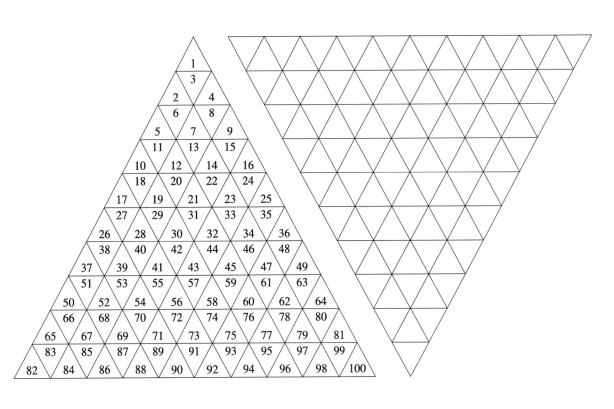

Variations of Hundred Charts: B

-9	-8	-7	-6	-5	-4	-3	-2	-1	0
1	2	3	4	5	6	7	8	9	10
11	12	13	14	15	16	17	18	19	20
21	22	23	24	25	26	27	28	29	30
31	32	33	34	35	36	37	38	39	40
41	42	43	44	45	46	47	48	49	50
51	52	53	54	55	56	57	58	59	60
61	62	63	64	65	66	67	68	69	70
71	72	73	74	75	76	77	78	79	80
81	82	83	84	85	86	87	88	89	90
91	92	93	94	95	96	97	98	99	100
101	102	103	104	105	106	107	108	109	110

101	102	103	104	105	106	107	108	109	110
111	112	113	114	115	116	117	118	119	120
121	122	123	124	125	126	127	128	129	130
131	132	133	134	135	136	137	138	139	140
141	142	143	144	145	146	147	148	149	150
151	152	153	154	155	156	157	158	159	160
161	162	163	164	165	166	167	168	169	170
171	172	173	174	175	176	177	178	179	180
181	182	183	184	185	186	187	188	189	190
191	192	193	194	195	196	197	198	199	200

Decimal or Percent Paper

Fraction Strips

1

$\frac{1}{2}$	$\frac{2}{2}$

$\frac{1}{3}$	$\frac{2}{3}$	$\frac{3}{3}$

$\frac{1}{4}$	$\frac{2}{4}$	$\frac{3}{4}$	$\frac{4}{4}$

$\frac{1}{5}$	$\frac{2}{5}$	$\frac{3}{5}$	$\frac{4}{5}$	$\frac{5}{5}$

$\frac{1}{6}$	$\frac{2}{6}$	$\frac{3}{6}$	$\frac{4}{6}$	$\frac{5}{6}$	$\frac{6}{6}$

$\frac{1}{8}$	$\frac{2}{8}$	$\frac{3}{8}$	$\frac{4}{8}$	$\frac{5}{8}$	$\frac{6}{8}$	$\frac{7}{8}$	$\frac{8}{8}$

$\frac{1}{9}$	$\frac{2}{9}$	$\frac{3}{9}$	$\frac{4}{9}$	$\frac{5}{9}$	$\frac{6}{9}$	$\frac{7}{9}$	$\frac{8}{9}$	$\frac{9}{9}$

$\frac{1}{10}$	$\frac{2}{10}$	$\frac{3}{10}$	$\frac{4}{10}$	$\frac{5}{10}$	$\frac{6}{10}$	$\frac{7}{10}$	$\frac{8}{10}$	$\frac{9}{10}$	$\frac{10}{10}$

$\frac{1}{12}$	$\frac{2}{12}$	$\frac{3}{12}$	$\frac{4}{12}$	$\frac{5}{12}$	$\frac{6}{12}$	$\frac{7}{12}$	$\frac{8}{12}$	$\frac{9}{12}$	$\frac{10}{12}$	$\frac{11}{12}$	$\frac{12}{12}$

$\frac{1}{20}$	$\frac{2}{20}$	$\frac{3}{20}$	$\frac{4}{20}$	$\frac{5}{20}$	$\frac{6}{20}$	$\frac{7}{20}$	$\frac{8}{20}$	$\frac{9}{20}$	$\frac{10}{20}$	$\frac{11}{20}$	$\frac{12}{20}$	$\frac{13}{20}$	$\frac{14}{20}$	$\frac{15}{20}$	$\frac{16}{20}$	$\frac{17}{20}$	$\frac{18}{20}$	$\frac{19}{20}$	$\frac{20}{20}$

$\frac{1}{24}$	$\frac{2}{24}$	$\frac{3}{24}$	$\frac{4}{24}$	$\frac{5}{24}$	$\frac{6}{24}$	$\frac{7}{24}$	$\frac{8}{24}$	$\frac{9}{24}$	$\frac{10}{24}$	$\frac{11}{24}$	$\frac{12}{24}$	$\frac{13}{24}$	$\frac{14}{24}$	$\frac{15}{24}$	$\frac{16}{24}$	$\frac{17}{24}$	$\frac{18}{24}$	$\frac{19}{24}$	$\frac{20}{24}$	$\frac{21}{24}$	$\frac{22}{24}$	$\frac{23}{24}$	$\frac{24}{24}$

Fraction Circles

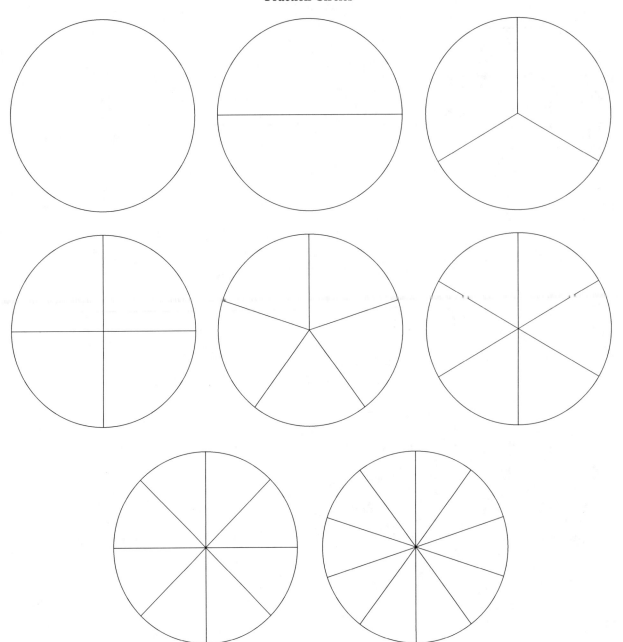

Basic Facts: Addition and Multiplication

+	0	1	2	3	4	5	6	7	8	9
0	0	1	2	3	4	5	6	7	8	9
1	1	2	3	4	5	6	7	8	9	10
2	2	3	4	5	6	7	8	9	10	11
3	3	4	5	6	7	8	9	10	11	12
4	4	5	6	7	8	9	10	11	12	13
5	5	6	7	8	9	10	11	12	13	14
6	6	7	8	9	10	11	12	13	14	15
7	7	8	9	10	11	12	13	14	15	16
8	8	9	10	11	12	13	14	15	16	17
9	9	10	11	12	13	14	15	16	17	18

x	0	1	2	3	4	5	6	7	8	9
0	0	0	0	0	0	0	0	0	0	0
1	0	1	2	3	4	5	6	7	8	9
2	0	2	4	6	8	10	12	14	16	18
3	0	3	6	9	12	15	18	21	24	27
4	0	4	8	12	16	20	24	28	32	36
5	0	5	10	15	20	25	30	35	40	45
6	0	6	12	18	24	30	36	42	48	54
7	0	7	14	21	28	35	42	49	56	63
8	0	8	16	24	32	40	48	56	64	72
9	0	9	18	27	36	45	54	63	72	81

Pattern Blocks

Green

Blue

Tan

Yellow

Orange

Red

Latice Multilication Blanks

Tangram

Polygonal Figures

Equilateral
Triangle

Regular
Quadrilateral
(Square)

Regular
Pentagon

Regular
Octagon

Regular
Decagon

Regular
Dodecagon

Regular
Hexagon

GLOSSARY

A

Absolute value
The absolute value of a number is the number of units the number is from zero.

Acute angle
An angl ewith measure *x*, such that $0° < x < 90°$.

Acute triangle
A triangle with only acute angles.

Additive
A numeration system is said to be additive if the value of the set of symbols representing a number is the sum of the values of the individual symbols.

Adjacent angles
Angles in a plane that share a common ray without their interiors intersecting are called adjacent angles.

Algorithm
A step-by-step procedure for performing a mathematical task.

Angle
An angle is formed when two rays join together at their endpoint.

Angle bisector
A ray that separates an angle into two congruent angles.

Arc
A connected subset of points of a circle.

Area of a planar shape
The area of a planar shape is the total region enclosed by the shape.

Arithmetic mean
The arithmetic mean of n numbers is their sum divided by n.

Arithmetic sequence
A pattern of numbers where the difference between any two terms of the sequence is the same quantity.

Associativity
A set is said to have the property of associativity under an operation * if for any three elements a, b, and c in it, $a * (b * c) = (a * b) * c$.

Average
A term widely used to refer to the arithmetic mean.

B

Bar graph
A graph, used to present frequency distributions or time series, which consists of bars (rectangles) of equal width, whose lengths are proportional to the frequencies (or values) they represent. A sample bar graph is shown below.

Base
A numeration system has a base if the numbers in that system reflect a process of repeated grouping by some number greater than one. The number is then called the base.

Box-and-whisker plot (or box plot)
A graph that displays the *5-number summary* of a set of data. A box-and-whisker plot for the following 12 quiz scores (10 points was the maximum score) is shown below: 8, 4, 9, 10, 10, 5, 7, 3, 8, 2, 9, 7.

A–lowest score **B**–1st quartile **C**–2nd quartile
D–3rd quartile **E**–highest score

C

Cardinal number
A number that refers to the number of objects in a set.

Cartesian coordinate system
The set of all points in a plane that are identified by a pair of *x*- and *y*-coordinates.

Cartesian product
The Cartesian product of sets A and B, denoted A × B, is the set of ordered pairs (x, y) that can be formed where the first element in the ordered pair is an element of set A and the second element in the ordered pair is an element of set B.

Central angle
An angle that has the center of a circle as its vertex, and has sides intersecting the circle.

Central tendency or measure of central tendency
This expression is sometimes used to refer to statistics—such as the mean, median, or mode—which indicate the average value of a data set.

Centroid
The point that is the intersection of the medians of a triangle.

Chord
Any line segment that has its endpoints on a circle.

Circle
A circle is formed by a set of points, all of which are at a constant distance from a fixed point.

Circular cone
A cone with a circular base.

Circular cylinder
A cylinder which has two congruent circles for bases.

Circumference
The distance around a circle.

Circumscribed circle
A circle that surrounds a polygon such that the vertices of the polygon lie on the circle.

Closure
A set is said to be closed with respect to an operation * if, for any two elements a and b in it, a * b belongs to the set.

Collinear points
Points that lie on the same line are called collinear points.

Combination
A selection of one or more of a set of distinct objects without regard to order. The number of possible combinations, each containing *k* objects, that can be formed from a collection of *n* distinct objects is given by $(n!)/(k!)(n-k)!$ and is denoted by (n, k), $_nC_k$, $C(n, k)$, or C_k^n. For example, the number of combinations of the letters of the alphabet, taken four at a time, is $26!/4!(26-4)! = 14950$.

Commutativity:
A set is said to have the property of associativity under an operation * if for any two elements a and b in it, $a * b = b * a$.

Complement
The complement of a set *A*, denoted *A*, is the set of all elements in the universal set that are not in *A*.

Complementary angles
Two angles whose sum is 90 degrees are called complementary angles.

Composite number
A positive integer that has more than two unique factors.

Compound statements
A statement formed by combining two statements.

Concave polygon
If every line joining any pair of two points inside a polygon does not lie completely within the polygon, we say it is concave.

Conclusion
A decision or judgment made regarding the truth of a hypothesis.

Conditional probability
The probability that A will occur given that B has occurred or will occur. If A and B are any two events and the probability of B is not equal to zero, then the conditional probability of A relative to B is denoted P(A|B) and given by P(A∩B)/P(B), where P(A∩B) is the probability of the joint occurrence of A and B.

Conditional statement
A statement of the form "if p then q." The statement p is called the hypothesis and the statement q is called the conclusion.

Cone
A simple closed surface comprised of a simple closed non-polygonal curve, its interior, and the line segments that connect each point of the curve to a point not in the plane of the curve.

Congruence modulo m
A number a is said to be congruent to a number b modulo m if m divides the number $(a - b)$.

Congruent angles
Angles that have the same measure.

Congruent polygons
Two polygons are said to be congruent if, when we superimpose one upon the other, the two polygons coincide completely.

Congruent segments
Segments that have equal lengths.

Conjecture
A guess or opinion based on inconclusive evidence.

Convex polygon
If a line joining any two points inside a polygon lies completely within the polygon, we say it is convex.

Coplanar points
Points that lie in the same plane are called coplanar points.

Cube
A right rectangular prism for which the length, width and height are equal.

Cylinder
A simple closed surface comprised of two congruent simple closed non-polygonal curves that are in parallel planes, their interiors, and the line segments that connect corresponding points on the curves.

D

Data
The results of an experiment, census, survey, and any kind of process or operation.

Decimal
A decimal representation is a means of writing a fraction in the base ten place-value system.

Deductive reasoning
Reasoning from a set of axioms or given general statements to derive or prove other specific statements or conclusions.

Dependent events
See INDEPENDENT EVENTS

Dependent variable
When considering the relationship between two variables, where the value of one *depends* on the value of the other, one of the variables is called a *dependent variable*, and the other is called an *independent variable*. For example, the number of apples you can purchase *depends* on the amount of money you have. In this situation, "number of apples" is a dependent variable, and "amount of money" is an independent variable.

Descriptive statistics
Any treatment of data which does not involve generalizations. (*See* INFERENTIAL STATISTICS).

Diameter
The length of a segment that has its endpoints on a circle and passes through the center of the circle.

Dihedral angle
An angle formed b the line of intersection of two planes and the union of the two half-planes.

Disjoint sets
Sets that have no elements in common other than the empty set.

Distribution
This term is used to refer to the overall scattering of observed data. It is often used as a synonym for *frequency distribution*.

Distributivity
Given a set with two operations, * and Â, we say * distributes over Â if, for any three elements, a, b and c in the set, $a * (b \hat{A} c) = a * b \hat{A} a * c$.

Divisible
A number, b, is said to be divisible by another number, a, if a is a factor of b. In other words, when b is divided by a, the remainder is 0.

Divisibility test for a number m
A quick and relatively easy method of determining if a given number is divisible by m without performing the actual division.

Divisor
A number, a, is said to be a divisor of another number, b, if a divides b without leaving a remainder.

Domain of a function
The set of all values that are allowed as input values of a function. For example, in the function

$$f(x) = \frac{1}{x - 5}$$

all real numbers *except* 5 could be in the domain. 5 cannot be in the domain because

$$F(5) = \frac{1}{5 - 5} = \frac{1}{0}$$

is undefined.

E

Element
A member of a set.

Empirical probability
The probability determined from data collected by conducting multiple rounds of an experiment.

Empty set
A set with no elements; also called the null set.

Equilateral triangle
A triangle with all three sides congruent.

Equally likely outcomes
Outcomes that have the same probability of occurring.

Equivalent fractions
Two or more fractions in which if all common factors between the numerator and the denominator of each fraction are removed, the fractions are the same.

Even number
A number is said to be even if it is divisible by 2.

Event
An event, in probability theory, is a subset of a sample space. For example, the event of getting an odd number when a die is tossed is the subset {1, 3, 5} of the sample space {1, 2, 3, 4, 5, 6}.

Expanded notation (or form)
A form of writing a number so as to represent the value of each digit using multiples of powers of the base.

Expected value
The expected value of a random variable is the mean of its distribution.

Experiment
Any activity in which different results can occur.

Experimental probability
probability of an event that is found by performing the experiment multiple times.

Exponent
A symbol placed above and after a number or expression, referred to as the base, that raises the base to the power designated by the symbol.

F

Face value
The numerical quantity represented by the symbol for a digit.

Factor
A number, a, is said to be a factor of another number, b, if a divides b without leaving a remainder.

Fair game
A game in which each participant has the same expectation; that is, a game which does not favor any player or group of players.

Fibonacci sequence
A sequence where each successive term is found by summing the two previous terms.

Figurate number
A number that can be represented by dots in some geometrical pattern.

Finite population
A well-defined set consisting of a finite number of elements, taken from a larger set. This larger set is called a population.

Five-number summary
The smallest value, the largest value, and the 3 quartile values—the first quartile, the second quartile (or median), and the third quartile—for a data set.

Fractal
A geometric figure that may result from an iterated function. Fractals typically have self-similarity, in which part of the figure is similar to larger parts of the figure. Examples include Koch's Snowflake curve and Sierpinski's triangle.

Fraction
A fraction is a number of the form a/b, where a and b are any numbers, and b • 0.

Fractions in simplest terms
A fraction is said to be in its simplest terms if the numerator and denominator do not share a common factor.

Frequency
The number of items, or cases, falling (or expected to fall) into a category or classification.

Frequency polygon
The graph of a frequency table obtain by drawing straight lines joining successive points representing the class frequencies, plotted at the corresponding class marks.
(*See* FREQUENCY TABLE)

Frequency table
A table (or other sort of arrangement) which displays the classes into which a set of data has been grouped together with the corresponding frequencies, that is the number of items falling into each class. Below is an example of a frequency table of the weights of 35 bags of beans taken from the production of a filling machine.

WEIGHT (IN POUNDS)	NUMBER OF BAGS
12.60—12.79	3
12.80—12.99	12
13.00—13.19	5
13.20—13.39	9
13.40—13.59	4
13.60—13.79	2

Function
A correspondence between a set A (the *domain*) and a set B (the *range*) in which each element of A is paired with exactly one element of B. The table below on the left could be a function. The table on the right could not be a function because one element of the domain (1) is paired with *two* elements of the range (2 and 3).

a	b
1	2
2	5
3	2

a	b
1	2
2	5
1	3

G

Geometric sequence
A pattern of numbers where each term is a constant multiple of the preceding term.

Glide reflection
A transformation on a plane in which every point in a set is translated and then reflected in a line parallel to the directed line segment.

Graph
A picture of information. In other words, a graph is a visual representation of data.

Great circle
A circle on a sphere that is formed by the intersection of the sphere and a plane passing through the center of the sphere.

Greatest common divisor
The greatest common divisor of two (or more) integers is the largest number that divides both (or all) of the numbers; also called the greatest common factor.

H

Heptagon
A polygon that has seven sides.

Hexagon
A polygon that has six sides.

Histogram
A graph of a frequency table obtained by drawing rectangles whose bases coincide with the class intervals and whose areas are proportional to the class frequencies. The sample histogram below shows the amount of money (in dollars) spent on food by a family over a 6-month period.

Hypotenuse
The side opposite the right angle in a right triangle.

Hypothesis
A statement that is assumed to be true.

I

Identity
We say that a set of numbers has an identity I, under the operation *, if, for any element x in the set, we have, $I * x = x * I = x$. We call I the *-identity of the set.

Incenter
The point that is the intersection of the angle bisectors of a triangle.

Independent events
Two events A and B are independent if the occurrence of either is not affect by the occurrence or not of the other (see mutually exclusive events). If the events are not independent, they are said to be *dependent*.

Independent variable
See DEPENDENT VARIABLE.

Inductive reasoning
Reasoning from the particular to the general.

Inferential statistics
Any decision, generalization, or estimate based on a sample.

Input variable
Same as *independent variable*. See *dependent variable* for a description.

Inscribed circle
A circle that is surrounded by a polygon such that the inscribed circle intersects each side of the polygon in exactly one point.

Integers
The set of numbers $\{\ldots, -3, -2, -1, 0, 1, 2, \ldots\}$, or numbers belonging to the set.

Interquartile range
A measure of variation given by the difference between the values of the third and first quartiles of a set of data; it represents the length of the interval which contains the middle 50 per cent of the data.

Intersection
The intersection of two sets is the set of all elements that are in both sets.

Inverse
An element, say x, belonging to a set that has a *- identity, say I, is said to have a *- inverse in the set if there

exists an element y in the set such that $x * y = y * x = I$.

Irrational number
A number that is not a rational number.

Isometry
A transformation that preserves the size and shape of the original figure.

Isosceles triangle
A triangle with at least two sides congruent.

Iterated function
A function that is "repeated" by taking the output and "feeding it back" to the function as the new input value. The first input of an iterated function is often referred to as the *seed*.

K

Kite
A quadrilateral with at least two distinct pairs of consecutive sides congruent.

L

Least common multiple
The least common multiple of two (or more) positive integers is the smallest non-zero multiple that is common to each number.

Legs of a right triangle
The two sides that form the right angle.

Line
Although line is an undefined term in geometry, we can describe a line as a one-dimensional set of an infinite number of points with direction.

Line of best fit
A line imposed on paired data in a scatterplot that best fits the trend of the data.

Line segment
A subset of a line that consists of two points on the line, called the endpoints of the line segment, and all the points on the line that are between the two endpoints.

Linear pair angles
Two adjacent angles in which their non-common sides form a straight angle (an angle of 180°).

M

Mathematical expectation
Consider the events $E_1, E_2, \ldots,$ and E_k to be mutually exclusive events. Furthermore, suppose a player re-

ceives an amount of money $M_1, M_2, \ldots,$ and M_k when events $E_1, E_2, \ldots,$ and E_k occur respectively. If $P_1, P_2, \ldots, P_k$ are the respective probabilities of these events, then the player's *mathematical expectation*—the amount of money he/she is expected to win in the long-run—is given by $E(M) = M_1P_1 + M_2P_2 + \cdots + M_kP_k$. In gambling game, for the game to be fair the expectation should equal the charge for playing the game.

Mean
The mean of n numbers is their sum divided by n. The mean is also known as the *arithmetic mean* or *average*.

Measures of variation
Statistical description such as the standard deviation, the mean deviation, or the range, which are indicative of the spread, or dispersion, of a set of data.

Median
If a list of numbers are arranged in increasing order, the median is the numerical value that marks the middle of the list. Hence, when there is an odd number of values, the median is the middle value in the ordered set of data. When there is an even number of values, the median is the mean of the two middle values.

Mode
This term is used to refer to the value which occurs with the highest frequency (most often) in a set of data. Note that a set of data can have more than one mode, or no mode at all when no two values are alike.

Modular arithmetic
For integers a, b, and m, a and b are congruent modulo m, written $a \equiv b$ mod m, if a and b have the same remainders when divided by m.

Multiple
A number, b, is said to be a multiple of another number, a, if a divides b without leaving a remainder.

Multiplicative
A numeration system is said to be multiplicative if each symbol in a number in that system represents a different multiple of the face value of that symbol.

Mutually exclusive events
Two events A and B are mutually exclusive if both events cannot occur at the same time.

N

Natural numbers
The set of counting numbers, that is, the set $\{1, 2, 3, \ldots\}$, or numbers belonging to this set.

Negation
The negation of a statement p, which is denoted ~p, is the statement "it is false that p."

Negative numbers
Numbers that are less than zero.

Normal distribution
A distribution of data in which the graphical representation of the data is a smooth, bell-shaped curve.

Null set
A set with no elements; also called the empty set.

Number
An idea that represents a numerical quantity.

Numeral
A written symbol used to represent a numerical quantity or number.

Numeration system
A system of writing numbers created to measure numerical quantities.

O

Oblique cylinder
A cylinder that is not a right cylinder.

Oblique prism
A prism with not all rectangles for the lateral faces.

Oblique regular pyramid
A pyramid with a regular polygon for a base but the lateral faces are not isosceles triangles.

Obtuse angle
An angle with measure x, such that $90° < x < 180°$.

Obtuse triangle
A triangle with one obtuse angle.

Octagon
A polygon that has eight sides.

Odd number
A number is said to be odd if it is not divisible by 2.

One-to-one correspondence
Two sets, A and B, have one-to-one correspondence if and only if each element of set A can be paired with exactly one element of set B and each element of set B can be paired with exactly one element of set A.

Operation
An arithmetic operation such as addition, subtraction, multiplication or division, defined on the elements of a set.

Ordinal number
A number that designates a comparative position or an order of some set of objects.

Orthocenter
The point that is the intersection of the altitudes of a triangle.

Outcome
A result that can occur during an experiment.

Output variable
Same as DEPENDENT VARIABLE.

P

Palindrome
A number that reads the same backward and forward.

Parallel lines
Lines in a plane that do not intersect no matter how far they are extended.

Parallelogram
A quadrilateral that has both pairs of opposite sides parallel.

Pascal's Triangle
A triangular pattern of numbers, written such that the first and last term in every row is 1, and every other term in a row is the sum of the two numbers directly above it.

Pattern
A design or relationship that is predictable in some manner or a schematic that can be followed.

Pentagon
A polygon that has five sides.

Percent
A ratio where one of the quantities being compared is 100.

Percentiles
The percentiles P_1, P_2, …, and P_{99} are values at or below which lie, respectively, the lowest 1, 2, …, and 99% of a set of data.

Perfect number
A number is said to be perfect if the sum of all its proper factors is equal to the number.

Perimeter
The perimeter of a planar shape is the total length of its boundaries.

Permutation
Any ordered subset of a collection of n distinct objects. The number of possible permutations, each containing k objects, that can be formed from a collection of n distinct object is given by $n(n - 1)\ldots(n - k + 1) = (n!)/(n - k)!$, and denoted $_nP_k$, $P(n, k)$, P_k^n or $(n)_k$. For example, the number of three-digit codes that can be formed using the number 0, 1, 2, …, 9 is $(10!)/(10 - 3)! = 720$.

Perpendicular bisector
A perpendicular bisector of a line segment is a line that is perpendicular to the line segment at its midpoint.

Perpendicular lines
Lines in a plane that intersect each other at an angle of ninety degrees.

Pictograph
A graph in which pictures are used to represent data.

Pie graph
A graph used to represent categorical distributions, especially categorical percentage distributions. A pie graph consists of a circle subdivided into a sectors whose sizes are proportional to the quantities or percentages they represent. An example, is shown below. During Spring Break, the expenses of 3 friends went to food, drink, gas, and lodging. The pie graph shows how the money was divided among these 4 categories (in percent).

Place value
A numeration system is said to be a place value system if the value of each digit in a number in the system is determined by its position in the number. The place value of a digit is a description of its position in a given number that determines the value of the digit.

Plane
Although plane is an undefined term in geometry, we can describe a plan as a two-dimensional set of an infinite number of points extending forever in all directions.

Point

Although point is an undefined term in geometry, we can describe a point as a location.

Polygon

A closed curve composed of line segments that starts and ends at the same point without crossing or retracing itself anywhere in its path is called a polygon.

Polyhedron

A simple closed surface composed entirely of polygonal regions.

Population

See FINITE POPULATION; SET.

Positive numbers

Numbers that are greater than zero.

Prime factorization

The decomposition of a number to express it as a product of its prime factors.

Prime number

A positive integer that has exactly two unique factors, 1 and itself.

Prism

A polyhedron comprised of two congruent faces that are in parallel planes and parallelograms for the remaining faces.

Probability of an event

If an event A occurs n times in t trials, the probability of event A, denoted by P(A),

$$P(A) = \frac{[\text{total occurrences of event A}]}{[\text{total number of trials}]}$$

Probability distribution

A list of all possible outcomes to an experiment along with the probabilities associated with each outcome.

Proof

A logical, irrefutable argument to demonstrate the truth of a mathematical result.

Proper subset

A is a proper subset of B if A is a subset of B but there is at least one element of B that is not an element of A.

Proportion

We say two ratios are in proportion if they represent equivalent fractions.

Pyramid

A polyhedron comprised of a polygon with n edges for its base, a point not in the plane of the base called the apex, and n triangular faces that are determined by the apex and the n edges of the base.

Pythagorean Theorem

If a right triangle has legs of lengths a and b and hypotenuse of length c, then $c^2 = a^2 + b^2$.

Q

Quadrilateral

A polygon that has four sides is called a quadrilateral.

Quartiles

The quartiles Q_1, Q_2, and Q_3 are values at or below which lie, respectively, the lowest 25, 50, and 75% of a set of data.

R

Random event

An unbiased event.

Randomness

An indiscriminate phenomenon.

Random process

A random process, also called a stochastic process, is a process which is carried at least in part by some random mechanism.

Random sample

A sample of size n from a finite population of size N is said to be random if it is chosen so that each of the $_NC_n$ possible samples has the same probability of being selected.

Random variable

A real-valued function defined over a sample space. It is often referred to as a chance variable, a stochastic variable, or a variate. The number of tails obtained in 12 flips of a coin is an example of random variable. A capital letter, say X, is often used to denote the random variables, and a lower case letter, say x, is used to denote their values.

Range

The set of all numbers that could occur as "output values" of a function. For example, in the function

$$f(x) = \frac{1}{x-5}$$

all real numbers *except* 0 could be in the range. Note that 0 cannot be in the range because in order for the value of the function to be 0, the numerator of the fraction would have to be equal 0.

Range of data set

The range of a set of data is given by the difference between the largest value and the smallest. For instance, the range of the number 3, 1, 5, 2, and 9 is $(9 - 1) = 8$.

Rate of change

Change in one variable, divided by the corresponding change in another variable. For example, if the temperature increases 10° in two hours, then the rate of change can be expressed as 5° per hour (i.e., 10°/2hrs. = 5°/hr.).

Ratio

A ratio is a pair of numbers, written as $a : b$, with $b \neq 0$.

Rational number

A rational number is a number of the form a/b, where a and b are any integers, and $b \neq 0$.

Raw data

Data which has not been subjected to any sort of statistical treatment.

Ray

A ray is a collection of points all of which lie on a line, that continues indefinitely in one direction.

Rectangle

A parallelogram with a right angle.

Reflection

A reflection is a transformation on a plane in which every point in a set is paired with a point in the image such that there is a line that is the perpendicular bisector of the line segment joining a point and its image.

Reflex angle

An angle that measures more than 180°.

Regular polygon

A polygon all of whose sides are of equal length.

Regular polyhedron

A convex polyhedron comprised of congruent regular polygons where at each vertex of the polyhedron there are the same number of edges meeting.

Relatively prime

Two integers are relatively prime if the only factor they have in common is 1.

Representative sample

A sample which contains the relevant characteristics of the population from which it came.

Rep-tile

A figure that serves as a building block for making a larger figure similar to the building block.

Rhombus
A parallelogram with all sides congruent.

Right angle
An angle measuring 90°.

Right circular cone
A circular cone is the set of all points joining the circumference of a circle in a plane to a point in space, such that the line joining the point to the center of the circle is perpendicular to the plane of the circle.

Right cylinder
A cylinder where the line segments joining corresponding points on the bases are perpendicular to the bases.

Right prism
A prism with all rectangles for the lateral faces.

Right regular pyramid
A pyramid with a regular polygon for its base and the lateral faces congruent isosceles triangles.

Right triangle
A triangle with one right angle.

Rotation
A rotation is a transformation on a plane in which every point in a set is moved the same number of units in the same direction by rotating about a point.

S

Sample
The subset of a population or sample space.

Sample space
The set of points representing the possible outcomes of an experiment is called the sample space for the experiment. The sample space is often denoted by the letter S. For example, when a die is tossed the sample space is $S = \{1, 2, 3, 4, 5, 6\}$.

Scalene triangle
A triangle with no sides congruent.

Scatter plot
A graph used to display the relationship between two variables. The scatter plot below displays the advertising expenditures and sales volume for a company for 8 selected months (both are measured in thousands of dollars).

Advertising Expenditures

Sector of a circle
A region of a circle formed by a central angle.

Seed
The first input value of an iterated function. For example, if we begin with 7, square it, square the new result, and so on, 7 is referred to as the seed.

Semicircle
An arc that consists of half of a circle.

Semi-regular tessellation
A tessellation comprised of more than one regular polygon such that each vertex has the same polygonal arrangement.

Set
A collection of objects or ideas.

Sieve of Eratosthenes
A method of finding all the prime numbers less than a given number, where numbers that are not prime are systematically crossed off a list of the natural numbers from 1 to the given number.

Similar polygons
Two polygons are said to be similar if their corresponding sides are proportional and their corresponding angles are equal.

Simple closed surface
A three-dimensional surface that is closed and has exactly one interior, no holes, and is hollow.

Size transformation
A transformation on a plane to the plane with center O and scale factor s $(s > 0)$ in which every point P in a set is paired with a point P', such that $OP' = s \cdot OP$ and O, P and P'

are collinear with O not between P and P'.

Skew lines
Any two lines that cannot lie in the same plane.

Skewed data
A distribution of data is skewed if it is not symmetric and it extends to one side more than the other.

Slope
Graphically, the "steepness" of a line. Numerically, slope is found in the same way as rate of change. It is calculated as follows:

$$slope = \frac{change\ in\ dependent\ variable}{change\ in\ independent\ variable}$$

A positive slope would indicate a positive rate of change, and would appear graphically as a line slanting upward from left to right. A negative slope would indicate a negative rate of change, and would appear as a line slanting downward from left to right. A slope of zero would indicate no change in the dependent variable, and would be seen as a horizontal line.

Solid
The set of points comprised of a simple closed surface and its interior.

Sphere
A sphere is the set of all points in space whose distance from a fixed point also in space is constant.

Square
A rectangle with all sides congruent.

Square root
The square root of a number is a number that when multiplied by itself produces the given number.

Standard Deviation
The standard of a sample of size n is given by the square root of the sum of the squared deviations from the mean divided by $(n - 1)$. Some mathematicians prefer to divide by n rather than by $(n - 1)$. If a set of data has x_j elements and $av(x)$ designates the mean of all the x_j's, for $j = 1, 2, \ldots k$. then the standard deviation is given by

$$SD = Sqrt\left[\frac{(Â\ (x_j - av(x))^2)}{(n\ or\ n-1)}\right], for\ j = 1, 2, \ldots k.$$

Statistic
A number obtained on the basis of a sample. Standard Deviation is an example of a statistic.

Statistics
The totality of methods employed in the collection and analysis of any kind of data and, more broadly, that branch of mathematics which deals with all aspects of the science of decision making in the face of uncertainty.

Stem-and-leaf plot
A two-column chart used to represent data in which the left column represents stems of data and the right column represents the leafs.

Straight angle
An angle that measures 180°.

Subset
A set A is a subset of another set B if every element in set A is also in set B.**Surface area**
The area of an object's surface

Supplementary angles
Two angles whose sum is 90 degrees are called supplementary angles.

Surface area
The surface area of a solid figure is the total area of its external surfaces.

T

Table
Data that have been arranged in rows and columns.

Tally chart
A chart used to record the frequency (how often) a certain piece of data occurs. Each occurrence of the piece of data is recorded by a short vertical bar. (See FREQUENCY TABLE). Below is an example of a tally chart.

Data	Tally	Frequency
apple	|||	4
orange	||| ||| |||	10
prune	||| ||| ||	8

Tessellation
A tessellation of the plane is the filling of the plane with repetitions of polygonal regions so that all corners meet at a vertex.

Theoretical probability
The probability determined by analyzing an experiment or situation.

Tiling
A tiling of the plane is the filling of the plane with repetitions of polygonal regions where corners do not necessarily meet at a vertex.

Transformation
A correspondence between all the points of a geometric figure in a plane and all the points of its image such that each point of the figure can be matched with exactly one point of its image, and each point of the image can be matched with exactly one point of the original figure.

Translation
A transformation on a plane in which every point in a set is moved the same number of units in the same direction.

Trapezoid
A trapezoid is a quadrilateral with at least one pair of parallel sides.

Tree diagram
A diagram in which individual paths represent all possible outcomes of an experiment.

Trial
A series of repeated experiments, such as that of tossing a die until a 5 is obtained.

Triangle
A triangle is a polygon that has three sides.

Twin primes
Two prime numbers that differ from each other by 1.

U

Union
The union of two sets is the set of all elements that are in either set or in both sets.

Unique representation
A numeration system is a unique representation system if each numeral refers to one and only one number.

Universal set
The set of all elements in a particular category.

V

Variable
A quality or quantity that may change or has the potential to change. For example, the amount of money in a person's savings account is variable, because it may change as a result of interest, deposits, withdrawals, and so on.

Variance
A statistic that indicates how data are dispersed around the mean. The variance is the mean of the squared deviation from the mean.

Vertical angles
Pairs of angles that are formed at the point of intersection of two intersecting lines.

Volume
The volume of a solid geometrical object is a measure of the amount of space that it encloses.

W

Weighted average
The average of a set of numbers obtained by multiplying each number by a weight expressing its relative importance, and then dividing the sum of these products by the sum of the weights.

Consider the set of numbers x_1, x_2, ..., x_k with their respective weight w_1, w_2, ..., w_k. The weighted average is given by $W_a = [x_1 w_1 + x_2 w_2 \ldots + x_k w_k]/[w_1 + w_2 + \ldots + w_k]$.

For example, if you work 3 hours at job A at $18 per hour, and 5 hours at job B for $24 per hour, then your (weighted) average earning per hour is $[(18)(3) + (5)(24)]/[8] = \$21.75$.

Whole numbers
The set of numbers {0, 1, 2, . . . }, or numbers belonging to the set.

Z

Z-score
The number of standard deviations that a given data value is above or below the mean.

INDEX

A

absolute value, 80
absolute value notation, 80
abundant integer, 107
acute angle, 313
acute triangle, 269
addends, 49
addition, 48
addition algorithms, 54
Addition Property of Equations, 232
Addition Property of Inequalities, 233
addition table, 51
additive, 33
additive identity, 52, 209
Additive Inverse Property, 81, 209
adjacent angles, 262
Agnesi, Maria, 236
Ahmes Papyri, 169, 317
al-Khwarizmi, 53
algorithm, 53
alternate exterior angles, 263
alternate interior angles, 263
altitude, 269, 271, 307
angle, 260
Angle-Angle-Side Triangle-Congruence Property, 290
Angle-Angle Triangle-Similarity Property, 295
Angle-Side-Angle Triangle-Congruence Property, 290
angle bisector, 280
annual percentage rate, 202
apex of a cone, 306
apex of a pyramid, 304
arc, 273
Archimedes, 198, 323, 335
area formulas, 321, 322, 323, 324
area model of multiplication, 65, 197
area of a planar shape, 319
arithmetic sequence, 120
array, 63
array division, 74
Array Multiplication, 63
Associative Property of Addition, 52, 208
Associative Property of Multiplication, 67, 208
Associative Property of the Intersection of Sets, 10
Associative Property of the Union of Sets, 9

B

Babylonian mathematics, 37, 175, 273, 312
Babylonian numeration system, 37
bar graph, 157
base, 245
base-60 system, 37
base-ten block model of addition, 54, 193
base-ten block model of division, 76
base-ten block model of multiplication, 69
base-ten block model of subtraction, 60, 195
base-ten system, 35
base-two system, 35
base of a cone, 307
base of a cylinder, 306
base of a polygon, 269
base of a prism, 303
base of a pyramid, 303
basic addition facts, 51
Bernoulli, Jakob, 129
between, 253
Bhaskara, 53
bilateral symmetry, 276
bimodal, 147
binary system, 36
Boethius, Anicius Manlius, 66
Borgh, Pieroi, 184
box-and-whisker plot, 155
Brahmagupta, 169, 175

C

Cantor, Georg, 2, 222
cardinal number, 45
Carroll, Lewis, 7
Cartesian Coordinate System, 234
Cartesian product, 9, 63
Cavalieri's Principle, 337
Cavalieri, Bonaventura, 337
Celsius, Anders, 338
center of a circle, 273
center of a sphere, 307
center of rotation, 353
central angle, 317
centroid, 287
certain event, 129
Charlemagne, 314
chord, 273
circle, 273
circle graph, 163
circular cone, 307
circular cylinder, 306

circumcenter, 285
circumference, 317
circumscribed circle, 284
class mark, 147
clock arithmetic, 117
Closure Property for Addition, 52, 207
Closure Property for Integer Subtraction, 85
Closure Property for Multiplication, 67, 208
cluster sampling, 145
collinear, 253
combination, 142
common denominator, 171
common fraction, 187
Commutative Property of Addition, 51, 52, 208
Commutative Property of Multiplication, 67, 208
Commutative Property of the Intersection of Sets, 9
Commutative Property of the Union of Sets, 9, 51
comparison subtraction, 59
compass, 274, 278
compensation, 49, 59
complementary angles, 263
complement of an event, 135
complement of a set, 8
composite number, 102
composition, 230
compounded interest, 203
compound statement, 15
concave polygon, 265
concave polyhedron, 303
conclusion, 14
concrete representation of an object, 45
concurrent lines, 257
conditional probability, 137
conditional statement, 16
cone, 307
congruent, 275, 288
conjecture, 14
conjunction, 15
constant of proportionality, 183
contrapositive statement, 17
converse statement, 17
convex polygon, 265
convex polyhedron, 303
coordinates, 234
coplanar, 254, 256
correlation, 162

corresponding angles, 263
counting back, 59
counting numbers, 44, 79
counting up, 49
cross multiplication, 172, 182
cube, 245, 333
cube of a number, 245
cubic unit, 331
cylinder, 306

D

Dantzig, George, 240
data, 144
data class, 158
Decagon, 265
decimal, 39, 184
decimal fraction, 184
decimal point, 184
decimal system, 39
deductive reasoning, 12
deficient integer, 107
degree Celsius, 338
degree Fahrenheit, 339
degree Kelvin, 338
degree unit, 312
denominator, 171
Density Property of Rational
Numbers, 207
dependent events, 137
Descartes, Rene, 234
de Meurs, Jean, 184
diagonal, 264
diameter of a circle, 273
diameter of a sphere, 307
difference, 58
dihedral angle, 301, 313
directed line segment, 351
directly proportional, 183
direct reasoning, 17
discrete models of division, 74
disjoint sets, 5, 48
disjunction, 15
distance formula, 344
distance postulate, 343
distribution curve, 152
Distributive Property of Intersection
over Union of Sets, 10
Distributive Property of
Multiplication
over Addition, 68, 209
dividend, 72
divisibility tests, 108
divisibility theorems, 108
divisible, 107

division, 72
division algorithms, 76
division by zero, 75
Division Property of Equations, 232
Division Property of Inequalities,
233
divisor, 72
dodecahedron, 305
domain, 227
double bar graph, 157
double plus one, 50
double plus two, 50

E

edge of a polyhedron, 303
Egyptian mathematics, 34, 63, 169,
171, 210, 215, 321, 329, 331
Egyptian numeration system, 34
element, 2
elimination method of solving
systems of equations, 243
empirical probability, 130
endpoints, 259
English System of Measurement,
314, 319, 331, 338, 339
equally likely outcomes, 129
equals sign, 232
equal additions method of
subtraction, 60
equal sets, 6
equation, 228, 232
equiangular polygon, 266
equilateral polygon, 266
equilateral triangle, 269
equivalent, 5
equivalent fractions, 171
equivalent ratios, 181
Escher, Maurits Cornelis, 347, 349
estimating products division
algorithm, 78
Euclid, 112, 254
Euclidean Algorithm, 113
Euler, 302
event, 127
even number, 108
experiment, 127
experimental probability, 130
exponent, 245
exterior angle, 263
exterior of an angle, 261

F

face of a polyhedron, 302
factor, 63, 108

factorial, 141
Fahrenheit, Gabriel, 339
Fermat's last theorem, 115
Fermat, Pierre de, 127
Fermat primes, 266
Fibonacci, 49, 120, 196
Fibonacci sequence, 121, 196, 291
figurate number, 122
finite, 3
finite set, 3, 207
45°-45°-90° right triangle, 341
fractal, 298
fraction, 169
fraction as part of a whole, 169
frequency, 158
frequency polygon, 160
frequency table, 158
function, 227
function machine, 229
Fundamental Counting Principle, 143
Fundamental Theorem of Arithmetic,
106

G

Gauss, Carl Friedrich, 81, 117, 266
Gaussian curve, 150
geometric sequence, 121
geometry, 252
Germain, Sophie, 115
glide reflection, 354
Goldbach's conjecture, 102
Golden Ratio, 180, 291
Golden Rectangle, 180, 291
Golden Rule, 182
gram, 338
graph, 228
Graunt, John, 144
greatest common divisor, 112
greatest common factor, 112, 173
great circle, 330
Grouping Property, 52
growing pattern, 121
guess and check, 20

H

heptagon, 265
Heron, 323
hexagon, 265
hieroglyphics, 169
Hindu-Arabic numeration system, 29,
39
Hippasus, 220
histogram, 160
horizontal bar graph, 157

hypotenuse, 340
hypothesis, 14, 144

I

icosahedron, 305
Identity Property of Multiplication, 67
image, 349
impossible event, 129
improper fraction, 175
incenter, 286
independent events, 137
indirectly proportional, 183
indirect reasoning, 18
inductive reasoning, 11
inequality, 233
infinite, 3
infinite set, 3, 207
inscribed circle, 286
integer, 80
integer addition, 80
integer division, 93
integer multiplication, 89
integer subtraction, 85
interest, 202
interest rate, 202
interior angles, 263
interior of an angle, 261
intersecting lines, 257
inverse, 17
inverse statement, 17
irrational number, 220
Islamic mathematics, 345, 347
isometry, 350
Isosceles-Triangle-Congruence Properties, 290
isosceles trapezoid, 271
isosceles triangle, 269

K

Karmarkar, Narendra, 243
kite, 271, 292
Klein, Felix, 351
Klein's Erlanger Programm, 351
Koch curve, 298
Kovalevsky, Sonya, 227

L

lateral face of a prism, 303
lateral face of a pyramid, 303
lateral surface area, 326
least common multiple, 115
legs of a right triangle, 340
length of a segment, 314

Leonardo of Pisa, 120, 196
Lindemann, Ferdinand, 284
line, 252
linear model of a rational number, 205
linear pair angles, 262
line graph, 160
line of best fit, 162
line of reflection, 354
line of symmetry, 276
line segment, 259
line symmetry, 276
Lobachevsky, Nicholai, 256
look for a pattern, 22

M

make an organized list, 23
make a table, 22
Mandelbrot, Benoit, 298
mapping, 229
mass, 338
Mayan numeration system, 34
mean, 146
median, 148
Mendel, Gregor, 146
mental computation, 49
Mesopotamia, 48
meter, 315
Metric System of Measurement, 315, 320, 331, 338, 339
midpoint, 259
midpoint formula, 344
midrange, 148
midsegment, 297
minuend, 58
missing-addend subtraction, 58
missing-factor division, 72
mixed decimal, 184
mixed number, 175
mode, 147
modular arithmetic, 118
modulus, 118
multimodal, 147
multiple, 108, 115
multiplication, 63
multiplication algorithms, 69
Multiplication Property of Equations, 232
Multiplication Property of Inequalities, 233
multiplication table, 66
multiplicative, 40
multiplicative identity, 67, 209
Multiplicative Inverse Property, 209

mutually exclusive events, 132

N

n-gon, 265
name, 45
natural number, 44, 79
negation, 15
negatively skewed data distribution, 152
negative correlation, 163
negative number, 79
negative sign, 79
negative slope, 236
net of the surface of a three-dimensional figure, 326
Nightingale, Florence, 146
non-mutually exclusive events, 132
nonagon, 265
noncollinear, 253
noncoplanar, 254, 256
nonterminating, nonrepeating decimal, 220
normal curve, 150
normal distribution, 152
nth term, 121
null set, 3
number, 45
number-line, 49
number-line model of division, 74
number-line model of multiplication, 65, 91
number-line model of subtraction, 59
number line model of addition, 49, 83
numeral, 45

O

oblique circular cone, 306
oblique cylinder, 306
oblique prism, 304
oblique regular pyramid, 304
obtuse angle, 313
obtuse triangle, 269
Octagon, 265
octahedron, 305
odds against an event, 136
odds in favor of an event, 136
odd number, 108
one-to-one correspondence, 5, 46
opposites, 80
ordered pair, 229, 234
Ordering Property, 52
order of a set, 6
order of operations, 96
ordinal number, 45

origin, 234
orthocenter, 287
outcome, 127
outlier, 162

P

Pacioli, Luca, 69, 72
paired data, 160
parallelogram, 271, 292
parallel lines, 258
Parallel Postulate, 256
partial products algorithm, 70
partial sums algorithm, 55
Pascal's Triangle, 141
Pascal, Blaise, 141
pattern, 120
Pellos, Francesco, 184
pentagon, 265
pentagonal number, 123
percent, 200
percentile, 154
percent change, 201
perfect integer, 107
perimeter, 316
perimeter formulas, 316
permutation, 142
perpendicular bisector, 282
perpendicular lines, 258
Petty, William, 144
pi, 220
pictograph, 156
pictorial model, 48
pie graph, 163
place value, 35, 39
plane, 254
plane of symmetry, 277
Plato, 300, 305
point, 252
point-slope form, 239
point symmetry, 276
Polya, George, 19
polygon, 264
polygonal region, 264
polyhedron (polyhedra), 302
population, 145
positively skewed data distribution, 152
positive correlation, 162
positive number, 79
positive sign, 79
positive slope, 236
power, 245
powers of 10, 34
prime factorization, 104

prime number, 102
Primitive numeration system, 29
principal, 203
prism, 203
probability, 127
probability distribution, 128
problem solving, 19
product, 63
proper divisor, 107
proper subset, 4
proportion, 182
proportional, 183
protractor, 278, 312
pyramid, 304
Pythagoras, 66, 220, 340
Pythagoreans, 220, 340
Pythagorean theorem, 340, 343

Q

quadrant, 234
quadrilateral, 265, 273
quartile, 154
Quetelet, Lambert Adolph, 150
quotient, 72, 170

R

radius (radii) of a circle, 273
radius (radii) of a sphere, 307
random sampling, 145
range, 148, 159, 227
rate, 181
ratio, 170, 180
rational exponent, 221
rational number, 204, 206
ray, 260
real number, 222
reciprocal, 218
rectangle, 271, 292, 316
reflection, 354
reflection symmetry, 276
reflex angle, 313
region model of a rational number, 204
regular polygon, 266
regular polyhedron, 305
relatively prime, 110, 112, 171
relative frequency, 163
rep-tile, 299
repeatand, 190
repeated addition multiplication, 63
repeated subtraction division, 72
repeating bar, 190
repeating decimal, 190

rhombus, 271, 294
right angle, 313
right circular cone, 307
right cylinder, 306
right prism, 304
right regular pyramid, 304
right triangle, 269
rigid transformation, 350
Robinson, Julia Bowman, 79
Roman numeration system, 29
rotation, 353
rotational symmetry, 276
Rudolff, Christoff, 184
ruler, 278
Rule of Three, 182

S

sample, 145
sample space, 127
scaffolding division algorithm, 78
scalene triangle, 269
scatterplot, 161
scientific notation, 247
scratch algorithm, 56
sector of a circle, 325
semicircle, 273
semiregular polyhedron, 305
semiregular tessellation, 348
set, 2
set-builder notation, 2
set model of a rational number, 205
set model of integer addition, 82
set model of integer division, 93
set model of integer multiplication, 90
set model of integer subtraction, 86
sharing division, 73
Side-Angle-Side Triangle-Congruence Property, 289
Side-Angle-Side Triangle-Similarity Property, 295
Side-Side-Side Triangle-Congruence Property, 289
Side-Side-Side Triangle-Similarity Property, 295
sides of an angle, 260
sides of a polygon, 264
Sierpinski triangle, 298
Sieve of Eratosthenes, 102
significant digits, 247
similar, 295
simplest form, 173
simplex method, 240

simple closed surface, 302
simple interest, 202
simulation, 128
size transformation, 356
skewed data distribution, 152
skew lines, 256
slant height, 330
slope, 236
slope-intercept form, 239
solid, 302
solve a simpler problem, 24
sphere, 307
square, 245, 271, 294, 316
square number, 122
square of a number, 245
square root, 220
standard addition algorithm, 54
standard deviation, 150
standard multiplication algorithm, 71
statement, 15
statistical data, 144
statistics, 144
stem-and-leaf plot, 164
Stevin, Simon, 193
straightedge, 278
straight angle, 313
stratified sampling, 145
subset, 4
substitution method of solving systems of equations, 243
subtraction, 58
subtraction algorithms, 61
Subtraction Property of Equations, 232
Subtraction Property of Inequalities, 233
subtractive, 35
subtrahend, 58

sum, 49
supplementary angles, 263
surface area, 326
symbol for zero, 38
systematic sampling, 145
system of equations, 240

T
table, 229
take-away subtraction, 58
temperature, 338
terminating decimal, 190
tessellation, 345
tetrahedron, 305
Thales, 11, 295
theoretical probability, 130
30°-60°-90° right triangle, 341
transformation, 349
transitional algorithm for addition, 56
transitional algorithm for division, 78
translation, 351
transversal, 263
trapezoid, 271, 291
tree diagram, 64, 104, 139
triangle, 269
Triangle Inequality, 342
triangular number, 122
triple bar graph, 157
truth tables, 16

U
undefined terms, 252
union of sets, 7, 48
unique representation, 29
Universe set, 5
use algebra, 24
use a visual aid, 21

V
van Hiele, Pierre, 308
van Hiele-Geldof, Dina, 308
variance, 150
Venerabilis, Beda, 66
Venn, John, 4
Venn Diagram, 4, 133
vertex (vertices), 260
vertical-line test, 230
vertical angles, 262
vertical bar graph, 157
volume, 331

W
Wallis, John, 245
Wantzel, Pierre, 266
Weierstrass, Karl, 93
weight, 338
weighted average, 149
Weyl, Hermann, 276
whole-number addition, 48
whole number, 47, 79
Wiles, Andrew, 115
work backward, 23

X
x-axis, 234
x-intercept, 238

Y
y-axis, 234
y-intercept, 238
Yoruba numeration system, 34

Z
z-score, 151
Zero Property of Multiplication, 67